THE 2nd MAMMOTH BOOK OF FUN & GAMES

Here are 500 pages chock-full of word games, quizzes, parlor tricks, pencil games, crosswords, threezies, puzzles, jokes, diamond puzzles, and many other kinds of entertainment for the whole family.

This is a book to be indulged in for months, with material for every kind of mood. And all of it is first-rate and challenging.

THE 2nd
MAMMOTH
BOOK OF
FUN & GAMES

Richard B. Manchester

A HART BOOK

A & W VISUAL LIBRARY • NEW YORK

PUBLISHED BY
A & W PUBLISHERS, INC.
95 MADISON AVENUE
NEW YORK, NEW YORK 10016

ISBN: 0-89104-170-2
LIBRARY OF CONGRESS CATALOG CARD NO. 79-93090
PRINTED IN THE UNITED STATES OF AMERICA

CONTENTS

5

CROSSWORD PUZZLES

THE 2nd
MAMMOTH
BOOK OF
FUN & GAMES

CORNUCOPIA

We have included in this quiz 22 questions pertaining to just about everything you can imagine. There's no method in this madness.

Check the answer you deem correct. Give yourself one point for each correct answer. If you get 10 right, you're okay; 12 is above average; 15 is good; 18 marks you as a master of trivia.

Answers on page 456

1. The Rosetta Stone is in:
   The British Museum   *Luxor, Egypt*   *Tiffany's, New York*

2. New South Wales is located in:
   The British Isles   *Australia*   *The Orkney Islands*

3. The Garden State is:
   California   *Florida*   *New Jersey*

4. The Kentucky Derby is held at:
   Epsom Downs   *Churchill Downs*   *Kentucky Downs*

5. The miniskirt was the rage in the:
   1900s   *1930s*   *1960s*

6. The basic Guatemalan unit of currency is the:
   Sombrero   *Quetzal*   *Peso*

7. The Florida State University football team is known as the:
   Sun Devils   *Gators*   *Seminoles*

8. An inland European city that has more miles of canals than Venice is:
   Vienna, Austria   *Hamburg, West Germany*
   Birmingham, United Kingdom

9. The modern nation you would visit to see the ruins of ancient Carthage is:
   Tunisia   *Turkey*   *Algeria*

10. The gestation period of an elephant is:
    6 months   *21 months*   *33 months*

11. The heaviest organ in the human body is the:
    Brain   *Stomach*   *Liver*

12. The dingo lives in:
     Central America   *Australia*   *Africa*

13. Vodka is distilled from:
     Blueberries   *Potatoes*   *Juniper berries*

14. Pasadena, California is the site of which football bowl?
     The Rose Bowl   *The Sugar Bowl*   *The Orange Bowl*

15. Gin gets its special flavor from:
     Juniper berries   *Thrice distilled Vermouth*   *Overripe grapes*

16. Bronze is an alloy made of:
     Brass and tin   *Zinc and tin*   *Copper and tin*

17. A Portuguese man-of-war is:
     A vest-pocket destroyer   *A boastful commander*
                    A stinging jellyfish

18. The man who served as vice-president under President Truman was:
     Henry Wallace   *Lyndon Johnson*   *Alben Barkley*

19. The most popular breed of dog in the United States today is:
     The Boxer   *The German Shepherd*   *The Poodle*

20. The Marx Brothers first went mad in:
     Horsefeathers   *The Coconuts*   *Duck Soup*

21. A prestidigitator is:
     A liar   *A radical*   *A conjurer*

22. A pawn is used in the game of:
     Ping-Pong   *Hockey*   *Chess*

13

EMPORIA OF IMPORT

Do you like to shop? Do you know the names of the world's most famous stores, and can you name the cities in which they are located?

Below is a list of 25 outstanding emporia. Some of them have more than one branch, but in every case, the main branch is the one that is well known. In the blank space, write the name of the city in which the main store is located.

A score of 11 is good; 14 is spiffy; and 19 indicates you've shopped around.

Answers on page 456

Answers on page 456

1. Neiman Marcus   _____
2. Macy's   _____
3. Selfridge's   _____
4. G. Fox and Company   _____
5. Filene's   _____
6. G.U.M.   _____
7. Galeries Lafayette   _____
8. Den Permanente   _____
9. Fauchon   _____
10. Christiana Glasmagasin   _____
11. Hammacher Schlemmer   _____
12. Gimbels   _____
13. Jordan Marsh   _____
14. Au Printemps   _____
15. Harrod's   _____
16. Marks and Spencer   _____
17. Galerias Preciados   _____
18. Saks Fifth Avenue   _____
19. Fortnum and Mason   _____
20. I. Magnin   _____
21. Marshall Field   _____
22. Sanborn's   _____
23. F.A.O. Schwarz   _____
24. Tiffany's   _____
25. Gucci   _____

DO YOU KNOW KIDS?

Read each statement and decide whether you think it is True or False. Give yourself two points for each correct response; but deduct one point for each incorrect answer. A score of 7 makes you a desirable baby sitter; 14 entitles you to work in a nursery program; and with a perfect score of 20 you can join the Harvard research team.

Answers on page 456

	TRUE	FALSE
1. Real intelligence and learning do not begin until the child is about six, which is why school usually begins at this age.	____	____
2. The cooing and babbling that babies engage in are meaningless.	____	____
3. The receptive vocabulary (words that are understood) of a six-year-old who has been raised in a family that talks and reads to him is between 15,000 and 25,000 words.	____	____
4. Small children are best kept in playpens where they can concentrate on one or two toys at a time.	____	____
5. Children's questions should be answered as seriously and correctly as possible, regardless of how silly or complex they may be.	____	____
6. A parent or baby-sitter should not encourage a child to read before the youngster has the guidance of a trained teacher.	____	____
7. Small children learn primarily through the sense of sight.	____	____
8. Children who are always "getting into things" are naughty and should be curbed because of the danger of accidents or disease.	____	____
9. Small children should be shown the correct way to play with their toys.	____	____
10. Small children should seldom, if ever, be taken on shopping trips with parents.	____	____

FIT FOR A DOG

Below, you will find 36 words, phrases, and expressions. Each one of these should suggest to you another expression which contains the word DOG. For example: a *fairway angle* would be a DOG*leg*. Fill in the correct expression on the line at the right.

A score of 15 is good; 20 is excellent; 25 is extraordinary; and 30 or more earns you a blue ribbon.

Answers on page 456

1. Worn and shabby _____

2. Deteriorated _____

3. In disfavor _____

4. Trivial or bad verse _____

5. Miserable, drab existence _____

6. Hardwood tree _____

7. Aerial skirmish _____

8. Quick, easy gait _____

9. Loaf on the job _____

10. Established opinion _____

11. Arctic vehicle _____

12. Obstinately determined _____

13. Teeming _____

14. Elementary swim stroke _____

15. Daisy _____

16. Architectural ornament _____

17. Marked by ruthless self-interest _____

18. Humorous tale involving
    a talking animal _____

19. Tuckered out _____

20. Small shark _____

21. Darned _____

22. Miserable, shameful end _____

23. One horse carriage _____

24. G.I. identification _____

25. Selfish hoarder of unneeded goods _____

26. For a very low price _____

27. Hot sultry period of summer _____

28. Infantryman _____

29. Leave well enough alone _____

30. Ball park refreshment _____

31. Night shift _____

32. Brief sleep _____

33. Pound employee _____

34. They come out in the midday sun _____

35. Dress up _____

36. Woebegone, forlorn _____

BELIEVE IT OR NOT

Below are 40 statements. If you agree with the statement, check TRUE; if you disagree, check FALSE. Answers include explanations.

Award yourself one point for every correct answer. A score of 20 is passing; 25 is capital; and 30 is truly splendid.

Answers on page 457

	TRUE	FALSE
1. Pandemonium is a disease of the lungs.	___	___
2. An octoroon is an almond cookie.	___	___
3. An accolade is a headache pill.	___	___
4. The Sugar Bowl is in Texas.	___	___
5. Finocchio is a vegetable with a licorice taste.	___	___
6. Gorgonzola is a character in *La Traviata*.	___	___
7. The great artist Picasso was Spanish.	___	___
8. Shakespeare wrote more tragedies than comedies.	___	___
9. The motto *E pluribus unum* means "Out of many, one."	___	___
10. David slew Goliath with a broadsword.	___	___
11. The sweetheart of Robin Hood was Maid Marian.	___	___
12. Insects possess two pairs of legs.	___	___
13. Rubber is made from the substance latex.	___	___
14. The first emperor of the Holy Roman Empire was Frederick the Great.	___	___
15. An estuary is a river breaking into two forks.	___	___
16. The Pleiades is a group of islands in the Caribbean.	___	___
17. A canard is a false and absurb report.	___	___
18. Emma Woodhouse is the heroine of a novel by George Eliot.	___	___
19. Maria Mitchell was the first American to discover a comet.	___	___

20. Seven United States Presidents were born in Ohio. —— ——

21. The 1932 Summer Olympics were held in London. —— ——

22. The longest river in the United States is the Mississippi. —— ——

23. The old name for the Turkish city of Izmir is Smyrna. —— ——

24. Socrates' wife was named Penelope. —— ——

25. Joan Fontaine and Joan Crawford are sisters. —— ——

26. Daylight saving time goes into effect in the U.S. at 2:00 A.M. on the last Sunday in May. —— ——

27. If you had a blot on your escutcheon, it would mean your reputation had been marred in some way. —— ——

28. The sewing machine was invented by Isaac Singer. —— ——

29. Florida is known as the Golden State. —— ——

30. Isaac Bashevis Singer won the Nobel Prize for literature in 1978. —— ——

31. The American poets, Stephen Vincent Benet and William Rose Benet, are not related. —— ——

32. Addison and Steele are English rock singers from Manchester. —— ——

33. A marimba is a Latin American dance. —— ——

34. The official language of Brazil is Spanish. —— ——

35. The Pacific Ocean is larger than the Atlantic Ocean. —— ——

36. The Bee Gees are an Australian rock group currently living in the U.S. —— ——

37. The disease which is the number one killer in the western world is cancer. —— ——

38. *Penrod and Sam* was written by Mark Twain. —— ——

39. The second and sixth presidents of the United States were father and son. —— ——

40. The world's longest river is the Amazon. —— ——

FREE-FOR-ALL

The 30 statements below have to do with everything and anything, and they add up to absolutely nothing. Can you recognize which of the statements are true and which statements false? Check TRUE or FALSE.

A score of 15 is fine; 20 is super; and 25 is awesome.

Answers on page 457

	TRUE	FALSE
1. The largest country in the world is China.	——	——
2. Harpo Marx was left-handed.		——
3. The skeleton of the earliest horse is estimated to be 45 million years old.	——	——
4. A tatterdemalion is a kind of lizard.	——	——
5. The most populous country in the world is India.	——	——
6. Parker Pyne is a detective invented by Agatha Christie.	——	——
7. Johnny Appleseed's real name was Paul Bunyan.	——	——
8. An oxymoron is a person of low intelligence.	——	——
9. In the movie *Gone With the Wind*, Scarlett O'Hara was played by Janet Leigh.	——	——
10. The average elevation of the United States, except for Alaska and Hawaii, is about 2,500 feet above sea level.	——	——
11. Tagliatelle was the name of a great 19th century ballerina.	——	——
12. Alexander Hamilton was killed in a duel with Benedict Arnold.	——	——
13. Mali is a country in Central America.	——	——
14. The comic strip *Alley Oop* was created by V.T. Hamlin.	——	——
15. A numismatist is a person who studies insects.	——	——
16. The modern mailbox was invented by novelist Anthony Trollope.	——	——

17. *Volpone* is a play by William Shakespeare.   —— ——

18. Aluminum is a good conductor of heat.   —— ——

19. The largest denomination of paper money printed in the United States today is the hundred dollar bill.   —— ——

20. The first New York newspaper was the *New York Times*.   —— ——

21. Something that is nugatory is worth its weight in gold.   —— ——

22. The trackless trolley originated in Los Angeles.   —— ——

23. Brass is an alloy of copper.   —— ——

24. Honoré de Balzac wrote 97 novels.   —— ——

25. The vacuum cleaner was invented by James Thurber.   —— ——

26. The native habitat of the griffin is New Zealand.   —— ——

27. The highest mountain is Everest.   —— ——

28. King Solomon was the son of David and Bathsheba.   —— ——

29. If you received your change in escudos, you would probably be in Peru.   —— ——

30. When it is noon in New York, it is 7:00 A.M. in Cairo.   —— ——

BEATLEMANIA

During the 1960s, the Beatles, an English rock group, took the United States by storm—yeah, yeah, yeah. How much do you know about this quartet of shaggy-haired crooners? Below are 25 questions about the Beatles. Check the answer you deem correct.

A score of 11 is fine; 15 is upbeat; 21 means you rock around the clock; and 23 marks you as a rock maven.

Answers on page 458

1. The fourth Beatle who came to the United States in 1964, along with John Lennon, Ringo Starr, and Paul McCartney, was:
   George Harrison   Bob Dylan   Barry Gibb

2. The original drummer for the Beatles was named:
   Ringo Starr   Peter Best   Stu Sutcliffe

3. The first American television show on which the Beatles appeared was:
   American Bandstand   Sonny and Cher   The Ed Sullivan Show

4. "All the lonely people, where do they all come from?"
   "All the lonely people, where do they all go to?"
   was the refrain to which one of the Beatles' hits?
   She Loves Me   Eleanor Rigby   Lucy in the Sky with Diamonds

5. The first Beatles' movie was:
   Help   A Hard Day's Night   Yellow Submarine

6. The Beatles' album *Sgt. Pepper's Lonely Hearts Club Band* was issued in what year?
   1962   1967   1969

7. Ringo Starr's real name was:
   Harvey Storch   Rick McSorley   Richard Starkey

8. The Beatles came from what British city?
   London   Liverpool   Manchester

9. The original manager of the Beatles was named:
   Arif Mardin   Brian Epstein   Karl Richards

10. George Harrison was born in what year?
    1940   1943   1948

11. The first Beatles' hit single was:
    Love Me Do   A Hard Day's Night
    You've Got to Hide Your Love Away

12. John Lennon divorced his first wife, Cynthia, to marry:

    Yoko Ono   Joan Baez   Samantha

13. *I Want to Hold Your Hand*, which eventually sold over 3 million copies, was the top record of what year?

    1962   1964   1970

14. The Beatles were originally named the Quarrymen. Their more famous name was inspired by The Crickets, an American rock group led by:

    Bill Haley   Buddy Holly   Dion

15. The Beatle who introduced Ravi Shankar to the West was:

    John Lennon   Paul McCartney   George Harrison

16. Most of the Beatles' most lyrical melodies were written by:

    Paul McCartney   Ringo Starr   John Lennon

17. Which of the following hit songs was not one of the Beatles'?

    Michelle   *Can't Buy Me Love*   *Satisfaction*

18. The Beatles separated in what year?

    1971   1974   1976

19. Paul McCartney's new band is called:

    Stones   Wings   Flying

20. Which Beatle was left-handed?

    Ringo Starr   Paul McCartney   George Harrison

21. How much money did the Beatles make during their two U.S. tours in 1964?

    $100,000 $1,000,000 $2,000,000

22. One of the American groups that influenced the Beatles originally was The Everly Brothers. The first names of the Everly Brothers were:

    Robin and Berry   Don and Phil   Frank and Karl

23. The Beatles' song *All You Need is Love* is on which album?

    Magical Mystery Tour   *Revolver*

              Sgt. Pepper's Lonely Hearts Club Band

24. The song *Lucy in the Sky with Diamonds* is about:

    The drug LSD   A rich girl   An aviatrix

25. The Beatles' album named after a street in London is:

    King's Road   Abbey Road   Pall Mall

23

IN YOUR CUPS

What do you know about booze? Below are 25 questions about alcoholic beverages. You have three choices. Check the answer you believe to be the right one.

A score of 16 is high; 18 is intoxicating; 21 is inebriating; and 23 certifies you as a bartender.

Answers on page 458

1. Vodka is distilled from:
   Blueberries   Potatoes   Juniper berries

2. Calvados is a French brandy made from:
   Oranges   Peaches   Apples

3. Dubonnet is generally served as:
   An afterdinner cordial   An apéritif   A chaser for whiskey

4. Aquavit is a Scandinavian liquor flavored with:
   Cloves   Chocolate liqueur   Caraway seed

5. Irish coffee is made with:
   Coffee and Kahlua   Coffee, whipped cream, and whiskey
   Coffee, vodka, and Cointreau

6. A Virgin Mary is:
   Vodka and tomato juice   Gin and tomato juice
   Plain tomato juice

7. A Grasshopper is made with:
   Crème de menthe, creme de cacao and cream
   Crème de menthe, Kahlua, and vodka
   Sloe gin and mint leaves

8. The liqueur that tastes like licorice is:
   Crème de menthe   Kahlua   Anisette

9. Champagne *brut* is:
   Very dry   Very sweet   Very old

10. A Black Russian is made with:
    Kahlua and vodka   Kahlua and cream
    Crème de cacao and Jack Daniels

11. Bourbon is distilled from:
    Corn   Rice   Wheat

12. An Americano contains:
    Campari   Bourbon   Tequila

13. Rum is obtained from fermented:

Potatoes   Sugar cane or molasses   Grain, such as rye or barley

14. Whiskey that is 86 proof contains what percent alcohol?

43 percent   86 percent   100 percent

15. An Old Fashioned consists of:

Whiskey, sugar, bitters, and club soda
Bourbon, mint leaves, sugar, and water
Gin, tonic, and a green olive

16. The initials *J* and *B* in J&B rare scotch stand for:

James and Billy   Juice and Brew   Justerini and Brooks

17. A Margarita contains:

Tequila, salt, lime juice, and Triple Sec
Tequila, vodka, and Kahlua
Tequila, orange juice, sugar, and Cointreau

18. A Martini is made with:

Gin, angostura bitters, and a maraschino cherry
Gin, a dash of vermouth, and a green olive (or lemon twist)
Gin, Campari, club soda, and a black olive

19. Tequila is distilled from:

The mescal cactus   A special Mexican white grape
The sap of the Mexican agave plant

20. Most wines contain what percent alcohol?

2 to 4 percent   8 to 12 percent   15 to 20 percent

21. The favorite toast of the Italians is:

Cin cin   Mama mia   Buon giorno

22. The portion of teetotalers in the United States is:

¼ of the population   ⅓ of the population   ½ of the population

23. A Side Car is made of:

Cointreau, lemon juice, and brandy
Vodka, white rum, and shaved ice
Gin, white crème de menthe, and sugar

24. Porter is a:

Vintage wine   Light beer similar to lager
Dark beer made from malt

25. A one-ounce measure is a:

Jigger   Pony   Shot

NAME THE PRODUCT

How well do you know advertising slogans? Below are 30 slogans or jingles that you've heard or seen frequently on TV or in magazines. Fill in the blank with the name of the product. For example, "Mm-mm good, mm-mm good. That's what *Campbell's Soups* are, mm-mm good."

Award yourself one point for every correct answer. A score of 15 is good; 19 makes you commercial-canny; and 24 means you prefer the commercials to the programs.

Answers on page 458

1. "Now it's _____ for those who think young."

2. "_____ tastes good, like a cigarette should."

3. "_____ _____ _____ is good to the very last drop."

4. "Come to _____ Country."

5. _____ _____: it chases dirt.

6. _____: the beer that made Milwaukee famous.

7. "It's _____ to be good."

8. "Have you got an _____ headache?"

9. "You get more tiny little tea leaves in _____ _____."

10. "Please don't squeeze the _____."

11. "Us _____ smokers would rather fight than switch."

12. "_____, the champagne of bottled beers."

13. "Things taste better with _____."

14. "Gentlemen prefer _____."

15. "Nothing says lovin' like something from the oven, and _____ says it best."

16. "_____ shakes brand loyalties."

17. "_____ _____ does it again."

18. "_____ _____ _____ is the heavenly coffee."

26

19. "There's always room for _____."

20. "_____, the breakfast of champions."

21. "Call for _____ _____."

22. "You're gonna swear you've got more hair with _____

_____ _____."

23. "Anticipation: _____ _____."

24. "_____ _____, the uncola."

25. "Don't wait to be told you need _____ _____."

26. "You asked for it, you got it: _____."

27. "We put everything we know into every bag _____

_____ _____."

28. "So thick you can watch a pearl drop: _____ _____."

29. "The clean makeup: _____ _____."

30. "Brush your breath with _____."

A LA MODE

Do you follow women's fashions? If so, this quiz is custom-made for you. Below are 27 questions. You have three choices. Check the answer you believe is correct.

A score of 12 says you are in vogue; 16 says you are a fashion plate; and a score of 21 means you're either a couturier or you know someone who is!

Answers on page 458

1. The mini-skirt was the rage in the:

    1900s   1930s   1960s

2. A designer noted for classic, conservatively-cut clothes is:

    Pierre Cardin   Pauline Trigère   Coco Chanel

3. A dress with the waistline just below the bust is said to be what style:

    Empire   Belle Epoque   Gibson Girl

4. The "flapper" look was the in-look of the:

    1890s   1920s   1950s

5. Crinoline is another name for:

    Bobby sox   A hoop skirt   Bloomers

6. The British "mod" look of the 1960s was introduced by designer:

    Bill Blass   Mary Quant   Yves St. Laurent

7. Before nylon was invented, stockings were generally made of:

    Rayon   Linen   Silk

8. Divided skirts disguised as pants are known as:

    Hot pants   Pantaloons   Culottes

9. A burnoose is a type of:

    Hooded cloak   Mutton-sleeved blouse   Sunbonnet

10. A beret is a type of:

    Hat   Jacket   Petticoat

11. Bustles were worn in what century?

    Fifteenth   Nineteenth   Twentieth

12. A type of hooded robe with a mask worn at 17th-century costume balls was a:

    Doublet   Dirndl   Domino

13. A type of fur often used to trim royal robes is:
    Mink   Sable   Ermine

14. A skirt worn over a series of hoops extending horizontally from the
    waist, fashionable in the 16th and 17th centuries was:
    A farthingale   A patrouche   A simballet

15. A fichu is a type of:
    Shoelace   Boot   Shawl

16. Before the days of panty hose, women often wore:
    Chastity belts   Garter belts   Knee socks

17. A type of hat made popular by Jackie Kennedy was the:
    Pillbox   Pokebonnet   Tam O'Shanter

18. An Indian cotton fabric that "bleeds" when you wash it is:
    Mohair   Madras   Calico

19. The shirtwaist look was popularized by:
    Charles Dana Gibson   Amelia Bloomer   Emilio Pucci

20. Organdy is a fabric once considered particularly appropriate for:
    Widows in mourning   Maternity dresses
                  Young girls' pinafores

21. Peter Pan refers to a type of:
    Headgear   Collar   High-button boot

22. A ceremonial dress worn by Japanese women is the:
    Sari   Caftan   Kimono

23. A sweater that buttons up or down completely is a:
    Turtleneck   Cardigan   Pullover

24. A cummerbund is worn around the:
    Neck   Ankle   Waist

25. Unisex is a look of the:
    1870s   1930s   1970s

26. The fashion designer, Bill Blass, is:
    French   American   English

27. Traditionally, the average family budget apportions what percent-
    age for clothing?
    8%   15%   25%

HOUSE BEAUTIFUL

Do you know a highboy from a lowboy?

This quiz is for furniture buffs. Below are 25 questions. There are three choices. Check the answer you believe is correct.

A score of 10 is good. A score of 16 makes you a chip off the old Chippendale. A score of 20 marks you as an interior decorator.

Answers on page 459

1. An English style of the late 18th century, noted for its light, graceful lines and concave curves was:
   Hepplewhite   Queen Anne   Chippendale

2. A spinet is a type of:
   Armchair   Piano   Desk

3. A four-poster is a type of:
   Tent for the backyard   Bed with a canopy   Wallpaper

4. A cloisonné tabletop is made of:
   Mahogany   Enamelware   Cherrywood

5. An escritoire is a type of:
   Bed   Dresser   Desk

6. A gateleg table is a drop leaf table with:
   Four immovable legs
   One immovable leg, shaped like a gatepost
   Four movable legs, arranged in pairs

7. A newel-post supports a:
   Dining table   Staircase   Franklin stove

8. Sheraton furniture was designed in what century?
   Fifteenth   Eighteenth   Twentieth

9. A piece of furniture with open shelves for ornaments or bric-a-brac is:
   An étagère   A rolltop desk   A highboy

10. If you were asked whether a chair had cabrioles, you would look at the:
    Seat   Back   Legs

11. A trivet has how many legs?
    Two   Three   Four

12. The primary wood used in the Tudor period was:
    Mahogany   Oak   Walnut

13. A trundle bed is:
    A bed on casters that can be rolled beneath a larger bed when
        not in use
    A queen-sized or matrimonial bed
    A bunkbed, with one bed permanently fixed on top of the other

14. A headpiece with stenciled designs was characteristic of the:
    French provincial bed Hepplewhite chair Boston rocker

15. The noted cabinetmaker, Duncan Phyfe, worked in:
    New York   London   Paris

16. Rya rugs originated in:
    Persia   Scandinavia   Turkey

17. Overstuffed furniture is characteristic of what period?
    Regency   Victorian   Danish Modern

18. A chair with a high spoked back and outward slanting legs con-
    nected by a crossbar is a:
    Morris chair   Windsor chair   Captain's chair

19. A wardrobe is where you keep:
    Dishes   Linens   Clothing

20. A wainscot is a type of:
    Damask upholstery Wood-paneling Quilted counterpane

21. A sideboard is found in what room?
    The dining room   The bedroom   The kitchen

22. A grandfather clock is:
    A clock that belonged to someone's grandfather
    A pendulum clock enclosed in a tall, narrow cabinet
    A highly ornamental clock that sits on a mantelpiece

23. A whatnot is a piece of furniture used to:
    Display bric-a-brac   Hold the pantry keys
         House sheet music

24. A settee is:
    A long wooden bench with arms
    A set of three pieces of furniture of the same design
    A low, circular table for children

25. Sterling silver contains a little copper and how much silver?
    80.5%   90%   92.5%

31

WHO WAS THAT LADY?

Many great movies bear the heroine's name in the title. Do you remember what actresses played the memorable heroines in the 50 movies listed below?

You have three choices. Check the answer you think is correct.

A score of 35 shows female intuition; 40 is matriarchal; and 45 is worthy of a femme fatale.

Answers on page 459

1. *Stella Dallas*
   Joanne Woodward   Barbara Stanwyck   Marilyn Monroe

2. *Mildred Pierce*
   Joan Fontaine   Joan Crawford   Joan Blondell

3. *Alice Adams*
   Katharine Hepburn   Olivia de Havilland   Katharine Houghton

4. *Jezebel*
   Bette Davis   Vivien Leigh   Donna Reed

5. *Marjorie Morningstar*
   Elizabeth Taylor   Shelley Winters   Natalie Wood

6. *Anna Christie*
   Liv Ullman   Greta Garbo   Julie Christie

7. *Theodora Goes Wild*
   Shirley Temple   Sandra Dee   Irene Dunne

8. *Sadie Thompson*
   Gloria Swanson   Carole Lombard   Joan Crawford

9. *Ninotchka*
   Greta Garbo   Gloria de Haven   May Britt

10. *Madame X*
    Ruth Gordon   Ruth Chatterton   Claudette Colbert

11. *Julia*
    Karen Black   Lynn Redgrave   Vanessa Redgrave

12. *Camille*
    Janet Leigh   Greta Garbo   Jane Wyman

13. *Sarah and Son*
    Lucille Ball   Ruth Chatterton   Katharine Hepburn

14. *Marie Antoinette*
    Norma Shearer   Celeste Holm   Judy Holliday

32

15. *Rebecca*
Merle Oberon   Joan Fontaine   Wendy Hiller

16. *Kitty Foyle*
Glenda Jackson   Ginger Rogers   Janet Suzman

17. *Annie Hall*
Diane Keaton   Jane Fonda   Lily Tomlin

18. *Madame Curie*
Irene Dunne   Greer Garson   Grace Kelly

19. *Gigi*
Jeanne Moreau   Jean Simmons   Leslie Caron

20. *Mrs. Miniver*
Bette Davis   Susan Hayward   Greer Garson

21. *Joan of Arc*
Marie Dressler   Ingrid Bergman   Joan Fontaine

22. *Sister Kenny*
Audrey Hepburn   Tuesday Weld   Rosalind Russell

23. *Violette*
Isabelle Huppert   Jeanne Moreau   Stephanie Audran

24. *All About Eve*
Joanne Woodward   Anne Baxter   Eva Marie Saint

25. *Irma La Douce*
Sophia Loren   Anna Magnani   Shirley MacLaine

26. *Juliet of the Spirits*
Giulietta Masina   Catherine Deneuve   Sophia Loren

27. *Mary Poppins*
Julie Andrews   Patricia Neal   Marsha Mason

28. *The Unsinkable Molly Brown*
Barbra Streisand   Barbara Stanwyck   Debbie Reynolds

29. *Georgy Girl*
Deborah Kerr   Lynn Redgrave   Sarah Miles

30. *Bonnie and Clyde*
Fay Wray   Faye Dunaway   Gena Rowlands

31. *Rachel, Rachel*
Raquel Welch   Mia Farrow   Joanne Woodward

32. *Isadora*
Ann Bancroft   Vanessa Redgrave   Leslie Browne

33. *Anne of the Thousand Days*
    Genevieve Bujold   Simone Signoret   Luise Rainer

34. *The Prime of Miss Jean Brodie*
    Claudette Colbert   Janet Gaynor   Maggie Smith

35. *Alice Doesn't Live Here Anymore*
    Diane Keaton   Ellen Burstyn   Cybill Shepherd

36. *Myra Breckenridge*
    Ali McGraw   Candice Bergen   Raquel Welch

37. *Rosemary's Baby*
    Mia Farrow   Sissy Spacek   Maureen O'Hara

38. *The Americanization of Emily*
    Julie Christie   Julie Andrews   Judith Anderson

39. *Harold and Maude*
    Ruth Chatterton   Ruth Gordon   Bette Davis

40. *Hello, Dolly!*
    Barbra Streisand   Liza Minnelli   Carol Channing

41. *Fanny*
    Simone Signoret   Jean Seberg   Leslie Caron

42. *Cleopatra*
    Elizabeth Taylor   Elizabeth Ashley   Mae West

43. *Daisy Miller*
    Mia Farrow   Cybill Shepherd   Tatum O'Neill

44. *The Perils of Pauline*
    Clara Bow   Lillian Gish   Pearl White

45. *McCabe and Mrs. Miller*
    Martha Scott   Julie Christie   Margaret Sullavan

46. *Carrie*
    Sissy Spacek   Tatum O'Neill   June Allyson

47. *Becky Sharp*
    Miriam Hopkins   Billie Burke   Loretta Young

48. *Auntie Mame*
    Rosalind Russell   Carol Channing   Maggie Smith

49. *Whatever Happened to Baby Jane?*
    Jill Clayburgh   Gloria Swanson   Bette Davis

50. *Lolita*
    Sue Lyon   Carol Baker   Tuesday Weld

34

GEM-DANDY!

Are you a connoisseur of precious stones? Below are 13 questions. You have three choices. Check the answer you believe is correct.

A score of five is precious; nine is sparkling; and 11 means you're a real jewel.

Answers on page 459

1. The most precious gem is the:
   Diamond   Emerald   Ruby

2. The Ruby Anniversary is the:
   20th   30th   40th

3. Amber is what color?
   Green   Red   Yellow

4. One carat equals:
   100 mg.   200 mg.   300 mg.

5. To bring out their natural color and brilliance, gems are usually:
   Cut   Polished   Cleaned in soap and water

6. Sapphire is a form of:
   Rutile   Corundum   Cassiterite

7. The hardest of all gems is the:
   Amethyst   Sapphire   Diamond

8. Garnet is the birthstone for the month of:
   January   February   July

9. The semiprecious stone malachite is found mainly in:
   Texas   India   Russia

10. The densest of all gems is:
    Tinstone   Ruby   Topaz

11. Pearls are found chiefly in:
    The western Pacific   The Aegean Sea   The eastern Atlantic

12. The diamond given to Elizabeth Taylor by Richard Burton in 1969 had how many carats?
    42 carats   69 carats   85 carats

13. The largest gem ever found was:
    A ruby   An aquamarine   A sardonx

35

DO YOU KNOW ART?

Are you an aficionado of the fine arts? This quiz tests your knowledge of famous painters and paintings. Three choices are given for each of the 26 questions. Check the answer you believe to be correct.

A score of 10 is fair; 16 is talented; 22 announces you as an art historian.

Answers on page 459

1. The *Mona Lisa* hangs in what famous art museum?
   The Metropolitan Museum of Art of New York City
   The Uffizi Galleries, Florence, Italy
   The Louvre, Paris, France

2. *La Primavera* was painted by:
   Botticelli   Leonardo da Vinci   Titian

3. A painter who belonged to the Fauve school of painters was:
   Monet   Vlaminck   Raphael

4. A painter renowned for his depictions of ballet dancers was:
   Reubens   Rembrandt   Degas

5. A group of painters who often painted outdoors, and used short brush strokes and bright colors were the:
   Dadaists   Impressionists   Cubists

6. Giotto, the famous Florentine painter, sculptor, and architect, lived in what century?
   Tenth   Fourteenth   Seventeenth

7. J.B.S. Chardin was a renowned 18th-century painter of:
   Landscapes   Portraits   Still lifes

8. The Jeu de Paume Museum in Paris is devoted entirely to the works of:
   The Impressionists   The Abstract Expressionists
   Italian painters of the 15th century

9. The leader of the Pre-Raphaelite Brotherhood was:
   Andrea del Sarto   Sir Joshua Reynolds   Dante Gabriel Rossetti

10. The American painter renowned for his portraits of George Washington was:
    Gilbert Stuart   Andrew Wyeth   John Singer Sargent

11. What nationality was Mary Cassatt?
    French   American   Swiss

12. The famous painter who was married to photographer Alfred Stieglitz is:
    Berthe Morisot   Helen Frankenthaler   Georgia O'Keeffe

13. Salvador Dali painted in what style?
    Abstract Expressionist   Barbizon School   Surrealist

14. A painter renowned for his madonnas was:
    J.M.W. Turner   Raphael   Cézanne

15. Robert Browning wrote a long poem about what painter?
    Fra Angelico   Fra Lippo Lippi   Veronese

16. Jackson Pollack introduced what new technique into painting?
    Chiaroscuro   Stain painting   Action painting

17. A 16th-century Flemish painter of peasant life was:
    Pieter Breughel   Piet Mondrian   Hieronymous Bosch

18. English art critic John Ruskin conducted a notorious vendetta against what painter?
    John Constable   J.A.M. Whistler   Sir Thomas Gainsborough

19. Which of the following painters was *not* an Impressionist?
    Monet   Renoir   Matisse

20. A painter famous for his paintings of sunflowers was:
    Vincent Van Gogh   Paul Gauguin   Jean Dufy

21. Picasso's *Guernica* commemorates:
    World War I   The Spanish Civil War
    The American Civil War

22. An English painter who was also a famous poet was:
    William Blake   John Everett Millais
    Sir Joshua Reynolds

23. A famous French Romantic painter was:
    Watteau   Corot   Delacroix

24. A Russian painter considered the originator of abstract painting, who was associated with the Bauhaus painters was:
    Marc Chagall   Wassily Kandinsky   Franz Kupka

25. A painter renowned for his elongated portraits of figures with almond-shaped eyes is:
    Robert Delauney   Modigliani   Van Dyke

26. If you wanted to see the marvelous collection in the renowned Hermitage museum, you would have to go to:
    Madrid   Amsterdam   Leningrad

COLOSSAL COUNTRIES

What are the 10 largest countries in the world? Below is a list of 20 countries. Check the 10 countries which you think are the largest, and rank the countries from largest to 10th largest.

You get two points for every country that you correctly identify as one of the 10 largest. Subtract one point for every wrong answer. Give yourself an extra five points for correctly identifying the world's largest country; three points for the second largest country; and two points for the third largest country.

A score of nine means you are a geographer; 12 earns you a gold star; and a score of 14 ranks you as topographical tops!

Answers on page 459

1. India

2. Algeria

3. Egypt

4. France

5. Brazil

6. Spain

7. Venezuela

8. Canada

9. New Zealand

10. United States

11. Germany

12. China

13. Japan

14. Mexico

15. Sudan

16. Great Britain

17. U.S.S.R.

18. Argentina

19. Saudi Arabia

20. Australia

SPELLING BEE

The sad tale set forth below looks even sadder than it sounds, for the unfortunate fellow, in addition to all his other troubles, was born a poor speller.

If your tears do not crinkle his autobiographical paragraphs, you should discern 20 misspelled words. You score five points for each misspelled word you underline. On the other hand, you lose 10 points for each correctly spelled word which you claim is misspelled.

Answers on page 459

SAD SACK

Did you ever have the kind of day that was simply disasterous? Well, yesterday I wanted to scream in frustration and dispair.

It all started when my usually trusty digital alarm failed to go off. If my phone hadn't wrung, I undoubtebly would have slept right through the day. It was, of course, a wrong number, but at least it woke me. To my horror and disbeleif, it was 9:30! And I had an important conferance with my boss scheduled for 10! It was not modern paraphenalia that had failed, but the human mind—I had forgotten to set the alarm!

I threw my clothes on and, sacrificing breakfeast, I raced out. As I waited for a cab, I automaticly felt for my wallet in my inside pocket. Wouldn't you know, in my haste I had forgotten it. Back up I raced to retreive my wallet. Then back to the street for a cab. Fortunately, one came along imediately. "Madison and 45th, and hurry, please."

He took off like greeced lightening. A couple of blocks down we had to stop for a traffic light. Sensing my impatience, the driver jumped the light. OK, you guessed it; we hit an oncoming vehical! Naturally, I hadn't put on the seat belt and I was thrown forward with a vengence. My arm was twisted into a pretzel! What can I tell you—the crowds gathered; cops sudenly appearred from no-where; an ambulance was called; and I wound up in the hospital.

By the time I could make the attendents understand that I had to call my boss, it was 11. Fortunately, I had an impecable excuse. How could my boss fire a guy who had just broken an arm trying to get to work on time?

You know what, he did! They say you'll be alright when you get out of the hospital, but as for me, *I'll* be a releif case!

A PANOPLY OF PHOBIAS

Psychiatrists call an obsessive fear a *phobia*. Below is a list of 15 unusual phobias—and the names of these phobias are pretty unusual, too! Can you pick out what the fearful object is to the sufferers from the following phobias? You have three choices.

You get one point for every correct answer. A score of seven is fearfully good; nine is terror-rific; 11 brands you as a psychoanalytic prodigy.

Answers on page 460

Answers on page 460

1. Acrophobia is fear of:
   Bees   *Heights*   *People*

2. Clinophobia is fear of:
   Clinics   *Beds*   *Disease*

3. Keraunophobia is a fear of:
   Thunder   *Leprechauns*   *Kites*

4. Taphephobia is a fear of:
   Candy   *Trees*   *Being buried alive*

5. Aileuophobia is a fear of:
   Cats   *Dogs*   *Allergies*

6. Bathophobia is a fear of:
   Taking baths   *Depth*   *Making decisions*

7. Claustrophobia is a fear of:
   Night   *Blood*   *Enclosed places*

8. Iatrophobia is a fear of:
   Storms   *Plants*   *Doctors*

9. Agoraphobia is a fear of:
   Typewriters   *Open places*   *Secretaries*

10. Hydrophobia is a fear of:
    Water   *Flowers*   *Monsters*

11. Necrophobia is a fear of:
    Nuclear bombs   *Rain*   *Dead bodies*

12. Ballistophobia is a fear of:
    Dancing   *Children*   *Bullets*

13. Pantophobia is a fear of:
    Trousers   *Women*   *Fears*

14. Sophophobia is a fear of:
    Learning   *Soap*   *Food*

15. Ombrophobia is a fear of:
    Insects   *Rain*   *Crossing bridges*

THE GAME OF STATES

On the left-hand side of this page you will find a list of 26 states. On the right-hand side, in a box, you will find the nicknames of these states. Can you match up which nickname belongs to what state?

Correctly identifying 15 states is good; 18 is excellent; and 21 means you are a geographical whiz.

Answers on page 460

1. Alabama
2. Arizona
3. California
4. Connecticut
5. Florida
6. Illinois
7. Indiana
8. Iowa
9. Kansas
10. Kentucky
11. Maine
12. Massachusetts
13. Michigan
14. Nebraska
15. Nevada
16. New Hampshire
17. New Jersey
18. New York
19. Ohio
20. Oklahoma
21. Oregon
22. South Carolina
23. South Dakota
24. Texas
25. Utah
26. Vermont

GREEN MOUNTAIN STATE
BEAVER STATE
BUCKEYE STATE
GRANITE STATE
BAY STATE
BLUEGRASS STATE
GARDEN STATE
WOLVERINE STATE
GOLDEN STATE
COTTON STATE
GRAND CANYON STATE
COYOTE STATE
SUNFLOWER STATE
HOOSIER STATE
LONE STAR STATE
PINE TREE STATE
PRAIRIE STATE
CORNHUSKER STATE
SILVER STATE
PALMETTO STATE
EMPIRE STATE
NUTMEG STATE
BEEHIVE STATE
SOONER STATE
HAWKEYE STATE
SUNSHINE STATE

CAN YOU SPOT THE INTRUDER?

Each of the groups of words below contains one word which doesn't belong. Can you tell which one is the outsider, and why?

Answers on page 460

1.	John	George	Ringo	Peter
2.	Tandem	Trike	Bicycle	Berth
3.	Tuba	Cello	Coronet	Oboe
4.	Wolf	Deer	Elephant	Crocodile
5.	Stallion	Llama	Steed	Mare
6.	Cougar	Pinto	Impala	Edsel
7.	Chin	Eye	Elbow	Lip
8.	Pen	Ruler	Pencil	Chalk
9.	Ode	Ballad	Sonnet	Concerto
10.	Beer	Brandy	Soda	Wine
11.	Farcical	Comic	Droll	Pathetic
12.	Milk	Flour	Cheese	Butter
13.	Threw	Thought	Feel	Bought
14.	Brother	Father	Uncle	Aunt
15.	Eyes	Teeth	Feet	Hands
16.	Stride	Saunter	Sway	Stroll
17.	Finish	Complete	Commence	Terminate
18.	Sun	Earth	Mars	Venus

PRESIDENTS AND VICE-PRESIDENTS

You have heard the names of all the Presidents of the United States. You've heard many of the names of the Vice-presidents of the United States. It's rather difficult to tell which Vice-president served under which president. On the left-hand side of this page you have a list of Presidents. On the right-hand side, you have a list of Vice-presidents. Can you match them up correctly?

A score of eight is average, and a score of 11 is extraordinary. If you can handle them all, that should be considered a tour de force.

Answers on page 460

PRESIDENTS	VICE-PRESIDENTS
1. Harry Truman	**JOHN ADAMS**
2. Herbert Hoover	**THOMAS JEFFERSON**
3. Warren Harding	**CHARLES FAIRBANKS**
4. William Taft	**JAMES SHERMAN**
5. Dwight Eisenhower	**THOMAS MARSHALL**
6. John Adams	**CALVIN COOLIDGE**
7. Gerald Ford	**CHARLES DAWES**
8. George Washington	**CHARLES CURTIS**
9. Franklin Roosevelt	**ALBEN BARKLEY**
10. William McKinley	**RICHARD NIXON**
11. Calvin Coolidge	**LYNDON JOHNSON**
12. John Kennedy	**SPIRO AGNEW**
13. Theodore Roosevelt	**NELSON ROCKEFELLER**
14. Richard Nixon	**THEODORE ROOSEVELT**
15. Woodrow Wilson	**HARRY TRUMAN**

GAME FOR THE GOURMET

Are you a connoisseur of culinary specialties? The 26 questions below all concern the composition of gourmet dishes. There are three choices. Check the answer you believe to be correct.

A score of 12 is savory; 16 is delectable; and 21 is delicious!

Answers on page 460

1. Chicken Marengo is made with:
    White wine and tomatoes   Saffron and beer
    Cognac and turnips

2. Eggs Benedict are poached eggs and ham served with:
    Hollandaise sauce   Béarnaise sauce   Brandied ketchup

3. Crepes suzettes are:
    German apple pancakes   Brazilian potato dumplings
    French pancakes with a flaming orange sauce

4. A steak dish eaten virtually raw is:
    Steak Diane   Steak Tartare   Salisbury steak

5. Chicken Tetrazzini is served on a bed of:
    Spinach   Brown rice   Spaghetti

6. Genoise is a:
    Cheese sauce   Cake   Pasta cooked in cream

7. Sukiyaki is a Japanese dish consisting primarily of:
    Beef and onions   Pork and cabbage   Veal and oyster sauce

8. Szechuan cooking is:
    Meatless   Spicy   Indigenous to Thailand

9. One of the ingredients of Sachertorte is:
    Gooseberry jam   Macadamia nuts   Apricot jam

10. Coquilles St. Jacques is made with:
    Shrimp   Filet of sole   Scallops

11. North African Couscous uses:
    Crushed grain   Potato flour   Steamed milk

12. Santa Lucia buns are made with:
    Allspice   Saffron   Chopped maraschino cherries

13. Croissants are:
    A Viennese dessert made with semisweet chocolate
    A Brazilian dish made with pork sausage
    A French roll made with lots of butter

14. An important seasoning in paella is:
    Oregano   Saffron   Cumin

15. Spaghetti al pesto is made with:
    A fresh basil sauce   An egg and cream sauce
                A tomato and meat sauce

16. Southern-style spareribs are:
    Baked in orange juice and white wine
    Barbecued in a tomato and molasses sauce
    Parboiled and served plain

17. Zabaglione is an Italian dessert made with:
    Egg yolks, sugar, and wine   Ice cream   Cream and cheese

18. Chilis rellenos is a Mexican dish consisting of:
    Corn wafers stuffed with ground meat and drenched in
          tomato sauce
    Green peppers stuffed with meat or cheese
    Chicken with a spicy chocolate sauce

19. Lentils are a prime ingredient of:
    Soupe niçoise   Mulligatawny soup   French onion soup

20. A soupçon is:
    A heaping tablespoon   A dash   A cup-and-a-half

21. A Waldorf salad contains:
    Celery, apples, and walnuts   Tuna and anchovies
          Croutons and bacon bits

22. Veal Parmigiana is made with:
    Mozzarella cheese and tomato sauce   Marsala and mushrooms
         White wine, lemon juice, and herbs

23. Calzone are stuffed with:
    Ricotta cheese and sometimes ham   Shrimp and minced clams
         Brazil nuts and sweet chocolate

24. Curry is composed of:
    Basil, thyme, and oregano   Cinnamon, cloves, and nutmeg
         Cumin, coriander, turmeric, and other pungent spices

25. Filet mignon is:
    A fish dish cooked in white wine and garnished with almonds
    A dessert made with bananas and ricotta cheese
    A choice steak dish, cooked in butter

26. If you ordered pommes soufflés, you would be eating:
    Apples   Cheese   Potatoes

ALL ABOUT EVE

Below are 35 questions about great women and their achievements. There are three choices. Check the answer you believe is correct.

A score of 15 shows your consciousness is raised. If you score 21, you're probably a feminist. If you score 28, you're well-grounded in history—or should we say herstory!

Answers on page 461

1. Marie Curie, the renowned discoverer of radium, was born in:
   France   England   Poland

2. Jane Addams was the founder of what settlement house?
   Hull House   The Henry St. Settlement   Denison House

3. Diane Arbus is renowned for her excellence in:
   Sculpting   Photography   Mathematics

4. The leader of the British suffragettes was:
   Elizabeth Cady Stanton   Beatrice Webb   Emmeline Pankhurst

5. Elizabeth I of England ascended the throne in:
   1533   1558   1588

6. The woman who was called "Mother of the Russian Revolution" was:
   Catherine the Great   Catherine Breshkovsky   Rosa Luxemburg

7. Babe Didrikson Zaharias was:
   A champion athlete   A famous novelist   A leading Zionist

8. The leader of the "Underground Railroad" that brought Southern Black slaves to freedom in the North prior to the Civil War was:
   Harriet Beecher Stowe   Harriet Ross Tubman   Cicely Tyson

9. Maria Montessori, the first woman in Italy to become a medical doctor, was famous for her innovations in:
   Biology   Elementary education   Business

10. The founder of home economics, who was also the first woman to attend M.I.T., was:
    Elizabeth Blackwell   Fanny Farmer   Ellen Swallow Richards

11. *Middlemarch* is a novel by Mary Ann Evans, who wrote under the pen name:
    Charlotte Brontë   George Eliot   George Sand

12. Dorothy Arzner was a top:

    Dress designer   Film director   Advertising executive

13. The reformer known as "The Angel of the Prisons" was:

    Joan of Arc   Elizabeth Fry   Dorothea Dix

14. Margaret Sanger was a noted:

    Birth control pioneer   Primitive painter   Political scientist

15. Florence Nightingale accomplished important public health reforms during:

    The American Revolution   The Napoleonic Wars

        The Crimean War

16. The Irish revolutionary, Constance Gore-Booth Markiewicz, was also:

    The first woman cabinet member in Europe

    Winner of the Nobel Prize for Poetry

    The first Irish aviator

17. Margaret Mead was:

    A psychoanalyst   An anthropologist   A writer of novels

18. The first woman prime minister of Israel was:

    Henrietta Szold   Emma Lazarus   Golda Meir

19. The discoverer of the first effective treatment against poliomyelitis was:

    Mother Cabrini   Sister Kenny   Clara Barton

20. The founder of the Christian Science religion was:

    Antoinette Brown Blackwell   Mary Baker Eddy

        Louisa May Alcott

21. The author of *Women and Economics*, an important 19th-century feminist document, was:

    Charlotte Perkins Gilman   Margaret Fuller

        Mary Wollstonecraft Godwin

22. Martha Graham is a well-known:

    Mountain climber and explorer   Ecologist

        Dancer and choreographer

23. The Soong sister who is currently a vice-premier of Communist China is:

    Meiling Soong Chiang   Ailing Soong Kung

        Chingling Soong Sun

24. The teacher of Helen Keller was:

    Laura Bridgman   Emma Willard   Anne Sullivan Macy

25. The first American-trained opera singer to sing at the Metropolitan Opera was:

    Rosa Ponselle   Beverly Sills   Maria Callas

26. Sojourner Truth was:

    The founder of a religious sect that preached that God is black
    A freed slave who was the first black to win a court action
        against whites
    A self-taught lawyer and polemicist

27. The first woman to swim the English Channel received a ticker-tape welcome in New York City. Her name was Gertrude Ederle, and the year of her achievement was:

    1916   1926   1936

28. The author of *Kristin Lavransdatter* received the Nobel Prize for literature in 1928. Her name is:

    Sigrid Undset   Baroness Orczy   Edith Wharton

29. The first nation to grant its female citizens the right to vote did so in 1893. The country was:

    Denmark   Switzerland   New Zealand

30. Isabella Beeton, the 19th century author of the famed work on cookery and domestic science entitled *Household Management*, died at the age of:

    29   49   79

31. The noted American anthropologist, author of *Patterns of Culture* was:

    Margaret Mead   Ruth Benedict   Carolyn Wells

32. The doctor who created a test that evaluates a baby's condition within one minute after birth is:

    Margaret Sanger   Marie Stopes   Virginia Apgar

33. The Bandit Queen, a confederate of the notorious Jesse James gang was:

    Sadie Thompson   Belle Starr   Kitty Black

34. The originator of the world-famous wax works exhibited in London was:

    Mary Beale   Florence Artaud   Marie Tussaud

35. Johanna Spyri, the author of the famous children's book, *Heidi*, was:

    Norwegian   Swiss   Russian

VOCABULARY QUIZ

You have undoubtedly encountered these 30 words in newspapers, magazines, and books. You probably know approximately what they mean; but do you know exactly what they mean?

Mark the choice you believe to be correct. Check your answers; give yourself two points for each correct answer, but deduct one point for each incorrect response. A total score of 34 means you're a highly verbal person; 42 means you should join Webster's staff; and a perfect score of 60 means you're a lexicographer.

Answers on page 461

1. FANFARE
    Blast of trumpets   *Cost of transportation to ball games*
    Spanish menu item   *Fee deductible from income tax*

2. OENOLOGY
    Study of seashells   *Science of wines*
    Ocean biology   *An Eastern religion*

3. PUERILE
    Valuable   *Enamel*
    Childish   *Sterile*

4. EFFULGENT
    Brassy   *Brittle*
    Brilliant   *Bruised*

5. CONCUPISCENT
    Lustful   *Attractive*
    Clever   *Costly*

6. ANODYNE
    Mercurochrome   *Rare bone disease*
    Painkiller   *In the year of Our Lord*

7. CLANDESTINE
    A famous family   *Musical instrument*
    Secret   *Brightly colored*

8. DONNYBROOK
    Brawl   *Large farm*
    Small stream   *Scottish national bird*

9. GOSSAMER
    Young goose   *Gaseous*
    Gauzy   *Bitter-tasting*

10. TRENCHANT

    Foxhole   *Incisive*

    Ditchdigger   *Wooden platter*

11. ENCOMIUM

    Praise   *Prison*

    Prize   *Price*

12. WINSOME

    Victorious   *Lucky*

    Unappealing   *Charming*

13. EPITOME

    Circumference   *Essence*

    Grandeur   *Large book*

14. RECIDIVIST

    Democrat   *Habitual criminal*

    Socialist   *Front-desk secretary*

15. CRASS

    Unfeeling   *Salad green*

    Synthetic metal   *Emotional*

16. GAFFE

    Desert animal   *Lady's hat*

    Blunder   *Nonsense*

17. PARIAH

    Outcast   *Outhouse*

    Outdoors   *Outlandish*

18. VICARIOUS

    Clerical   *Funny*

    Dangerous   *Substitute*

19. ICONOCLASTIC

    Durable plastic   *Traditional*

    Strong elastic   *Revolutionary*

20. NADIR

    Lowest point   *Governmental official*

    Poor   *Hindu garment*

21. DEPREDATE

    Plunder   *Belittle*

    Intercede   *Precede*

22. MAUDLIN
    Ordinary   *Purple*
    Stately   *Sentimental*

23. MILITATE
    March   *Lessen*
    Have effect   *Conscript*

24. RESCIND
    Sin again   *Revoke*
    Rekindle   *Tough rind*

25. PEREGRINATION
    Journey   *Dovelike*
    Puzzle   *Disease*

26. SUBSIST
    Be a category of *Continue to exist*
    Hang up   *Flood with water*

27. INTERLOPER
    Dramatist   *Conversationalist*
    Aviator   *Intruder*

28. HARBINGER
    Omen   *Magician*
    Gambler   *Type of horse*

29. DIFFIDENCE
    Shyness   *Trust*
    Distinction   *Stubbornness*

30. HALCYON
    Sanctified   *Chalice*
    Tranquil   *Synthetic*

BALLETOMANIA

Are you a balletomane—a devoted fan of the classical ballet? Below are 25 questions. You have three choices. Check the answer you believe is correct.

A score of 10 shows you're on your toes; 15 earns you bravos; and 20 makes you a *mâitre de ballet*.

Answers on page 461

1. A *pirouette* is:
    A rapid turn on the toe or ball of the foot
    A series of leaps executed in rapid succession
    Five *pliés* performed in second position

2. The music to *Swan Lake* was composed by:
    Stravinsky   Tchaikovsky   Debussy

3. The leading contemporary choreographer of plotless ballets is:
    George Balanchine   Agnes De Mille   Bronislav Nijinska

4. Swanhilda is a character in what ballet?
    Swan Lake   *Les Sylphides*   *Coppelia*

5. The Royal Ballet of England was formerly called:
    Ballet Theater   Sadler's Wells   The Ballet Russe

6. Ballet originated in the 16th century in what country:
    Russia   France   Italy

7. The tutu came into use in what century:
    18th   19th   20th

8. The first of the great Russian choreographers was:
    Marius Petipa   Sergei Diaghilev   Michel Fokine

9. Anna Pavlova, considered to be the greatest ballerina of the first three decades of the 20th century, was particularly associated with what ballet:
    Le Baiser de la Fée   *The Dying Swan*   *Scheherezade*

10. In Tchaikovsky's *Sleeping Beauty*, the title character's name is:
    Rose   Aurora   Giselle

11. The male ballet dancer who starred in the movie *The Turning Point* was:
    Rudolph Nureyev   Mikhail Baryshnikov   Jacques D'Amboise

12. Suzanne Farrell, a leading ballerina of the New York City Ballet, is usually partnered by:

    Peter Martins   Rudolph Nureyev   Anton Dolin

13. The ballet which requires the *première danseuse* to execute 32 *fouettés* in the third act is:

    Romeo and Juliet   *Swan Lake*   *Sleeping Beauty*

14. Which of the following ballets was composed by Igor Stravinsky?

    Fall River Legend   *Nutcracker Suite*   *The Firebird*

15. The director of the Cuban Ballet is:

    Marcia Haydée   Maria Tallchief   Alicia Alonso

16. Moira Shearer starred in a ballet movie called:

    The Turning Point   *Tina, the Ballerina*   *The Red Shoes*

17. The first ballerina to dance the title role of *Giselle* was:

    Carlotta Grisi   Marie Taglioni   Alicia Markova

18. The oldest ballet in the standard repertory is:

    La Sylphide   *L'Après-Midi d'un Faune*   *La Fille Mal Gardée*

19. The ballet about three puppets brought to line by a Russian charlatan is:

    Petrouchka   *Sebastian*   *Til Eulenspiegel*

20. In the American premiere of the complete *Swan Lake*, performed by the Sadler's Wells Company at the Metropolitan Opera House in New York on October 20, 1949, the roles of Odette and Odile were danced by:

    Svetlana Beriosa   Margot Fonteyn   Beryl Grey

21. A *pas de deux* requires how many dancers:

    Two, a ballerina and a danseur.
    Three, a ballerina and two danseurs.
    As many dancers as there are in the company's corps de ballet.

22. The great 18th-century ballet innovator who abolished the mask and simplified ballet costumes was:

    Pierre Beauchamps   Jean Georges Noverre   Charles Didelot

23. There are how many ballet positions:

    Five   Ten   An infinite number

24. *Giselle* is what type of ballet:

    Romantic   Psychological   Divertissement

25. The bluebird *pas de deux* comes from what ballet?

    Don Quijote   *The Firebird*   *Nutcracker Suite*

53

THE DOODLE QUIZ

We all do it. The cave men did it. Children scribble their doodles. The powerful and renowned, the man on the street, even you and I leave behind us on walls, telephone books, and bits of paper the projection of our thoughts as we unconsciously make lines which may or may not resemble reality.

The following are doodles of people famous in politics and the arts. You are given three choices. Pick out the name of the person you think made the doodle, and check the name.

A score of six is average; eight is very good; 10 is excellent; 14 is extraordinary; and 15 makes it clear that you're a professional psychologist.

Answers on page 461

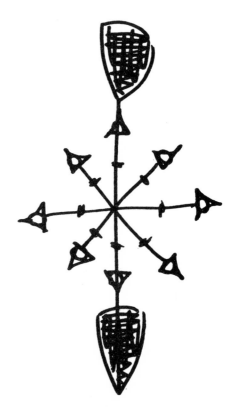

1. Joan Miró
Ringo Starr
Ed Koch

2. Sophia Loren
Frank Sinatra
Hugh Carey

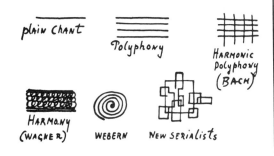

3. Sir Alec Guinness
Woody Allen
Telly Savalas

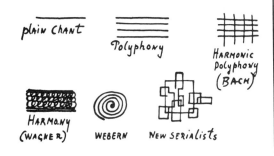

4. Isaac Stern
Igor Stravinsky
Leonard Bernstein

5. Reggie Jackson
Merv Griffin
Norman Rockwell

6. Leonardo da Vinci
Joseph Teller
Albert Einstein

7. Johnny Carson
Elia Kazan
Ginger Rogers

55

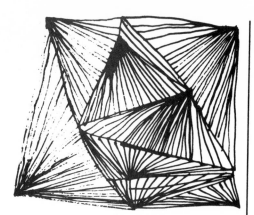

8. Richard Nixon
   Adolph Ochs
   Cyrus Vance

11. Bette Davis
    Ethel Barrymore
    Cornelia Otis Skinner

9. Jean Dubuffet
   Joe Di Maggio
   Rosa Ponselle

10. Arthur Burns
    Bob Hope
    The Shah of Iran

12. Norman Mailer
    James Michener
    Saul Bellow

13. Lily Pons
Joan Sutherland
Beverly Sills

15. Queen Elizabeth
Princess Grace of Monaco
Golda Meir

14. Tony Randall
Pat Boone
Paul Newman

16. Betty Grable
Teddy Kennedy
Humphrey Bogart

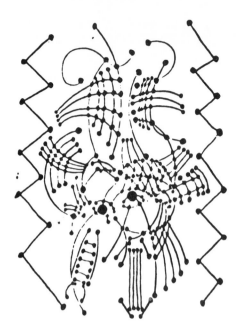

17. Joan Didion
Cardinal Spellman
Pablo Picasso

19. Lyndon Johnson
Arturo Toscanini
Enrico Caruso

18. Charles de Gaulle
Duke Ellington
Yves Montand

20. Paul Klee
Mikhail Baryshnikov
Frank Lloyd Wright

STREETWISE

Do you know the names of the world's famous highways and byways? Below are the names of 25 internationally famous streets. In the blank spaces, write the names of the cities in which these streets are located.

A score of 11 means you've been around; 17 makes you a boulevardier; and 23 makes you a walking street dictionary.

Answers on page 462

1. Les Champs Élysées   _____

2. Bond Street   _____

3. Wall Street   _____

4. Sunset Boulevard   _____

5. Via Veneto   _____

6. Madison Avenue   _____

7. Beacon Street   _____

8. Boulevard St. Michel   _____

9. Wilshire Boulevard   _____

10. Peachtree Street   _____

11. Hans Christian Andersen Boulevard   _____

12. Nevsky Prospekt   _____

13. Kurfurstendam   _____

14. Promenade des Anglais   _____

15. Dizengoff   _____

16. Mott Street   _____

17. Piccadilly   _____

18. Unter den Linden   _____

19. Michigan Boulevard   _____

20. Bourbon Street   _____

21. Market Street   _____

22. Basin Street   _____

23. Fleet Street   _____

24. Pennsylvania Avenue   _____

25. The Strand   _____

FOR BOGART FANS

Who can ever forget Bogie? How much do you remember about the actor who for over a quarter of a century was the idol of American film-goers?

Three choices are given for each of the 27 questions. Check the answer you believe to be the right one.

A score of 13 is good; 18 is superior; 22 dates you; 24 means you're a revival buff.

Answers on page 462

Answers on page 462

1. Bogart's last film, made in 1956, was:
   The African Queen   *The Harder They Fall*
                          The Left Hand of God

2. Humphrey Bogart's mother was a famous:
   Doctor   Stage actress   Magazine illustrator

3. Bogart began his theatrical career as:
   A stage manager   A set designer
                  A stage actor, playing juvenile leads

4. Bogart's first stage role was as a Japanese houseboy in the play:
   The Manchurian Candidate   *Madame Butterfly*   *The Drifter*

5. Bogart's first wife was actress:
   Lauren Bacall   Helen Mencken   Bette Davis

6. Under Bogart's first film contract, his weekly salary was:
   $75 $750 $7,500

7. Bogart's first film part was a minor role in *A Devil with Women* (1930). The star of this film was:
   Spencer Tracy   Victor McLaglen   Charles Farrell

8. Bogart's first gangster role was in the movie:
   Three on a Match   *The Petrified Forest*   *High Sierra*

9. Bogart called his fourth wife, Lauren Bacall:
   Laurie   Becky   Betty

10. The detective character immortalized by Bogie in *The Maltese Falcon*, based on the Dashiell Hammett mystery novel, was named:
    Nero Wolfe   Ellery Queen   Sam Spade

11. Bogart's famous line, "I was misinformed," was spoken in which movie?
    The Petrified Forest   *Casablanca*   *Dark Victory*

12. Bogie co-starred with Lauren Bacall in her first picture, released in 1945. The film was:

    The Big Sleep   *To Have and Have Not*   *Key Largo*

13. Bogie's co-star in *The African Queen* was:

    Lauren Bacall   Bette Davis   Katharine Hepburn

14. Bogie and his close friends, who included Frank Sinatra, Sid Luft, and others, were known as The Clan, or:

    Our Gang   The Rat Pack   The Dirty Dozen

15. The director of the Bogart hit *The Treasure of Sierra Madre* was:

    John Huston   John Ford   Howard Hawks

16. Bogart considered his worst picture to be:

    Knock on Any Door   *We're No Angels*   *Swing Your Lady*

17. Humphrey Bogart was the father of how many children?

    Two   Four   Six

18. Bogart died in 1957 of:

    A heart attack   Cancer   Pancreatitis

19. Captain Queeg was a character played by Bogart in what film?

    Moby Dick   *The Caine Mutiny*   *San Quentin*

20. In Bogart's second movie, *Up the River*, the female lead was played by:

    Bette Davis   Ingrid Bergman   Claire Luce

21. In which movie did Barbara Stanwyck play Bogart's wife?

    The Big Sleep   *Stella Dallas*   *The Two Mrs. Carrolls*

22. Bogart appeared with Bette Davis and Ronald Reagan in what film?

    Dark Passage   *Dark Victory*   *Now, Voyager*

23. Bogie owned a 55-foot yacht named:

    The African Queen   *The Santana*   *The Betty*

24. The script for the movie *Beat the Devil*, featuring Bogie, Jennifer Jones, Gina Lollobrigida, and Peter Lorre, was written by:

    William Inge   Truman Capote   Gore Vidal

25. Bogie won his first Oscar for which picture?

    Casablanca   *The African Queen*   *The Petrified Forest*

26. Bogart played the role of Philip Marlowe in:

    Dark Victory   *The Big Sleep*   *To Have and Have Not*

27. Which of one of these people did *not* play in *The Petrified Forest*?

    Bette Davis   Leslie Howard   Peter Lorre

POT-AU-FEU

We have here a stew of 29 unrelated bits and pieces of information. See how good a chef you are. Choose the answer you think is right.

Award yourself one point for each correct answer. A score of 13 makes the grade; 18 is commendable; and 23 earns you a cordon bleu.

Answers on page 462

1. Which country has the highest death rate?
   Panama   Angola   Bangladesh

2. A neophyte is a:
   New golf club   New type of carriage   Beginner

3. Katharine Hepburn's first movie was:
   Alice Adams   *A Bill of Divorcement*   *The Philadelphia Story*

4. The first Little League World Series took place in:
   1910   1947   1967

5. Which animal lives the longest?
   A camel   A tortoise   A parrot

6. Which of the following birds can *not* fly?
   The magpie   The bobwhite   The cormorant

7. A vendetta is a:
   Feud   Spanish marketplace   Large advertised sale

8. A backlist is:
   A list of books published previously
   A published list of insurance prospects
   A list of retired military officers

9. The largest desert in the world is:
   The Great Gobi   The Sahara   Death Valley

10. Stephen Crane's novel *The Red Badge of Courage* was published in:
    1845   1895   1955

11. A troglodyte is:
    A cave dweller   A large amphibian
    An attic window transparent to the sky

12. The largest bird in the world is the:
    Eagle   Ostrich   Emu

13. A famous battle of World War I was:
    The Battle of the Bulge   The Battle of the Marne
    The Battle of Waterloo

14. Kleig lights are:
    High-powered laser beams   Bright lights used in the theatre
            Illegal illuminations used by smugglers

15. What President of the United States became Chief Justice of the Supreme Court after he left the Presidency?
    Taft   Polk   Buchanan

16. A pinafore is a:
    Type of musical instrument   Large safety pin   Children's apron

17. The last bare-knuckle fight was held in:
    1869   1889   1919

18. The most expensive food in the world, the white truffle of the Piedmont district of Italy, sells for about:
    $20 per pound $200 dollars per pound $2,000 per pound

19. The Thousand Islands are located:
    In the Southwest Pacific   In the Great Lakes   Off Alaska

20. A dromedary is a:
    Date   Camel   Mohammedan calendar

21. Puck is a character in Shakespeare's:
    Twelfth Night   *The Tempest*   *Midsummer Night's Dream*

22. The artist associated with the Sistine Chapel was:
    Leonardo da Vinci   Giotto   Michelangelo

23. A palimpsest is a:
    Grapefruit   Cordovan pocketbook
        Manuscript in which later writing is superimposed on earlier writing

24. What is meant by the phrase "killing the fatted calf?"
    Feasting and rejoicing   Wasting without limit
            Destroying one's source of sustenance

25. A knight errant was a:
    Knight who had fallen from grace   Wandering knight
        Knight in a chess game which has been turned into a king

26. The fur nutria comes from a large South American water rodent called a:
    Coypu   Weasel   Ferret

27. The capital of the State of Delaware is:
    Wilmington   Elsmere   Dover

28. The author of *Wuthering Heights* was:
    Charlotte Brontë   Emily Brontë   Jane Austen

29. If someone called you a profligate, it would mean you are:
    Stingy   Wasteful   Vain

63

WHERE, OH, WHERE?

You need not have seen all this world's sights to know where these landmark monuments are. In the blank spaces, write the name of the city in which (or near which) the monument is located.

Give yourself two points for every correct answer. Deduct one point for every incorrect answer. A score of 30 is worthy of Atlas; 36 is monumental; and 44 means you're a walking Michelin guide!

Answers on page 462

1. The Statue of Liberty is in _____.

2. The Wailing Wall stands in _____.

3. The Eiffel Tower is in _____.

4. The Great Pyramids stand near _____.

5. The Spanish Steps are in _____.

6. The Hermitage is in _____.

7. The Sphinx is near _____.

8. The Leaning Tower is in _____.

9. The Vatican is in _____.

10. The Empire State Building is in _____.

11. The Taj Mahal is in _____.

12. Saint Mark's Cathedral is in _____.

13. Big Ben is in _____.

14. The Blarney Stone is in _____.

15. The Kremlin is in _____.

16. La Scala Opera House is in _____.

17. The Alhambra is in _____.

18. The Golden Gate Bridge is in _____.

19. The Parthenon is in _____.

20. Westminster Abbey is in _____.

21. The Kaaba is in _____.

22. Notre Dame Cathedral stands in _____.

23. The Prado is in _____.

24. Faneuil Hall is in _____.

GRAND TOUR

Who doesn't dream of making that deluxe grand tour around the world, staying at the most elegant five-star hotels in each city? Here is a list of 25 famous hotels located in cities all over the world that have given luxurious accommodation to traveling notables. Can you say in which city each of these hostelries is located?

A score of 10 shows you read the travel pages; 15 makes you travelwise; and 20 practically makes you a travel agent.

Answers on page 462

Answers on page 462

 1. PLAZA-ATHENÉE _____

 2. NEW STANLEY _____

 3. KING DAVID _____

 4. GRANDE-BRETAGNE _____

 5. SACHER _____

 6. LA MAMOUNIA _____

 7. CLARIDGE'S _____

 8. HASSLER'S VILLA MEDICI _____

 9. REGENCY _____

10. NEGRESCO _____

11. GRESHAM _____

12. LIBERTADOR _____

13. PENINSULA _____

14. DAN CARMEL _____

15. PALACE _____

16. GEORGE V _____

17. RAFFLES _____

18. FONTAINBLEU _____

19. BRISTOL KEMPINSKI _____

20. SHILLA _____

21. BAUR AU LAC _____

22. SHAH ABBAS _____

23. MARK HOPKINS _____

24. SOUTHERN CROSS _____

25. CONNAUGHT _____

FOR CHAPLIN FANS

Many film buffs consider Charlie Chaplin the greatest personage in motion-picture history. How much do you know about this beloved star and his movies?

Below are 25 questions. You have three choices. Check the answer you believe is correct.

A score of 14 is admirable; 21 means you're a movie aficionado; and 24 means you win the Chaplin Emmy.

Answers on page 463

1. A Charlie Chaplin sobriquet was:
   The Little Tramp   The Sheik   Pagliaccio

2. Charlie was born in:
   1859   1889   1905

3. How many times did Charlie marry?
   Two   Four   Six

4. Charlie Chaplin began his film career as an extra for which director?
   D.W. Griffith   Cecil Hepworth   Cecil De Mille

5. The leading lady who starred with Charlie in 35 films was:
   Marie Dressler   Lillian Gish   Edna Purviance

6. Which of these was the earliest Chaplin film?
   A Night Out   *City Lights*   *Monsieur Verdoux*

7. *The Great Dictator* is considered a satire on:
   Bismarck   Hitler   Nixon

8. Charlie Chaplin was born in what city?
   New York   London   Glasgow

9. In 1919, United Artists was formed by Chaplin, D.W. Griffith, Douglas Fairbanks, and:
   Mack Sennett   Mary Pickford   Spencer Chaplin

10. Charlie's last wife, Oona, was the daughter of:
    Samuel Beckett   Eugene O'Neill   William Gibson

11. Charlie's first feature length film (six reels) was:
    The Kid   *A Day's Pleasure*   *Modern Times*

12. In which Chaplin film is "the little fella" so starved that he cooks his shoelaces and eats them like spaghetti?

    City Lights   *The Kid*   *The Gold Rush*

13. Which character did Charlie play in *The Gold Rush?*

    Big Jim   The Lone Prospector   Black Larson

14. How long did it take to film *City Lights?*

    Six months   Two years   Four years

15. Which of these leading ladies was Chaplin's third wife?

    Claire Bloom   Marilyn Nash   Paulette Goddard

16. Charlie's last film, made in 1967, was:

    A Countess from Hong Kong   *The Great Dictator*
    A King in New York

17. Charlie had how many children by his various wives?

    Two   Five   Eight

18. Charlie's leading lady in *Modern Times* was:

    Mary Pickford   Paulette Goddard   Pola Negri

19. After being attacked during the McCarthy Era as a "fellow traveler," Charlie Chaplin left the U.S. and settled in what country?

    Switzerland   England   U.S.S.R.

20. Chaplin did not return to the United States, following his exile, until what year?

    1965   1972   1977

21. Charlie was involved in a notorious paternity suit brought by starlet:

    Joan Barry   Lita Grey   Claire Windsor

22. What was the name of the dog befriended by Charlie in *A Dog's Life?*

    Fido   Scraps   Mergatroid

23. Which of Charlie's daughters has become a well-known actress in her own right?

    Josephine   Victoria   Geraldine

24. The idea for *Monsieur Verdoux*, which is based on the life of an infamous French murderer named Landru, was suggested to Charlie by:

    Alexander Korda   Orson Welles   Charles De Gaulle

25. Charlie Chaplin died in:

    1973   1977   1979

GRAB BAG

In this quiz, we have gathered together 25 questions pertaining to just about anything you can imagine. There was absolutely no method to our madness.

Check the answer you deem correct. Give yourself one point for each correct answer. A score of 10 does credit to your capacity for retaining useless information; 15 is a track record to be proud of; and 20 earns you the trivia trophy of the year.

Answers on page 463

1. A cretin is:

    A person of low intelligence   A small wildflower

           An inhabitant of one of the Greek islands

2. The highest city in the world is:

    Lhasa, Tibet   Bogota, Columbia   Addis Ababa, Ethiopia

3. Who said, *"Hope springs eternal in the human breast?"*

    William Shakespeare   Alexander Pope   Arthur Godfrey

4. Venison is the meat of a:

    Buffalo   Yak   Deer

5. The country with the lowest life expectancy is:

    Guinea, Africa   Chad, Africa   Nigeria, Africa

6. A marimba is a:

    Cuban dance   Guatemalan stew

          Musical instrument which resembles a xylophone

7. The hottest city in the world is:

    Khartoum, Sudan   Timbuktu, Mali   Niamey, Nigeria

8. Atavism is:

    The study of birds   Very limited eyesight

        Reversion to characteristics in one's remote ancestors

9. "The Little Brown Wren" was the nickname of which Hollywood film star?

    Bette Davis   Olivia de Havilland   Natalie Wood

10. Someone referred to as Brobdingnagian is likely to be:

    Gigantic   A native of a town in Siberia   Puppetlike

11. A trapezoid is:
    A quadrilateral rectangle having only two sides parallel
    A snare used to catch especially wild animals
    An order of monks, which still flourishes in French-speaking
        Switzerland

12. *Song of Myself* is a long poem by:
    William Wordsworth   Walt Whitman
              Henry Wadsworth Longfellow

13. The greatest harness-racing horse that ever lived was:
    Dancer's Image   Goldsmith Maid   My Friend, Flicka

14. Comestibles are:
    Things which catch fire easily   Eatables
              Rubbers made of gutta percha and tin

15. The fastest hockey skater, Bobby Hull, has been timed at:
    19.7 mph   29.7 mph   49.7 mph

16. The Rosetta Stone is in:
    The British Museum   Luxor, Egypt   Tiffany's, New York

17. The opera *Il Trovatore* was written by:
    Arturo Toscanini   Gaetano Donizetti   Giuseppe Verdi

18. Mickey Wright is a great:
    Jockey   Golfer   Rock singer

19. New South Wales is located in:
    The British Isles   Australia   The Orkney Islands

20. The first person in history to swim the English Channel was:
    Matthew Webb   Gertrude Ederle   Johnny Weissmuller

21. Apiphobia is a fear of:
    Enclosed spaces   Cats   Bees

22. The Garden State is:
    California   Florida   New Jersey

23. The heaviest planet in the universe is:
    Venus   Jupiter   Earth

24. The Kentucky Derby is held at:
    Epsom Downs   Churchill Downs   Kentucky Downs

25. Sandy Hook is a:
    Fishing rod   Candy bar   Stretch of land off New Jersey

69

DRIVE, HE SAID

Are you an auto buff? Below are 25 questions. Check the answer you believe is correct. You have three choices.

A score of 10 shows you're in high gear; 15 is as swift as a Ferrari; and 20 makes you a champion of the road!

Answers on page 463

1. There are how many automobiles per person in the United States?

   One per person   One per two persons   One per three persons

2. The first person to patent a high-speed, four-stroke automobile engine was:

   Gottlieb Daimler   Henry Ford   Nicholas Cugnot

3. The first practical gasoline-powered car with a modern-style chassis and gears was called the:

   Mercedes-Benz   Landaulet   Panhard

4. The Duryea brothers built their first automobile in:

   1873   1893   1913

5. The first automobile race in America was held in:

   1885   1895   1905

6. The Detroit-Flint corridor in Michigan produces what percentage of American cars?

   25 percent   50 percent   75 percent

7. The most popular car in America is the:

   Oldsmobile   Ford   Chevrolet

8. Which car was named for the founder of Detroit?

   The Buick   The Cadillac   The Pontiac

9. How many licensed drivers are there in the United States?

   50 million   100 million   125 million

10. The Mercury was introduced in:
    1929   1939   1949

11. The world's leading producer of automobiles is:
    The United States   Germany   Japan

12. Car registration began in 1901 in what state?
    Michigan   Ohio   New York

13. The first modern traffic light appeared in:
    1903   1914   1935

14. The world's most reckless drivers, based on accident rates, are the:
    Americans   Italians   Austrians

15. The speed limit on *all* American highways is:
    45 mph   55 mph   60 mph

16. The most expensive standard car now on the market is made by:
    The Mercedes-Benz Co.   The Rolls-Royce Co.
                    The Cadillac Co.

17. The first automobile racer to drive over a mile-course in excess of 600 miles was:
    Gary Gabelick   Sir Malcolm Campbell   Craig Breedlove

18. The first patented automobile heater was invented by:
    Henry Ford   Augusta M. Rogers   John Dunlop

19. The car that finished first at the Indianapolis 500 in 1924, 1925, and 1927 was the:
    Dusenberg   Alfa-Romeo   Porsche

20. The maximum speed obtained by a 1904 Rolls-Royce was:
    20 mph   30 mph   40 mph

21. The four-wheel brake was introduced into automobiles in the:
    1920s   1930s   1940s

22. The first European automobile company to mass-produce its cars was:
    Ferrari   Citroen   Horch

23. The Grand Prix is held in:
    Indianapolis   Le Mans   Dieppe

24. Cars run more smoothly in the:
    Early morning   Late afternoon   Evening

25. In 1908, Ford's Tin Lizzie sold for:
    $450 $850 $1,110

HOOP-LA!

How much do you know about basketball? Below are 25 questions about America's biggest sport. See how many answers you know. You have three choices. Check the answer you believe is correct.

A score of 11 is good; 14 is superb; and 21 nets you a championship rating.

Answers on page 463

1. The longest collegiate basketball shot, estimated at 55 feet by Madison Square Garden officials, was made on March 14, 1946, by a 5'10" player named Ernie Calverley. He was playing for:

   Rhode Island State   Oklahoma Aggies   St. John

2. Who was the highest professional scorer in history?

   Larry Costello   Bob Petit   Wilt Chamberlain

3. The originator of modern basketball was:

   Abner Doubleday   Bill Tilden   James Naismith

4. Kareem Abdul-Jabbar was born with the name:

   Tom Chamberlain   Ferdinand Lewis Alcindor   Andy Wright

5. What team did Bill Russell play on?

   Los Angeles Lakers   Boston Celtics   New York Knickerbockers

6. A basketball attendance record was set in 1951, at Olympic Stadium in West Berlin, Germany. How many fans appeared to watch the Harlem Globetrotters' high jinks?

   50,000   75,000   100,000

7. The tallest basketball player in the history of the game was:

   Bob Lanier of Detroit   Mu Tieh-Chu
   George Mikan of Minneapolis

8. The driving genius of the original Celtics was:

   Nat Holman   Dutch Leonard   James Naismith

9. Approximately how many high school basketball teams are there in America?

   10,000   20,000   50,000

10. The first country outside the United States to adopt basketball was:

    England   China   Canada

11. Worldwide, how does basketball rank among sports as a popular spectator sport:

    First   Third   Fifth

12. The only college team to win both the NCAA and the NIT championships in the same year was:
     City College of New York   UCLA   New York University

13. Wilt Chamberlain's nickname is:
     Runty   The Stilt   Mr. Basketball

14. Women's basketball began in the:
     1840s   1890s   1920s

15. There are how many teams in the four divisions of the NBA?
     15   22   32

16. Who was the best professional foul shooter ever?
     Julius Erving   Oscar Robertson   Bill Sharman

17. Goaltending refers to:
     Interference with the ball on its final arc toward the basket
     Guarding the best forward on the opposite team
     Staying in your own court, so when a teammate gets the ball, he
       can throw it to you

18. The first intercollegiate basketball game, with seven men per team, was played in 1896. The teams were:
     Harvard and Princeton   Wesleyan and Yale
               University of Chicago and UCLA

19. Professional basketball games are played in four quarters. Each quarter lasts how many minutes?
     12   20   35

20. Basketball has been part of the Olympic Games since:
     1910   1936   1945

21. In basketball, it is illegal to:
     Dribble the ball   Roll the ball   Run holding the ball

22. What is the greatest number of points ever scored by a single player in one game:
     60   80   100

23. The time limit for an offensive team to make a shot is:
     15 seconds   24 seconds   38 seconds

24. The lowest free-throw percentage for the 1976-77 season was set by center Kim Hughes of the New Jersey Jets. His percentage was:
     .275   .325   .395

25. The men's basketball gold medal in the 1976 summer Olympics was won by what country?
     U.S.S.R.   Canada   United States

73

ALTERNATE CHOICE

Each of the 25 questions which follow offers four prospective answers. Underscore the answer you consider correct.

A score of 10 is average; 13 is excellent; and 18 is extra special.

Answers on page 464

1. Biblical Samson angrily called his new bride a:
    Heifer   *Pullet*   *Ewe*   *Filly*

2. Which one of these is most interested in pigments?
    Physician   *Butcher*   *Farmer*   *Painter*

3. A jaundiced person is most likely having trouble with his:
    Thyroid   *Heart*   *Liver*   *Stomach*

4. Which title is most suggestive of the number 12?
    Superintendent   *Foreman*   *President*   *Treasurer*

5. Honey is produced by creatures living in an:
    Aviary   *Fold*   *Farrowing house*   *Apiary*

6. Which saw requires the least skill?
    Hacksaw   *Buzz saw*   *Seesaw*   *Bucksaw*

7. Which nicknamed creature is the enemy of the other three?
    Elsie   *Leo*   *Nanny*   *Peter*

8. A vixen is the mate of which nicknamed creature?
    Bruin   *Dobbin*   *Reynard*   *Chanticleer*

9. A slick chick with a classy chassis would be found in which group?
    Herd   *Drove*   *Pack*   *Bevy*

10. A chuck roast made which sound while on foot?
    Moo   *Oink*   *Baa-baa*   *Cluck*

11. Which one of these is not in a college curriculum?
    Embryology   *Biology*   *Numerology*   *Psychology*

12. Which one of these is usually for the shortest period of time?
    Charter   *Permit*   *Lease*   *Franchise*

13. The slang term "juice" suggests which worker?
    Carpenter   *Barber*   *Electrician*   *Plumber*

14. Which one of these indicates a crooked spine?
    Osmosis   *Pyrosis*   *Nephrosis*   *Kyphosis*

15. Which creature makes a gray paper nest shaped like a football?
    Wasp   *Spider*   *Bumblebee*   *Hornet*

16. Which type of fuel is found nearest the surface of the ground?
    Peat   *Anthracite coal*   *Lignite*   *Oil*

17. Ancient Diogenes went around with a lamp looking for which type
    of man?
    Rich   *Handsome*   *Religious*   *Honest*

18. During a coronary heart attack, the patient is in most need of:
    Digitalis   *Morphine*   *Oxygen*   *Glucose*

19. Shellac is derived from which one of these?
    Trees   *Coal tar*   *Insects*   *Creosote*

20. Which of these was Rosencrantz's sidekick?
    Polonius   *Holofernes*   *Guildenstern*   *Falstaff*

21. Which Constitutional amendment necessitated the 21st?
    16th   *17th*   *18th*   *19th*

22. Which one would you not properly address as Your Excellency?
    Foreign Ambassador   *Archbishop*   *Bishop*   *Cardinal*

23. Which one of these would you be least likely to find in a zoo?
    Unicorn   *Wapiti*   *Phalanger*   *Manatee*

24. Whom would you like most to have with you when you go fishing?
    Etymologist   *Numismatist*   *Ichthyologist*   *Phrenologist*

25. Which kind of review would make an actor feel bad?
    Laudatory   *Disparaging*   *Panegyrical*   *Eulogistic*

PSEUDONYMITY

Many celebrated artists, performers, and other notables have changed their names or adopted an alias. Do you know the real names of these celebrities?

Below are 50 names of people as they are generally known. The box contains the real names of these people; these real names are not in any particular order. Write the real name next to the pseudonym in the space provided.

You score two points for each correct answer. You lose one point for each incorrect answer. A score of 50 is good; 65 is excellent.

Answers on page 464

 1. Woody Allen _____

 2. Fred Astaire _____

 3. Jack Benny _____

 4. Sarah Bernhardt _____

 5. Voltaire _____

 6. Rocky Graziano _____

 7. Joseph Stalin _____

 8. John Wayne _____

 9. Roy Rogers _____

10. Calamity Jane _____

11. Cary Grant _____

12. Adolf Hitler _____

13. Harry Houdini _____

14. Mark Twain _____

15. Moliere _____

16. Mary Pickford _____

17. Billy the Kid _____

18. Father Divine _____

19. Gerald Ford _____

20. Edward G. Robinson _____

21. Lewis Carroll _____

22. George Orwell _____

23. Marlene Deitrich _____

24. Saki _____

25. Tintoretto _____

26. Leon Trotsky _____

27. Sugar Ray Robinson _____

28. O. Henry _____

29. Nikolai Lenin _____

30. Dean Martin _____

31. Sophia Loren _____

32. Maxim Gorki _____

33. W.C. Fields _____

34. Greta Garbo _____

35. Judy Garland _____

36. Marilyn Monroe _____

37. Paul Muni _____

38. Joseph Conrad _____

39. "Legs" Diamond _____

40. Boris Karloff _____

41. Elizabeth Arden _____   46. Marion Davies _____

42. Hedy Lamarr _____   47. Rocky Marciano _____

43. George Eliot _____   48. George Sand _____

44. Bette Davis _____   49. Ringo Starr _____

45. Bing Crosby _____   50. Vivien Leigh _____

Martha Jane Burke	**William Claude Dukinfield**
Jean Baptiste Poquelin	**Eric Blair**
George Baker	**Norma Jean Baker**
Leslie L. King, Jr.	**Muni Weisenfreund**
Ehrich Weiss	**Marion Douras**
Adolf Schicklgruber	**William Henry Pratt**
Francois Marie Arouet	**Ruth Elizabeth Davis**
Allen Stewart Konigsberg	**Florence N. Graham**
Tom Barbelo	**Vivian Hartley Holman**
Frederick Austerlitz	**Hector Hugh Moore**
Samuel Clemens	**Mary Ann Evans**
Henry McCarty	**Jacopo Robusti**
Leonard Slye	**Lev D. Bronstein**
Emmanuel Goldberg	**Richard Starkey**
Iosif V. Dzhugashvili	**Amandine Aurore Lucie Dupin**
Marion Morrison	**William Sidney Porter**
Gladys Smith	**Vladimir Ilich Ulyanov**
Benny Kubelsky	**Rocco Marchegiano**
Rosine Bernard	**John T. Nolan**
Archibald Leach	**Teodor J.K. Korzeniowski**
Sofia Scicolone	**Harry Crosby**
Hedwig Kiesler	**Magdalene van Losch**
Dino Crocetti	**Walker Smith**
Frances Gumm	**A. Max Peshkov**
Greta Gustaffson	**C.L. Dodgson**

77

HOW TO SOLVE DIAMONDS

The goal is to form as many words of four letters or more as you possibly can from the letters in the diamond. The following rules must be observed:

1. A letter may only be used once in any word.

2. Each word must include the letter in the center of the diamond.

3. Find one word which uses all nine letters.

4. Plurals, foreign words, and proper names are taboo.

DIAMOND 1

At least 27 words of four letters or more—including one nine-letter word—can be formed from the letters in this diamond.

If you get 15 that's very good; 20 is excellent; and 25 is super!

Answers on page 464

1. _____   10. _____   19. _____

2. _____   11. _____   20. _____

3. _____   12. _____   21. _____

4. _____   13. _____   22. _____

5. _____   14. _____   23. _____

6. _____   15. _____   24. _____

7. _____   16. _____   25. _____

8. _____   17. _____   26. _____

9. _____   18. _____   27. _____

DIAMOND 2

We found 26 words in this diamond, including one nine-letter word. How many can you come up with?

A score of 13 is fair; 17 is lovely; and 22 is magnificent.

Answers on page 464

1. _____
2. _____
3. _____
4. _____
5. _____
6. _____
7. _____
8. _____
9. _____

10. _____
11. _____
12. _____
13. _____
14. _____
15. _____
16. _____
17. _____

18. _____
19. _____
20. _____
21. _____
22. _____
23. _____
24. _____
25. _____
26. _____

DIAMOND 3

There are at least 28 words hidden in this diamond.

If you find 15, you get a star; 19 rates you a medal; and 24 earns you a trophy.

Answers on page 465

1. _____   10. _____   20. _____
2. _____   11. _____   21. _____
3. _____   12. _____   22. _____
4. _____   13. _____   23. _____
5. _____   14. _____   24. _____
6. _____   15. _____   25. _____
7. _____   16. _____   26. _____
8. _____   17. _____   27. _____
9. _____   18. _____   28. _____
                    19. _____

81

DIAMOND 4

We list 19 words that can be formed from the letters in this diamond.
A score of 10 is adequate; 14 is ample; and 17 is prodigious.

Answers on page 465

1. _____	7. _____	14. _____
2. _____	8. _____	15. _____
3. _____	9. _____	16. _____
4. _____	10. _____	17. _____
5. _____	11. _____	18. _____
6. _____	12. _____	19. _____
	13. _____	

DIAMOND 5

There are at least 20 words buried in this diamond. How many can you find?

A score of 10 is not bad; 14 is grand; and 17 is top-notch.

Answers on page 465

1. _____	8. _____	14. _____
2. _____	9. _____	15. _____
3. _____	10. _____	16. _____
4. _____	11. _____	17. _____
5. _____	12. _____	18. _____
6. _____	13. _____	19. _____
7. _____		20. _____

DIAMOND 6

There are at least 27 words to be made from the letters in this diamond.
A score of 13 is fine; 18 is dandy; and 23 is to write home about.

Answers on page 465

1. _____   10. _____   19. _____
2. _____   11. _____   20. _____
3. _____   12. _____   21. _____
4. _____   13. _____   22. _____
5. _____   14. _____   23. _____
6. _____   15. _____   24. _____
7. _____   16. _____   25. _____
8. _____   17. _____   26. _____
9. _____   18. _____   27. _____

DIAMOND 7

We found 18 words in this diamond. Can you match or top it?

Getting 9 is good going; 12 is cooking with gas; and 15 is record-breaking.

Answers on page 465

1. _____	7. _____	13. _____
2. _____	8. _____	14. _____
3. _____	9. _____	15. _____
4. _____	10. _____	16. _____
5. _____	11. _____	17. _____
6. _____	12. _____	18. _____

DIAMOND 8

There are at least 31 words to be formed from the letters in this diamond.

A score of 16 is not bad; 22 is good; and 29 is grand.

Answers on page 465

1. _____ 11. _____ 22. _____

2. _____ 12. _____ 23. _____

3. _____ 13. _____ 24. _____

4. _____ 14. _____ 25. _____

5. _____ 15. _____ 26. _____

6. _____ 16. _____ 27. _____

7. _____ 17. _____ 28. _____

8. _____ 18. _____ 29. _____

9. _____ 19. _____ 30. _____

10. _____ 20. _____ 31. _____

21. _____

DIAMOND 9

We found 38 words in this diamond.

    If you list 18, you're doing fine; 25 shows good concentration; and 32 shows an impressive vocabulary.

Answers on page 465

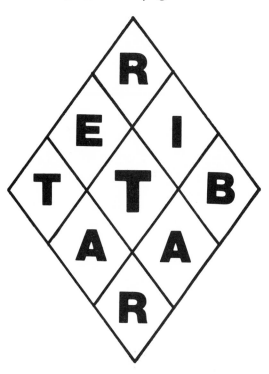

1. _____
2. _____
3. _____
4. _____
5. _____
6. _____
7. _____
8. _____
9. _____
10. _____
11. _____
12. _____
13. _____

14. _____
15. _____
16. _____
17. _____
18. _____
19. _____
20. _____
21. _____
22. _____
23. _____
24. _____
25. _____

26. _____
27. _____
28. _____
29. _____
30. _____
31. _____
32. _____
33. _____
34. _____
35. _____
36. _____
37. _____
38. _____

DIAMOND 10

We have listed 26 words that can be formed from the letters in this diamond.

A score of 13 is fine; 17 is laudable; and 22 is meritorious.

Answers on page 465

1. _____	10. _____	18. _____
2. _____	11. _____	19. _____
3. _____	12. _____	20. _____
4. _____	13. _____	21. _____
5. _____	14. _____	22. _____
6. _____	15. _____	23. _____
7. _____	16. _____	24. _____
8. _____	17. _____	25. _____
9. _____		26. _____

DIAMOND 11

There are at least 31 words to be made from the letters in this diamond.
A score of 15 is good; 22 is superior; and 29 is exceptional.

Answers on page 466

1. _____
2. _____
3. _____
4. _____
5. _____
6. _____
7. _____
8. _____
9. _____
10. _____

11. _____
12. _____
13. _____
14. _____
15. _____
16. _____
17. _____
18. _____
19. _____
20. _____
21. _____

22. _____
23. _____
24. _____
25. _____
26. _____
27. _____
28. _____
29. _____
30. _____
31. _____

DIAMOND 12

Hidden in this diamond there are at least 57 words of four letters or more (including one nine-letter word) each containing the letter A from the center of the diamond.

A score of 30 is good; 40 is excellent; and 50 makes you a word detective.

Answers on page 466

1. _____	20. _____	39. _____
2. _____	21. _____	40. _____
3. _____	22. _____	41. _____
4. _____	23. _____	42. _____
5. _____	24. _____	43. _____
6. _____	25. _____	44. _____
7. _____	26. _____	45. _____
8. _____	27. _____	46. _____
9. _____	28. _____	47. _____
10. _____	29. _____	48. _____
11. _____	30. _____	49. _____
12. _____	31. _____	50. _____
13. _____	32. _____	51. _____
14. _____	33. _____	52. _____
15. _____	34. _____	53. _____
16. _____	35. _____	54. _____
17. _____	36. _____	55. _____
18. _____	37. _____	56. _____
19. _____	38. _____	57. _____

CLASSIC DEDICATIONS

Vice-President Tom Marshall dedicated his memoirs:
To President Woodrow Wilson, from his only Vice.

Franklin P. Adams inscribed one volume of verse:
To my loving wife, but for whose constant interruptions, this book would have been finished six months earlier.

Carl Winston dedicated *How to Turn a Million into a Shoestring* thus:
I should be remiss, indeed, if I failed to acknowledge my indebtedness to the People's Bank of Bridgeport, the Connecticut Light and Power Co., the New England Telephone Co., Sears Roebuck, Casey Fuel, the West Redding Market, the Internal Revenue Department, and another creditor whose name is Morris H. Legion. The total is $17,886.05. Hi, Fellows!

Inscription on a cigarette lighter:
To My Matchless Wife.

Al Jaffee of *Mad* Magazine dedicated one of his books:
To myself, without whose inspired and tireless efforts this book would not have been possible.

An RKO director dedicated his first book:
To my wife, without whose absence this could not have been written.

Inez McEwen dedicated her book *So This Is Ranching:*
To my infant grandson, the only gent on whom I've been able to pin anything.

TYPESETTER'S HEADACHE

Roger is learning to operate a computer typewriter. He started on this simple machine which has only four keys. However, each key has a combination of two letters, a symbol, and a number. Roger is having trouble remembering which letters go with which symbols and numbers. From the 7 clues below you should be able to straighten him out. Remember, = means "goes with;" ≠ means "does not go with."

Solution on page 466

1. **XY = 57**   3. **LK = %**   6. **39 ≠ #**

2. **TR = $**   4. **68 ≠ ES**   7. **LK ≠ 39**

                     5. **101 = @**

TREE HOUSES

Four trees stand in a row, and in them four friends have their tree houses. The four boys have painted their tree houses four different colors.

   With the clues below, can you fill in the information and make sure each tree house is correctly given an owner, a color, and a tree?

PAR: 5 MINUTES

Solution on page 466

	Tree No. 1	Tree No. 2	Tree No. 3	Tree No. 4
OWNER				
COLOR				
TYPE OF TREE				

1. Pete's house is red.

2. Jeff is in tree #3.

3. Luke's house is in the cherry tree.

4. The blue house is in the maple.

5. The elm tree is #1.

6. The house in #2 is not the yellow one.

7. The green house is in #4.

8. Tom's house is in the maple, not in the oak.

FLY ME

Five planes are lined up at the runway waiting for takeoff. Each, of course, has its own pilot and stewardess. Each plane belongs to a different airline and each is headed for a different city.

Using the clues below, can you figure it all out and complete the chart. If you do it in six minutes or less, you certainly come off with flying colors.

Solution on page 466

	Joe	Jim	Dan	John	Bob
Airline					
Stewardess					
Destination					

1. Jim is a pilot for TWA.

2. Marge does not fly for TWA.

3. The Eastern flight is going to Miami.

4. Dan is flying to New York.

5. Lore works for Delta.

6. John does not work for Delta.

7. Bob is flying to Chicago.

8. Jim does not work with Donna.

9. Doris is flying to New York.

10. The United flight is to Chicago.

11. The TWA flight is to Los Angeles.

12. Marge and Bob do not work for the same airline.

13. John is not going to Dallas.

14. Lynn does not work for Pan Am.

TRIPLET TROUBLE

As usual, the three Smith sisters were giggling. They were always giggling. Sue, Sarah, and Sandy Smith are triplets, and they look exactly alike. Nobody can tell them apart—even their mother has trouble. Sometimes they take advantage of the confusion this creates. The only one who can really tell them apart is their younger brother, Sam.

The girls take turns walking their dog, Skipper, alternating each day.

"Whose turn is it to walk Skipper today?" asked Mrs. Smith on Wednesday.

"Not mine!" said Sue.

"Not mine!" said Sarah.

"Not mine!" said Sandy.

"Well, it has to be someone's turn," Mrs. Smith said exasperatedly.

"Don't you know?" the girls asked, giggling.

Mrs. Smith shook her head. "But Sam knows," she said. "Don't you?"

Yes," Sam admitted. He knew whose turn it was, but he didn't want his sisters to get mad at him.

"It can't be my turn," Sue said. "I walked Skipper Monday. I don't have to walk him again until tomorrow."

"*I* walked the dog Monday, not Sue," Sarah said.

"One of them is telling the truth," Sam told his mom.

"I don't know who walked Skipper Monday," Sandy said. "But I walked him Tuesday."

Sue protested. "Sarah walked Skipper Tuesday, not Sandy. I saw her."

"One of them is telling the truth," Sam told his mom.

"I did not walk Skipper Tuesday," Sarah said. "I told you before I walked him Monday. But I saw Sue walking him Tuesday," Sarah added.

"One of Sarah's statements is true," Sam said.

Mrs. Smith thought for a few minutes. "I know whose turn it is," she said.

Do you?

You should be able to figure out whose turn it is from Sam's hints. You should also be able to figure out who walked Skipper Monday and Tuesday.

Solution on page 467

TRUTH IN LABELING

On a shelf in Ann's pantry are five home-canned jars. Her neighbors gave them to her at various times and she is very happy to have them. She carefully wrote on each jar what it contained, who gave it to her, and when. But her son tore off the labels. Using the 15 clues below, can you help Ann sort out the information and relabel the jars correctly?

Solution on page 467

1. Pat gave the corn.

2. The tomato juice is between two other jars.

3. The green beans were canned in 1974.

4. The sweet pickles are in the first jar.

5. The grape juice is next to the tomato juice.

6. Carol gave the fifth jar.

7. Maggie gave the jar canned in 1973.

8. Kris gave the middle jar.

9. The 1972 jar is neither on an end nor in the center.

10. The oldest jar was packed in 1969.

11. Lois gave one of the end jars.

12. The tomato juice was packed in 1973.

13. The second jar has corn in it.

14. The green beans are between two other jars.

15. 1971 was a good year for grape juice.

BUGS! BUGS! BUGS!

A school district with five high schools (Davis, Lee, Jackson, Forrest, and Stephens) held a science fair, and each school was invited to send one student in each category. Three prizes and two honorable mentions were given in each category.

With the clues below, can you fill in the information about the contestants in insect study?

TIME: 6 MINUTES

Solution on page 467

	Craig	Joan	Margaret	Bert	Peter
School					
Insect					
Award					

1. Craig and Joan took the honorable mentions.

2. The fly collector doesn't go to Forrest or Stephens.

3. Margaret collects butterflies.

4. The Forrest student took third place.

5. Peter goes to Davis High.

6. Joan goes to Lee High.

7. Bert took second place with his beetle collection.

8. The ant collector got an honorable mention.

9. The Jackson student collects ants.

10. The bee collection won first place.

THE LAW PROFESSOR
AND HIS STUDENT

In ancient Athens, a young but impecunious student came to a noted professor of law and asked to be accepted as a student. After the professor found that the young man had no means to pay for his instruction, the following bargain was struck between the two:

Said the professor: "You have no money to pay me now, but sooner or later you will be earning money. Suppose you pay me for my full course of instruction after you have won your first case."

The student agreed to this proposal.

After two years passed, the student was well-grounded in the intricacies of the law. Soon after he left the professor's academy, a fairly large sum fell into his hands through a bequest from a relative.

The professor then demanded money. The student refused, and the professor brought him to court.

The professor argued before the tribunal: "If I win this case, and my claim is deemed just and correct, then this young man must pay me what he owes me. However, if I lose this case, then my student will have won his first case; and then, according to the terms of our bargain, he must pay me because he will have won his first case."

Now it was the student's turn to speak. He had been well-trained by the master. Said he to the court: "If I win this case, then of course, I don't have to pay, because the judgment of this court will be in my favor and the claim of my professor will have been rejected. However, if I lose this case, then I certainly don't have to pay because the terms of our bargain were that I should pay instruction fees only after I won my first case."

The court was in a dilemma. Do you have an answer? After 3,000 years, no one seems to have been able to solve this one.

MATERNITY WARD

Zorba Memorial Hospital had five births in five successive days. All 10 beaming parents, and all five beaming infants, are doing fine.

Using the 15 clues given below, you should be able to figure out which infant was born on which day, and to which parents.

TIME: 10 MINUTES

Solution on page 467

	April 29	April 30	May 1	May 2	May 3
Infant					
Mother					
Father					

1. Diane is Bob's wife.

2. Maureen was born on May 2.

3. Carol was not born in April.

4. Jim is not Annie's husband.

5. Chuck's father is Lee.

6. Carol's mother is Diane.

7. George's father is Kevin.

8. The baby born on May 1 was a girl.

9. Bill was born on April 30.

10. Wilma is married to Lee.

11. Donna's baby was born May 2.

12. Maureen's father is Tom.

13. Barbara's baby was a boy.

14. The baby born on May 3 was a boy.

15. Wilma's son was born on April 29.

THE SOCCER TOURNAMENT

Four high schools—Central, Madison, Lakeside, and Western—competed in an all-city soccer tournament. Each school played each of the others once. In each game, two points were at stake: the winner received two points, but if the two teams tied, each received one point.

At the end of the tournament, the total was: Madison, 5 points; Central, 3 points; Western, 3 points; Lakeside, 1 point.

In the entire tournament, a total of thirteen goals was scored, seven of them by Central High alone; Western High scored no goals at all.

In the game between Central and Lakeside, Central won four goals to one.

Can you fill in the scores of the other five games?

TIME: 12 MINUTES

Solution on page 467

Central-Madison	_____
Central-Lakeside	4-1
Central-Western	_____
Madison-Lakeside	_____
Madison-Western	_____
Lakeside-Western	_____

QUINTUPLET QUIZ

The Chandlers are very proud parents. Their five sons, quintuplets, are all about to graduate from college, where they were all varsity athletes, but in five different sports. All five of them are also about to get married, but, of course, to five different women.

With the eight clues below, can you make sure each brother gets the credit for the right sport and winds up with the right bride?

TIME: 7 MINUTES

Solution on page 468

	Pat	Bob	Tim	Steve	Bill
FIANCEE					
SPORT					

1. Pat earned his letter in football.

2. Susan, the sister of Bob's fiancée, is engaged to one of the other brothers.

3. Tim's fiancée is Pam.

4. Karen is engaged to the swimmer.

5. Alice is engaged to the quarterback.

6. Bill got his letter in baseball.

7. Sharon is engaged to the basketball champion.

8. Steve is neither the wrestler nor the swimmer.

CRIB CRISIS

In Kildare Memorial Hospital are five newborn infants, and they have been assigned to five numbered cribs in the nursery. With the clues below, can you make sure each baby is in the right crib with the right mother's name on it?

TIME: 6 MINUTES

Solution on page 468

	Crib #1	Crib #2	Crib #3	Crib #4	Crib #5
Baby's Name					
Mother's Name					

1. Andy goes in crib #2.

2. Carla Moore's baby does not go on either end.

3. Paul and Dennis belong in end cribs.

4. Melody Barnes's son is not Paul.

5. Sean is Susan O'Leary's son.

6. Todd is in the middle crib.

7. Alice Hamilton's son is in crib #1.

8. Sharon Adams's baby is between Andy and Sean.

101

SUGAR AND SPICE

It is Friday night after the big game. Six cheerleaders from Naughton High School are having a slumber party. Besides their boyfriends (of course), the girls talk about their favorite TV shows. No two of them have the same favorite program, and, luckily, no two of them have the same boyfriend. The girls are sleeping in sleeping bags of six different colors. Given the clues below, can you indicate in the grid which girl has which boyfriend; which girl has which sleeping bag; and which girl watches what TV show?

TIME: 7 MINUTES

Solution on page 468

	Lois	Mary	Margie	Shirley	Diane	Sharon
BAG						
BOYFRIEND						
TV SHOW						

1. Lois dates Scott and watches *M*A*S*H**.

2. Ken's girlfriend brought a plaid sleeping bag.

3. Mary brought a blue sleeping bag.

4. Margie dates Andy.

5. Sharon never misses *American Bandstand*, but someone else prefers *Maude*.

6. The owner of the green sleeping bag dates Ed.

7. Shirley likes *Laverne and Shirley*.

8. Diane's favorite show is not *Hawaii Five-O*, but it is someone else's favorite.

9. Margie did not bring the red sleeping bag.

10. Ben's date watches *Happy Days* faithfully.

11. Sharon brought the plaid bag, not the yellow one.

12. Diane dates Al and brought a black sleeping bag.

PAPA'S PLANTS

Everyone in our family has a hobby—Papa raises plants. In our house each room has one window, and each window faces a different direction. Papa has a different plant in each window, and each plant has a different color pot. Of course, Papa knows exactly which pot each plant is in, and which direction each plant faces; but the rest of the family keeps forgetting.

Using the 11 clues below, can you figure out which room each plant is in; the color of the pot each plant is in; and the direction each plant faces?

Solution on page 468

1. The African violet has a north window.

2. The yellow pot does not have a west window.

3. The red pot is in the playroom.

4. The blue pot is not in the living room.

5. The philodendron is in the den.

6. The coleus is not in the playroom.

7. The kitchen has a south window.

8. The spider plant is not in the living room.

9. The green pot faces south.

10. The spider plant has an east view.

11. The coleus is in the green pot.

THE FIVE DWARFS

Less well known than their distant cousins who played host to Snow White are the five dwarfs of this puzzle, who seldom have company of any kind. These five dwarfs are not miners like their relatives, but lumberjacks. When they go into the woods each day, each dwarf wears a different color hat. In this age of specialization, each dwarf chops down only one kind of tree.

With the clues below, can you match each dwarf to his cap and tree?

TIME: 5 MINUTES

Solution on page 469

	Tipsy	Greasy	Cruddy	Clumsy	Shnook
Tree					
Cap Color					

1. Cruddy wears a red cap.

2. Greasy chops down elm trees.

3. The oak cutter does not wear the yellow cap.

4. The wearer of the green cap cuts down spruce trees.

5. Clumsy does not wear the yellow cap.

6. Shnook wears the blue cap, not the black one.

7. Clumsy chops maple trees.

8. The dwarf with the blue cap chops down pines.

CRAZY QUILT

Six women have a sewing circle. They are working on six different projects with six different fabrics of six different colors. Can you fill in the grid below to show who is making what out of what?

TIME: 13 MINUTES

Solution on page 469

	Ann	Barb	Chris	Dee	Edna	Fran
Project						
Color						
Fabric						

1. Ann is making curtains.

2. The dress is to be white.

3. The denim is for a jacket.

4. The cotton is not for the shirt.

5. Chris's fabric is brown.

6. The felt is green.

7. The flannel is blue.

8. Ann's fabric is yellow.

9. Edna is using satin.

10. The pants will be brown.

11. The green fabric is for toys.

12. The jacket is Barb's project.

13. The yellow fabric is not corduroy.

14. Barb's fabric is red.

15. Dee is not working with felt.

RETIREMENT RIDDLE

Four elderly friends gather daily in the park to play games and talk about their grandchildren. No two have the same hair color, and no two have the same favorite game. With the seven clues provided, show in the grid what each gent looks like and what his favorite game is.

PAR TIME: 12 MINUTES

Solution on page 469

	Mr. Jones	Mr. Smith	Mr. Kelly	Mr. Robson
Hair				
Game				

1. Mr. Kelly has brown hair.

2. The croquet player is bald.

3. Someone likes horseshoes, but it's not Mr. Robson.

4. Mr. Smith likes checkers.

5. The chess player has white hair.

6. Mr. Jones prefers another game to croquet.

7. Mr. Jones is not the one with gray hair.

HOW TO SOLVE THREEZIES

You are given a sequence of three letters. List all the words you can think of which contain these three letters *in exact sequence*.

The sequence may seem quite unlikely. For example, a sequence of letters R R H at first sight might seem completely hopeless, yet with a little thought you may come up with the words *catarrh* and *myrrh*. If the given three letters were M B S, you might find that out of this strange sequence you can form the words *numbskull* and *tombstone*.

The rules of the game are very simple. You may use only one form of the word. For example, if the threezie were N D L, a proper answer would be HANDLE. But then you couldn't use the words HANDLES, HANDLED, OR HANDLING, since all these words are forms of the same root. However, where words have a completely different usage, then they may both be used even though the roots are similar. Thus, since FOND is an adjective and FONDLE is a verb, you could score with the word FOND-LY and also with the word FONDLE.

Proper names are off limits; hyphenated words are not allowed.

C H O

We have found 31 words which contain the letters CHO in sequence. How many can you find? A score of 18 is good; 22, excellent; 27, outstanding; and 30 is supercolossal.

Answers on page 469

1. _____	11. _____	22. _____
2. _____	12. _____	23. _____
3. _____	13. _____	24. _____
4. _____	14. _____	25. _____
5. _____	15. _____	26. _____
6. _____	16. _____	27. _____
7. _____	17. _____	28. _____
8. _____	18. _____	29. _____
9. _____	19. _____	30. _____
10. _____	20. _____	31. _____
	21. _____	

ADE

There are at least 52 words that contain the letter sequence ADE. A score of 25 is fair; 35 is a good deal better; and 45 is first-rate.

Answers on page 469

1. _____	18. _____	36. _____
2. _____	19. _____	37. _____
3. _____	20. _____	38. _____
4. _____	21. _____	39. _____
5. _____	22. _____	40. _____
6. _____	23. _____	41. _____
7. _____	24. _____	42. _____
8. _____	25. _____	43. _____
9. _____	26. _____	44. _____
10. _____	27. _____	45. _____
11. _____	28. _____	46. _____
12. _____	29. _____	47. _____
13. _____	30. _____	48. _____
14. _____	31. _____	49. _____
15. _____	32. _____	50. _____
16. _____	33. _____	51. _____
17. _____	34. _____	52. _____
	35. _____	

NDM

We have found nine words which contain the letters NDM in sequence. How many can you find? Five is good; seven is terrific!

Answers on page 469

1. _____	4. _____	7. _____
2. _____	5. _____	8. _____
3. _____	6. _____	9. _____

ARL

We have found 36 words which have a letter sequence of ARL. How many can you find? A score of 18 is fine; 24 is excellent; and 32 is noteworthy.

Answers on page 470

1. _____	13. _____	25. _____
2. _____	14. _____	26. _____
3. _____	15. _____	27. _____
4. _____	16. _____	28. _____
5. _____	17. _____	29. _____
6. _____	18. _____	30. _____
7. _____	19. _____	31. _____
8. _____	20. _____	32. _____
9. _____	21. _____	33. _____
10. _____	22. _____	34. _____
11. _____	23. _____	35. _____
12. _____	24. _____	36. _____

ROB

There are at least 27 words that contain the letter sequence ROB. A score of 14 is very agreeable; 18 is superb; and you really went overboard with 22.

Answers on page 470

1. _____	10. _____	19. _____
2. _____	11. _____	20. _____
3. _____	12. _____	21. _____
4. _____	13. _____	22. _____
5. _____	14. _____	23. _____
6. _____	15. _____	24. _____
7. _____	16. _____	25. _____
8. _____	17. _____	26. _____
9. _____	18. _____	27. _____

N G O

There are at least 11 words that contain the letter sequence NGO. Finding five is good; anything more is great.

Answers on page 470

1. _____   5. _____   8. _____
2. _____   6. _____   9. _____
3. _____   7. _____   10. _____
4. _____   11. _____

E R U

We found 12 words that have the letter sequence ERU. If you list five, that's fine; anything more is outstanding.

Answers on page 470

1. _____   5. _____   9. _____
2. _____   6. _____   10. _____
3. _____   7. _____   11. _____
4. _____   8. _____   12. _____

O U P

We found only 14 words with the letter sequence OUP. Can you match or top this? Anything over seven is commendable.

Answers on page 470

1. _____   6. _____   10. _____
2. _____   7. _____   11. _____
3. _____   8. _____   12. _____
4. _____   9. _____   13. _____
5. _____   14. _____

IEN

We found 24 words with the letter sequence IEN. A score of 12 is good; 16 is excellent; and 20 earns kudos.

Answers on page 470

1. _____   9. _____   17. _____
2. _____   10. _____   18. _____
3. _____   11. _____   19. _____
4. _____   12. _____   20. _____
5. _____   13. _____   21. _____
6. _____   14. _____   22. _____
7. _____   15. _____   23. _____
8. _____   16. _____   24. _____

OCO

We have found 17 words which have a letter sequence of OCO. How many can you find? A score of eight is nice; 11 is very good; and 14 is wunderbar!

Answers on page 470

1. _____   7. _____   12. _____
2. _____   8. _____   13. _____
3. _____   9. _____   14. _____
4. _____   10. _____   15. _____
5. _____   11. _____   16. _____
6. _____   17. _____

SSA

There are at least 37 words that contain the letter sequence SSA. A score of 18 is fair; 25 is very good; and 32 is superb.

Answers on page 470

1. _____	13. _____	26. _____
2. _____	14. _____	27. _____
3. _____	15. _____	28. _____
4. _____	16. _____	29. _____
5. _____	17. _____	30. _____
6. _____	18. _____	31. _____
7. _____	19. _____	32. _____
8. _____	20. _____	33. _____
9. _____	21. _____	34. _____
10. _____	22. _____	35. _____
11. _____	23. _____	36. _____
12. _____	24. _____	37. _____
	25. _____	

NFA

There are at least 24 words that contain the letter sequence NFA. A score of 12 is good; 16 is outstanding; and 21 is, in fact, a knockout.

Answers on page 470

1. _____	9. _____	17. _____
2. _____	10. _____	18. _____
3. _____	11. _____	19. _____
4. _____	12. _____	20. _____
5. _____	13. _____	21. _____
6. _____	14. _____	22. _____
7. _____	15. _____	23. _____
8. _____	16. _____	24. _____

NGE

At least 65 words contain the letter sequence NGE. How many can you list? A score of 33 is commendable; 45, laudatory; and 57 brings highest encomiums.

Answers on page 471

1. _____
2. _____
3. _____
4. _____
5. _____
6. _____
7. _____
8. _____
9. _____
10. _____
11. _____
12. _____
13. _____
14. _____
15. _____
16. _____
17. _____
18. _____
19. _____
20. _____
21. _____
22. _____

23. _____
24. _____
25. _____
26. _____
27. _____
28. _____
29. _____
30. _____
31. _____
32. _____
33. _____
34. _____
35. _____
36. _____
37. _____
38. _____
39. _____
40. _____
41. _____
42. _____
43. _____

44. _____
45. _____
46. _____
47. _____
48. _____
49. _____
50. _____
51. _____
52. _____
53. _____
54. _____
55. _____
56. _____
57. _____
58. _____
59. _____
60. _____
61. _____
62. _____
63. _____
64. _____
65. _____

FFE

There are at least 41 words with the letter sequence FFE. A score of 20 is good; 27 is notable; and 34 is fit for a scholar.

Answers on page 471

1. _____   15. _____   28. _____
2. _____   16. _____   29. _____
3. _____   17. _____   30. _____
4. _____   18. _____   31. _____
5. _____   19. _____   32. _____
6. _____   20. _____   33. _____
7. _____   21. _____   34. _____
8. _____   22. _____   35. _____
9. _____   23. _____   36. _____
10. _____   24. _____   37. _____
11. _____   25. _____   38. _____
12. _____   26. _____   39. _____
13. _____   27. _____   40. _____
14. _____   41. _____

OWB

We found 21 words that contain the letter sequence OWB. A score of 10 is fine; 14 is very good; and if you get 17 or more—oh, boy!

Answers on page 471

1. _____   8. _____   15. _____
2. _____   9. _____   16. _____
3. _____   10. _____   17. _____
4. _____   11. _____   18. _____
5. _____   12. _____   19. _____
6. _____   13. _____   20. _____
7. _____   14. _____   21. _____

RGO

There are at least 16 words that contain the letter sequence RGO. If you list eight that's pretty good; 12 or more is phenomenal.

Answers on page 471

1. _____   6. _____   12. _____
2. _____   7. _____   13. _____
3. _____   8. _____   14. _____
4. _____   9. _____   15. _____
5. _____   10. _____   16. _____
                     11. _____

IBU

We can list a dozen words that contain the letter sequence IBU. How many can you find? Six or more is noteworthy.

Answers on page 471

1. _____   5. _____   9. _____
2. _____   6. _____   10. _____
3. _____   7. _____   11. _____
4. _____   8. _____   12. _____

LEF

There are at least eight words with the letter sequence LEF. A score of four is good.

Answers on page 471

1. _____   4. _____   6. _____
2. _____   5. _____   7. _____
3. _____   8. _____

A B B

There are at least 27 words that contain the letter sequence ABB. A score of 14 is good; 19 is excellent; and 23 is superior.

Answers on page 471

1. _____	10. _____	19. _____
2. _____	11. _____	20. _____
3. _____	12. _____	21. _____
4. _____	13. _____	22. _____
5. _____	14. _____	23. _____
6. _____	15. _____	24. _____
7. _____	16. _____	25. _____
8. _____	17. _____	26. _____
9. _____	18. _____	27. _____

L L B

We can list 12 words with the letter sequence LLB. How many can you find? A score of six or better is a feather in your cap.

Answers on page 471

1. _____	5. _____	9. _____
2. _____	6. _____	10. _____
3. _____	7. _____	11. _____
4. _____	8. _____	12. _____

RRE

There are at least 45 words that have the letter sequence RRE. A score of 25 is fair; 32 is very good; and 39 shows rrreal ability!

Answers on page 472

1. _____	16. _____	31. _____
2. _____	17. _____	32. _____
3. _____	18. _____	33. _____
4. _____	19. _____	34. _____
5. _____	20. _____	35. _____
6. _____	21. _____	36. _____
7. _____	22. _____	37. _____
8. _____	23. _____	38. _____
9. _____	24. _____	39. _____
10. _____	25. _____	40. _____
11. _____	26. _____	41. _____
12. _____	27. _____	42. _____
13. _____	28. _____	43. _____
14. _____	29. _____	44. _____
15. _____	30. _____	45. _____

MBA

There are at least 18 words with the letter sequence MBA. A score of nine is fine; 12 is quite good; and 15 is notable.

Answers on page 472

1. _____	7. _____	13. _____
2. _____	8. _____	14. _____
3. _____	9. _____	15. _____
4. _____	10. _____	16. _____
5. _____	11. _____	17. _____
6. _____	12. _____	18. _____

INA

We have listed 85 words that contain the letter sequence INA. A score of 45 shows you're in a hurry; 60 means you're in a more studious mood; and 70 places you up front in a schoolroom.

Answers on page 472

1. _____
2. _____
3. _____
4. _____
5. _____
6. _____
7. _____
8. _____
9. _____
10. _____
11. _____
12. _____
13. _____
14. _____
15. _____
16. _____
17. _____
18. _____
19. _____
20. _____
21. _____
22. _____
23. _____
24. _____
25. _____
26. _____
27. _____
28. _____

29. _____
30. _____
31. _____
32. _____
33. _____
34. _____
35. _____
36. _____
37. _____
38. _____
39. _____
40. _____
41. _____
42. _____
43. _____
44. _____
45. _____
46. _____
47. _____
48. _____
49. _____
50. _____
51. _____
52. _____
53. _____
54. _____
55. _____
56. _____
57. _____

58. _____
59. _____
60. _____
61. _____
62. _____
63. _____
64. _____
65. _____
66. _____
67. _____
68. _____
69. _____
70. _____
71. _____
72. _____
73. _____
74. _____
75. _____
76. _____
77. _____
78. _____
79. _____
80. _____
81. _____
82. _____
83. _____
84. _____
85. _____

O R P

There are at least 23 words that contain the letter sequence ORP. Finding 12 is good; 16 shows skill and purpose; and 19 is gorgeous.

Answers on page 472

1. _____
2. _____
3. _____
4. _____
5. _____
6. _____
7. _____
8. _____

9. _____
10. _____
11. _____
12. _____
13. _____
14. _____
15. _____

16. _____
17. _____
18. _____
19. _____
20. _____
21. _____
22. _____
23. _____

R M Y

We found only six words that have the letter sequence RMY. Can you identify them? If you come up with more than four, that's excellent!

Answers on page 472

1. _____
2. _____

3. _____
4. _____

5. _____
6. _____

L F I

At least nine words share the letter sequence LFI. If you list four, that's not half bad.

Answers on page 472

1. _____
2. _____
3. _____

4. _____
5. _____
6. _____

7. _____
8. _____
9. _____

HOW TO SOLVE A REBUS

Rebus games are fun; they are fun for everyone in the family. You will find solving the rebus puzzle a delight.

SOLUTION

Perhaps the best way to explain the rebus game is to start with a simple example. Let's work it together:

1. HAND - AND = H.

   Cross out the A, the N, and the D, and what you have left is one H.

2. Add the word CHAIN. Now you have HCHAIN.

3. The next picture shows a CAN. So you cross out CAN from HCHAIN and you are now left with HHI.

4. Add a T, and you now have HHIT.

5. Take away one H, and what is left is the three letter word HIT.

Let's check this out with what the cartoons say. The first cartoon figure says, "What a batter dreams about." Well, of course, a batter dreams about a hit.

The second cartoon character says that the word means "A great popular performance." You'll agree that this is a hit.

You can always check your answer in two ways:

1. The answer should fit exactly into the boxes provided.

2. The answer should fit with what the characters say.

REBUS GAME NO. 1

Solution on page 472

REBUS GAME NO. 2

Solution on page 472

REBUS GAME NO. 3

Solution on page 472

REBUS GAME NO. 4

Solution on page 473

122

REBUS GAME NO. 5

Solution on page 473

REBUS GAME NO. 6

Solution on page 473

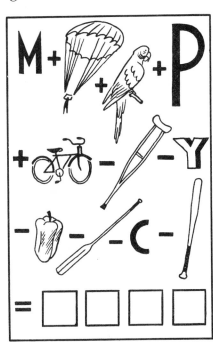

123

REBUS GAME NO. 7

Solution on page 473

REBUS GAME NO. 8

Solution on page 473

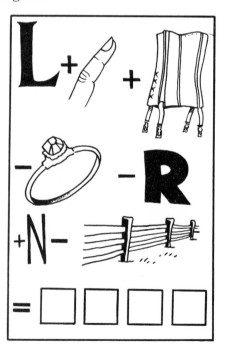

REBUS GAME NO. 9

Solution on page 473

REBUS GAME NO. 10

Solution on page 473

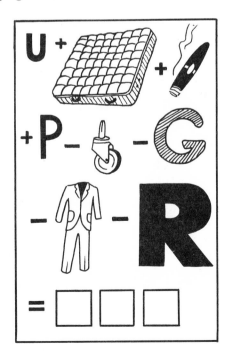

REBUS GAME NO. 11

Solution on page 473

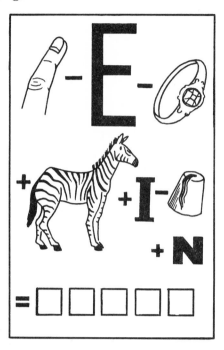

REBUS GAME NO. 12

Solution on page 473

REBUS GAME NO. 13

Solution on page 473

REBUS GAME NO. 14

Solution on page 473

REBUS GAME NO. 15

Solution on page 473

REBUS GAME NO. 16

Solution on page 473

REBUS GAME NO. 17

Solution on page 473

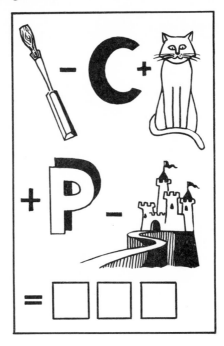

REBUS GAME NO. 18

Solution on page 473

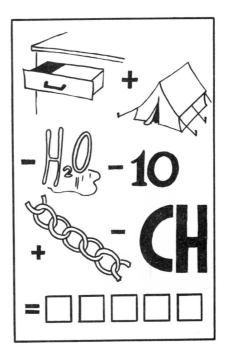

129

REBUS GAME NO. 19

Solution on page 473

REBUS GAME NO. 20

Solution on page 473

REBUS GAME NO. 21

Solution on page 473

REBUS GAME NO. 22

Solution on page 473

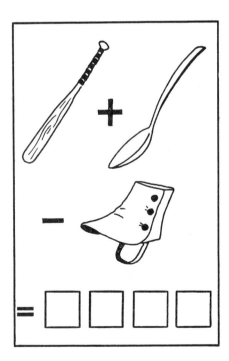

REBUS GAME NO. 23

Solution on page 473

REBUS GAME NO. 24

Solution on page 473

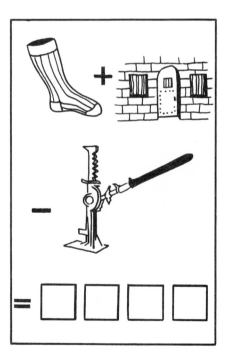

REBUS GAME NO. 25

Solution on page 474

REBUS GAME NO. 26

Solution on page 474

THE OWL-CRITIC

JAMES T. FIELDS

"Who stuffed that white owl?" No one spoke in the shop,
The barber was busy, and he couldn't stop;
The customers, waiting their turns, were all reading
The *Daily*, the *Herald*, the *Post*, little heeding
The young man who blurted out such a blunt question;
Not one raised a head, or even made a suggestion;
    And the barber kept on shaving.

"Don't you see, Mr. Brown,"
Cried the youth, with a frown,
"How wrong the whole thing is,
How preposterous each wing is,
How flattened the head is, how jammed down the neck is—
In short, the whole owl, what an ignorant wreck 'tis.
I make no apology;
I've learned owl-eology.
I've passed days and nights in a hundred collections,
And cannot be blinded to any deflections
Arising from unskillful fingers that fail
To stuff a bird right, from his beak to his tail.
Mister Brown! Mister Brown!
Do take that bird down,
Or you'll soon be the laughing-stock all over town!"
    And the barber kept on shaving.

"I've *studied* owls,
And other night-fowls,
And I tell you
What I know to be true;
An owl cannot roost
With his limbs so unloosed;
No owl in this world
Ever had his claws curled,
Ever had his legs slanted,
Ever had his bill canted,
Ever had his neck screwed
Into that attitude.
He can't *do* it, because
'Tis against all bird-laws.

"Anatomy teaches,
Ornithology preaches,
An owl has a toe
That *can't* turn out so!
I've made the white owl my study for years,
And to see such a job almost moves me to tears!
Mr. Brown, I'm amazed
You should be so gone crazed
As to put up a bird
In that posture absurd!
To *look* at that owl really brings on a dizziness
The man who stuffed *him* don't half know his business!"
    And the barber kept on shaving.

"Examine those eyes.
I'm filled with surprise
Taxidermists should pass
Off on you such poor glass;
So unnatural they seem
They'd make Audubon scream,
And John Burroughs laugh
To encounter such chaff.
Do take that bird down;
Have him stuffed again, Brown!"
    And the barber kept on shaving.

"With some sawdust and bark
I could stuff in the dark
An owl better than that.
I could make an old hat
Look more like an owl
Than that horrid fowl,
Stuck up there so stiff like a side of coarse leather.
In fact, about *him*, there's not one natural feather."

Just then, with a wink and a sly normal lurch,
The owl, very gravely, got down from his perch,
Walked around, and regarded his fault-finding critic
(Who thought he was stuffed) with a glance analytic,
And then fairly hooted, as if he should say:
"Your learning's at fault *this* time, anyway;
Don't waste it again on a live bird, I pray.
I'm an owl; you're another. Sir Critic, good day!"
    And the barber kept on shaving.

THE GOAT AND
THE THREE RED SHIRTS

There was a man, now please to note,
There was a man, who had a goat;
He loved that goat, indeed he did,
He loved that goat, just like a kid.

One day that goat felt frisk and fine,
Ate three red shirts from off the line.
The man he grabbed him by the back,
And tied him to a railroad track.

But when the train hove into sight,
That goat grew pale and green with fright.
He heaved a sigh, as if in pain,
Coughed up those shirts and flagged the train!

137

CASEY AT THE BAT

ERNEST LAWRENCE THAYER

The outlook wasn't brilliant for the Mudville nine that day,
The score stood two to four with just one inning left to play;
And so, when Cooney died at first, and Burrows did the same,
A sickly silence fell upon the patrons of the game.

A straggling few got up to go in deep despair. The rest
Clung to the hope that springs eternal within each human breast;
They thought if only Casey could but get a whack at that—
They'd put up *even money* now, with Casey at the bat.

But Flynn preceded Casey, and so did Jimmy Blake,
And the former was a washout, and the latter was a fake;
So upon that stricken multitude grim melancholy sat,
For there seemed but little chance of Casey's getting to the bat.

But Flynn let drive a single to the wonderment of all,
And Blake whom all had sneered at, tore the cover off the ball;
And when the dust had lifted, and they saw what had occurred,
There was Jimmy safe on second and Flynn a-huggin' third!

Then from the gladdened multitude went up a joyous yell,
It rumbled in the mountaintops, it rattled in the dell,
It struck upon the hillside and rebounded on the flat;
For Casey, mighty Casey, was advancing to the bat.

There was ease in Casey's manner as he stepped into his place,
There was pride in Casey's bearing, and a smile on Casey's face;
And when, responding to the cheers, he lightly doffed his hat,
No stranger in the crowd could doubt 'twas Casey at the bat.

Ten thousand eyes were upon him as he rubbed his hands with dirt;
Five thousand tongues applauded when he wiped them on his shirt.
Then while the writhing pitcher ground the ball into his hip,
Defiance gleamed in Casey's eye, a sneer curled Casey's lip.

And now the leather-covered sphere came hurtling through the air,
And Casey stood a-watching it in haughty grandeur there;
Close by the sturdy batsman the ball unheeded sped:
"That ain't my style," said Casey. "Strike one!" the umpire said.

From the benches, black with people, there went up a muffled roar,
Like the beating of the storm-waves on a stern and distant shore;
"Kill him! Kill the umpire!" shouted someone in the stands.
And it's sure they would have killed him had not Casey raised his hand.

With a smile of Christian charity great Casey's visage shone;
He stilled the rising tumult; he bade the game go on;
He signaled to the pitcher, and once more the spheroid flew,
But Casey still ignored it; and the umpire said, "Strike two!"

"Fraud!" cried the maddened thousands, and the echo answered "Fraud!"
But one scornful look from Casey and the audience was awed;
They saw his face grow stern and cold, they saw his muscles strain.
And they knew that Casey wouldn't let that ball go by again.

The sneer is gone from Casey's lip, his teeth are clenched with hate;
He pounds with cruel violence his bat upon the plate;
And now the pitcher holds the ball, and now he lets it go.
And now the air is shattered by the force of Casey's blow.

Oh, somewhere in this favored land the sun is shining bright;
The band is playing somewhere, and somewhere hearts are light;
And somewhere men are laughing, and somewhere children shout;
But there is no joy in Mudville—*mighty Casey has struck out!*

CASEY—
TWENTY YEARS LATER

CLARENCE PATRICK McDONALD

The Bugville team was surely up against a rocky game;
The chances were they'd win defeat and undying fame;
Three men were hurt and two were benched; the score stood six to four.
They had to make three hard-earned runs in just two innings more.

"It can't be done," the captain said, a pallor on his face;
"I've got two pitchers in the field, a mutt on second base;
And should another man get spiked or crippled in some way,
The team would sure be down and out, with eight men left to play.

"We're up against it anyhow as far as I can see;
My boys ain't hitting like they should and that's what worries me;
The luck is with the other side, no pennant will we win;
It's mighty tough, but we must take our medicine and grin."

The eighth round opened; one, two, three; the enemy went down;
The Bugville boys went out the same, the captain wore a frown;
The first half of the ninth came round, two men had been called out,
When Bugville's catcher broke a thumb and could not go that route.

A deathly silence settled o'er the crowd assembled there.
Defeat would be allotted them; they felt it in the air;
With only eight men in the field 'twould be a gruesome fray,—
Small wonder that the captain cursed the day he learned to play.

"Lend me a man to finish with," he begged the other team;
"Lend you a man?" the foe replied; "My boy, you're in a dream;
We want to win the pennant, too—that's what we're doing here.
There's only one thing you can do—call for a volunteer."

The captain stood and pondered in a desperate sort of way;
He never was a quitter and would not be today!
"Is there within the grandstand here"—his voice rang loud and clear—
"A man who has the sporting blood to be a volunteer?"

Again that awful silence settled o'er the multitude;
Was there a man among them with such recklessness imbued?
The captain stood with cap in hand, while hopeless was his glance,
And then a short and stocky man cried out, "I'll take a chance."

Into the field he bounded with a step both firm and light;
"Give me the mask and mitt," he said; "let's finish up the fight.
The game is now beyond recall; I'll last at least a round;
Although I'm ancient you will find me muscular and sound."

His hair was sprinkled here and there with little streaks of gray;
Around his eyes and on his brow a bunch of wrinkles lay.
The captain smiled despairingly and slowly turned away.
"Why, he's all right," one rooter yelled. Another, "Let him play."

"All right, go on," the captain sighed; the stranger turned around,
Took off his coat and collar, too, and threw them on the ground.
The humor of the situation seemed to hit them all,
As he donned the mask and mitt, the umpire called, "Play ball!"

Three balls the pitcher at him hurled, three balls of lightning speed;
The stranger caught them all with ease and did not seem to heed.
Each ball had been pronounced a strike, the side had been put out,
And as he walked in towards the bench, he heard the rooters shout.

One Bugville boy went out on strikes, and one was killed at first;
The captain saw his awkward pose, and gnashed his teeth and cursed.
The third man smashed a double and the fourth man swatted clear,
Then, in a thunder of applause, up came the volunteer.

His feet were planted in the earth, he swung a warlike club;
The captain saw his awkward pose and softly whispered, "Dub!"
The pitcher looked at him and grinned, then heaved a mighty ball;
The echo of that fearful swat still lingers with us all.

High, fast, and far that spheroid flew; it sailed and sailed away;
It ne'er was found, so it's supposed it still floats on today.
Three runs came in, the pennant would be Bugville's for a year;
The fans and players gathered round to cheer the volunteer.

"What is your name?" the captain asked. "Tell us your name," cried all,
As down his cheeks great tears were seen to run and fall.
For one brief moment he was still, then murmured soft and low:
"I'm mighty Casey who struck out—just twenty years ago."

CASEY'S REVENGE

GRANTLAND RICE

There were saddened hearts in Mudville for a week or even more;
There were muttered oaths and curses—every fan in town was sore.
"Just think," said one, "how soft it looked with Casey at the bat,
And then to think he'd go and spring a bush league trick like that!"

All his past fame was forgotten—he was now a hopeless "shine."
They called him "Strike-Out Casey," from the mayor down the line;
And as he came to bat each day his bosom heaved a sigh,
While a look of hopeless fury shone in mighty Casey's eye.

He pondered in the days gone by that he had been their king,
That when he strolled up to the plate they made the welkin ring;
But now his nerve had vanished, for when he heard them hoot
He "fanned" or "popped out" daily, like some minor league recruit.

He soon began to sulk and loaf, his batting eye went lame;
No home runs on the score card now were chalked against his name;
The fans without exception gave the manager no peace,
For one and all kept clamoring for Casey's quick release.

The Mudville squad began to slump, the team was in the air;
Their playing went from bad to worse—nobody seemed to care.
"Back to the woods with Casey!" was the cry from Rooters' Row.
"Get someone who can hit the ball, and let that big dub go!"

144

The lane is long, someone has said, that never turns again,
And Fate, though fickle, often gives another chance to men;
And Casey smiled; his rugged face no longer wore a frown—
The pitcher who had started all the trouble came to town.

All Mudville had assembled—ten thousand fans had come
To see the twirler who had put big Casey on the bum;
And when he stepped into the box, the multitude went wild;
He doffed his cap in proud disdain, but Casey only smiled.

"Play ball!" the umpire's voice rang out, and then the game began.
But in that throng of thousands there was not a single fan
Who thought that Mudville had a chance, and with the setting sun
Their hopes sank low—the rival team was leading "four to one."

The last half of the ninth came round, with no change in the score;
But when the first man up hit safe, the crowd began to roar;
The din increased, the echo of ten thousand shouts was heard
When the pitcher hit the second and gave "four balls" to the third.

Three men on base—nobody out—three runs to tie the game!
A triple meant the highest niche in Mudville's hall of fame;
But here the rally ended and the gloom was deep as night,
When the fourth one "fouled to catcher" and the fifth "flew out to right."

A dismal groan in chorus came; a scowl was on each face
When Casey walked up, bat in hand, and slowly took his place;
His bloodshot eyes in fury gleamed, his teeth were clenched in hate;
He gave his cap a vicious hook and pounded on the plate.

But fame is fleeting as the wind and glory fades away;
There were no wild and woolly cheers, no glad acclaim this day;
They hissed and groaned and hooted as they clamored: "Strike him out!"
But Casey gave no outward sign that he had heard this shout.

The pitcher smiled and cut one loose—across the plate it sped;
Another hiss, another groan. "Strike one!" the umpire said.
Zip! Like a shot the second curve broke just below the knee.
"Strike two!" the umpire roared aloud; but Casey made no plea.

No roasting for the umpire now—his was an easy lot;
But here the pitcher whirled again—was that a rifle shot?
A whack, a crack, and out through the space the leather pellet flew,
A blot against the distant sky, a speck against the blue.

Above the fence in center field in rapid whirling flight
The sphere sailed on—the blot grew dim and then was lost to sight.
Ten thousand hats were thrown in the air, ten thousand threw a fit,
But no one ever found the ball that mighty Casey hit.

O, somewhere in this favored land dark clouds may hide the sun,
And somewhere bands no longer play and children have no fun!
And somewhere over blighted lives there hangs a heavy pall,
But Mudville hearts are happy now, *for Casey hit the ball.*

TO MY LOVE

I love my love with a deep purple love;
She fascinates me like a fly struggling in a pot of glue.
Her eyes are gray, like twin ash cans just emptied.
About which still hovers a dainty mist.
Her disposition is as bright as a 50-cent shine,
Yet her kisses are tender and goulashy.
I love my lady with a deep purple love.

THE CITY OF COLOGNE

SAMUEL TAYLOR COLERIDGE

In Koln, a town of monks and bones,
And pavements franged with murderous stones,
And rags, and hags, and hideous wenches,
I counted two-and-seventy stenches,
All well defined, and separate stinks!
Ye nymphs that reign o'er sewers and sinks,
The river Rhine, it is well known,
Doth wash your city of Cologne;
But tell me, nymphs, what power divine
Shall henceforth wash the river Rhine?

147

SHE WAS POOR, BUT SHE WAS HONEST

She was poor, but she was honest,
    Victim of the squire's whim:
First he loved her, then he left her,
    And she lost her honest name.

Then she ran away to London,
    For to hide her grief and shame;
There she met another squire,
    And lost her name again.

See her riding in her carriage,
    In the Park and all so gay:
All the nibs and nobby persons
    Come to pass the time of day.

See the little old-world village
    Where her aged parents live,
Drinking the champagne she sends them;
    But they never can forgive.

In the rich man's arms she flutters,
    Like a bird with broken wing:
First he loved her, then he left her,
    And she hasn't got a ring.

See him in the splendid mansion,
    Entertaining with the best,
While the victim of his passions
    Trails her way through mud and slime.

Standing on the bridge at midnight,
    She says: "Farewell, blighted Love."
There's a scream, a splash—Good Heavens!
    What is she a-doing of?

Then they drag her from the river,
    Water from her clothes they wrang,
For they thought that she was drowned;
    But the corpse got up and sang:

"It's the same the whole world over,
    It's the poor that gets the blame,
It's the rich that gets the pleasure.
    Isn't it a blooming shame?"

IVAN SKAVINSKY SKAVAR

The sons of the Prophet are brave men and bold,
    And quite unaccustomed to fear;
But the bravest by far, in the ranks of the Shah,
    Was Abdul Abulbul Amir.

If you wanted a man to encourage the van,
    Or harass the foe from the rear,
Storm fort or redoubt, you had only to shout
    For Abdul Abulbul Amir.

Now the heroes were plenty and well known to fame,
    In the troops that were led by the Czar,
And the bravest of these was a man by the name
    Of Ivan Skavinsky Skavar.

He could jump fifty yards and tell fortunes at cards,
    And strum on the Spanish guitar,
In fact quite the cream of the Muscovite team
    Was Ivan Skavinsky Skavar.

One day this bold Russian, he shouldered his gun
    And donned his most insolent sneer,
Downtown he did go, where he trod on the toe
    Of Abdul Abulbul Amir.

"Young man," Abdul roared, "With your life are you bored?
    Do you wish to end your career?
Vile infidel, know, you have trod on the toe
    Of Abdul Abulbul Amir!

"So take your last look at sunshine and brook,
    And send your regrets to the Czar—
For by this I imply, you are going to die,
    Count Ivan Skavinsky Skavar!"

Then this bold Mameluke drew his trusty skibouk,
    Singing, "Allah Il Allah! Al-hah"
And with murd'rous intent, he ferociously went,
    For Ivan Skavinsky Skavar.

They parried and thrust, they side-stepped and cussed,
Of blood they both spilled a great part;
For they both were so tough, so strong and so rough—
'Twas a wonderful fight from the start!

They fought all that night 'neath the pale yellow moon;
The din it was heard from afar,
And huge multitudes came, so great was the fame,
Of Abdul and Ivan Skavar.

As Abdul's long knife was exacting the life,
In fact, he was shouting "Huzzah!"
He felt himself struck by the wily Kalmuck,
Count Ivan Skavinsky Skavar.

The Sultan rode by in his red-breasted fly,
 Expecting the victor to cheer,
But as he drew nigh he heard the last sigh
 Of Abdul Abulbul Amir.

There's a tomb rises up where the Bosphorus rolls,
 And carved there in characters clear,
Is, "Stranger, when passing, oh pray for the soul
 Of Abdul Abulbul Amir."

In a Muscovite town 'long the Volga's green banks,
 'Neath the light of the cold Northern Star,
A maid tends the grave of her hero so brave,
 Ivan Skavinsky Skavar!

THE BLIND MEN
AND THE ELEPHANT

JOHN GODFREY SAXE

It was six men of Indostan
    To learning much inclined,
Who went to see the Elephant
    (Though all of them were blind),
That each by observation
    Might satisfy his mind.

The *First* approached the Elephant,
    And happening to fall
Against his broad and sturdy side,
    At once began to bawl:
"God bless me! but the Elephant
    Is very like a wall!"

The *Second*, feeling of the tusk,
    Cried, "Ho! what have we here
So very round and smooth and sharp?
    To me 'tis mighty clear
This wonder of an Elephant
    Is very like a spear!"

The *Third* approached the animal,
    And happening to take
The squirming trunk within his hands,
    Thus boldly up and spake:
"I see," quoth he, "the Elephant
    Is very like a snake!"

The *Fourth* reached out an eager hand,
    And felt about the knee.
"What most this wondrous beast is like
    Is mighty plain," quoth he;
"'Tis clear enough the Elephant
    Is very like a tree!"

The *Fifth* who chanced to touch the ear,
  Said, "E'en the blindest man
Can tell what this resembles most;
  Deny the fact who can,
This marvel of an Elephant
  Is very like a fan!"

The *Sixth* no sooner had begun
  About the beast to grope,
Than, seizing on the swinging tail
  That fell within his scope,
"I see," quoth he, "the Elephant
  Is very like a rope!"

And so these men of Indostan
  Disputed loud and long,
Each in his own opinion
  Exceeding stiff and strong,
Though each was partly in the right,
  And all were in the wrong!

THE MORAL:

So oft in theologic wars,
  The disputants, I ween,
Rail on in utter ignorance
  Of what each other mean,
And prate about an elephant
  Not one of them has seen!

THE SOCIETY
UPON THE STANISLAUS

BRET HARTE

I reside at Table Mountain, and my name is Truthful James;
I am not up to small deceit, or any sinful games;
And I'll tell in simple language what I know about the row
That broke up our society upon the Stanislow.

But first I would remark that it is not a proper plan
For any scientific gent to whale his fellow man,
And if a member don't agree with his peculiar whim,
To lay for that same member, so to razzle-dazzle him.

Now, nothing could be finer or more beautiful to see
Than the first six months' proceedings of that same society;
Till Brown of Calaveras brought a lot of fossil bones
That he found within a tunnel near the residence of Jones.

Then Brown, he read a paper, and he reconstructed there,
From those same bones, an animal that was extremely rare;
And Jones then asked the Chair for a suspension of the rules,
Till he could prove that those same bones was one of his lost mules.

Then Brown, he smiled a bitter smile, and said he was at fault,
It seemed he had been trespassing on Jones's family vault;
He was a most sarcastic man, this quiet Mr. Brown;
He had the kind of acrid smile that almost was a frown.

Now, I hold it is not decent for a scientific gent
To say another is an ass—at least, to all intent;
Nor should the individual who happens to be meant
Reply by heaving rocks at him to any great extent.

Then Abner Deal of Angel's raised a point of order, when
A chunk of old red sandstone took him in the abdomen;
And he smiled a kind of sickly smile, and curled up on the floor,
And the subsequent proceedings interested him no more.

For in less time than I write it, every member did engage
In a warfare with the remnants of a palaeozoic age;
And the way they heaved those fossils in their anger was a sin,
Till the skull of an old mammoth caved the head of Thompson in.

And this is all I have to say of these improper games
For I live at Table Mountain, and my name is Truthful James;
And I've told, in simple language, what I know about the row
That broke up our society upon the Stanislow.

BLOW ME EYES

WALLACE IRWIN

When I was young and full o' pride,
    A-standin' on the grass
And gazin' o'er the water-side,
    I seen a fisher lass.
"O, fisher lass, be kind awhile,"
    I asks 'er quite unbid.
"Please look into me face and smile"—
    And, blow me eyes, she did!"

      O, blow me light and blow me blow,
      I didn't think she'd charm me so—
         But, blow me eyes, she did!

She seemed so young and beautiful
    I *had* to speak perlite,
(The afternoon was long and dull,
    But she was short and bright).
"This ain't no place," I says, "to stand—
    Let's take a walk instid,
Each holdin' of the other's hand"—
    And, blow me eyes, she did!

      O, blow me light and blow me blow,
      I sort o' thunk she wouldn't go—
         But, blow me eyes, she did!

And as we walked along a lane
    With no one else to see,
Me heart was filled with sudden pain,
    And so I says to she:
"If you would have me actions speak
    The words what can't be hid,
You'd sort o' let me kiss yer cheek"—
    And, blow me eyes, she did!

        O, blow me light and blow me bloe,
        How sweet she was I didn't know—
            But, blow me eyes, *she* did!

But pretty soon me shipmate Jim
    Came strollin' down the beach,
And she began a-oglin' him
    As pretty as a peach.
"O, fickle maid o' false intent,"
    Impuslively I chid,
"Why don't you go and wed that gent?"
    And, blow my eyes, she did!

        O, blow me light and blow me blow,
        I didn't think she'd treat me so—
            But, blow me eyes, she did!

159

THE YARN OF THE NANCY BELL

W.S. GILBERT

'Twas on the shores that round our coast
　　From Deal to Ramsgate span,
That I found alone, on a piece of stone,
　　An elderly naval man.

His hair was weedy, his beard was long,
　　And weedy and long was he;
And I heard this wight on the shore recite,
　　In a singular minor key:—

"Oh, I am a cook and a captain bold,
　　And the mate of the Nancy brig,
And a bo'sun tight, and a midshipmite,
　　And the crew of the captain's gig."

And he shook his fists and he tore his hair,
　　Till I really felt afraid,
For I couldn't help thinking the man had been drinking,
　　And so I simply said:—

"Oh, elderly man, it's little I know
　　Of the duties of men of the sea,
But I'll eat my hand if I understand
　　How ever you can be

"At once a cook and a captain bold,
    And the mate of the Nancy brig,
And a bo'sun tight, and a midshipmite,
    And the crew of the captain's gig!"

Then he gave a hitch to his trousers, which
    Is a trick all seamen larn,
And having got rid of a thumping quid,
    He spun this painful yarn:—

"'Twas in the good ship Nancy Bell
    That we sailed to the Indian Sea,
And there on a reef we come to grief,
    Which has often occurred to me.

"And pretty nigh all o' the crew was drowned
    (There was seventy-seven o' soul);
And only ten of the Nancy's men
    Said 'Here!' to the muster-roll. .

"There was me, and the cook, and the captain bold,
    And the mate of the Nancy brig,
And the bo'sun tight and a midshipmite,
    And the crew of the captain's gig.

"For a month we'd neither vittles nor drink
    Till a-hungry we did feel,
So we drawed a lot, and accordin', shot
    The captain for our meal.

"The next lot fell to the Nancy's mate,
    And a delicate dish he made;
Then our appetite with the midshipmite
    We seven survivors stayed.

"And then we murdered the bo'sun tight,
    And he much resembled pig;
Then we whittled free, did the cook and me,
    On the crew of the captain's gig.

"Then only the cook and me was left,
    And the delicate question, 'Which
Of us two goes to the kettle?' arose,
    And we argued it out as sich.

"For I loved that cook as a brother, I did,
    And the cook he worshipped me;
But we'd both be blowed if we'd either be stowed
    In the other chap's hold, you see.

"'I'll be eat if you dines off me,' says Tom.
    'Yes, that,' says I, 'you'll be.
I'm boiled if I die, my friend,' quoth I;
    And 'Exactly so,' quoth he.

"Says he: 'Dear James, to murder me
    Were a foolish thing to do,
For don't you see that you can't cook *me*,
    While I can—and will—cook *you?*

"So he boils the water, and takes the salt
    And the pepper in portions true,
Which he never forgot, and some chopped shallot,
    And some sage and parsley, too.

"'Come here,' says he, with a proper pride,
    Which his smiling features tell;
'Twill soothing be if I let you see
    How extremely nice you'll smell.'

"And he stirred it round and round and round,
    And he sniffed at the foaming froth;
When I ups with his heels, and smothers his squeals
    In the scum of the boiling broth.

"And I eat that cook in a week or less,
    And as I eating be
The last of his chops, why I almost drops,
    For a vessel in sight I see.—

"And I never larf, and I never smile,
    And I never lark nor play;
But sit and croak, and a single joke
    I have—which is to say:

"Oh, I am a cook and a captain bold,
    And the mate of the Nancy brig,
And a bo'sun tight, and a midshipmite,
    And the crew of the captain's gig!"

THE BALLAD OF CHARITY

CHARLES GODFREY LELAND

It was in a pleasant depot, sequestered from the rain,
That many weary passengers were waiting for the train;
Piles of quite expensive baggage, many a gorgeous portmanteau,
Ivory-handled umberellas made a most touristic show.

Whereunto there came a person, very humble was his mien,
Who took an observation of the interesting scene;
Closely scanned the umberellas, watched with joy the mighty trunks,
And observed that all the people were securing Pullman bunks.

Who was followed shortly after by a most unhappy tramp,
Upon whose features Poverty had jounced her iron stamp;
And to make a clear impression as bees sting while they buzz,
She had hit him rather harder than she generally does.

For he was so awfully ragged, and in parts so awfully bare,
That the folks were quite repulsioned to behold him begging there;
And instead of drawing currency from out of their pocket-books,
They drew themselves asunder with aversionary looks.

Sternly gazed the first newcomer on the unindulgent crowd,
Then in tones which pierced the depot he solilicussed aloud:—
"I have traveled o'er this continent from Quebec to Saginaw,
But such a set of scalawags as these I never saw!

"You are wealthy, you are loaded, you have houses, lands and rent,
Yet unto a suffering mortal, you will not donate a cent;
You expend your missionaries all the way to Timbuktu,
But there isn't any heathen that is half as small as you.

"You are lucky—you have check-books and deposits in the bank,
And ye squanderate your money like titled folks of rank;
The onyx and the sardonyx upon your garments shine,
And you drink cocktails at dinner and wash them down with wine.

"You are going for the summer to the islands by the sea,
Where a sandwich sells for two bucks, and it's fifty cents for tea;
Ivory-handled umberellas do not come into my plan,
But I can give some comfort to my suffering fellow man.

"Handbags made of alligator are not truly at my call,
Yet in the eyes of Mercy, I am richer than you all,
For I can give five dollars where you cannot stand a dime,
And never miss it neither, nor regret it any time."

Saying this he drew a wallet from inside his fancy vest,
And gave the tramp a V-note which it was his level best;
Other people having seen him, soon to charity inclined—
One genuine real giver makes a hundred change their mind.

The first who gave five dollars led the other one about,
And at every contribution, he a-raised a joyful shout;
Exclaiming how 'twas noble to relieviate distress,
And remarking that our duty is our present happiness.

Eight hundred bucks in greenbacks were collected by the tramp,
When he bid them all good evening, and went out into the damp;
And was followed briefly after by the one who made the speech,
And who showed by good example how to practise as to preach.

Which soon around the corner the couple quickly met,
And the tramp produced the specie for to liquidate his debt;
And the man who did the preaching took five hundred of the sum,
Which five from eight collected left three hundred for the bum.

And the couple passed the summer at the seashore with the rest;
Greatly changed in their appearance and most elegantly dressed.
Any fowl with change of feathers may a brilliant bird become:
Oh, how hard is life for many! Oh, how sweet it is for some!

CURSES

We all learn to squelch, hide, or sublimate our feelings of anger and hostility. The curse is probably one of the more innocent ways of getting rid of those "bad" feelings, and sometimes in the process, we manage to get off some real literary gems.

Here is a list of special beauties that we think you will find delicious—the crème de la crème of maledictions.

May you be the proof that man can endure everything.

Break a leg and lose your crutch.

May you become so poor that you have to go around begging, and I hope you have to come to me for alms, and I hope I have nothing to give you.

Avoid old age—go hang yourself.

May you lose all your teeth except one—the one that has the toothache.

Take a nice walk and stumble on a skunk.

May you grow like an onion—with your head in the ground and your feet in the air.

May you romp with joy and skip right into a sewer.

May all your relatives move in on you.

May student barbers practice on your beard.

May all your baths be too hot and your women too cold.

May everything you cook stick to the bottom of the pot.

May you become famous—in medical history.

May all your shoes be too long and your haircuts too short.

May you be a liar with a poor memory.

May you spend the best part of your day sitting on a soft chair—my dentist's.

May you have only nightmares—and may all your dreams come true.

May your wife eat matzohs in bed, and may you roll in the crumbs.

May you spend your healthy days on your back, your sick days on your feet.

May your appetite enlarge and your digestion diminish.

May your wife be as much help to you as a lame horse.

May you have lots of money in a bank—a bankrupt one!

May you bargain with God and lose.

May you be like a lamp—hang all day and burn all night.

Go eat apples—and bite into worms.

May your hat be the right size, but your head too small.

MARK TIME

Each of the 28 definitions below should bring to mind a name, word, or expression which contains somewhere within it the word MARK. For example: *To assign boundaries* would be MARK *off.* How many can you figure out?

A score of 15 is not bad; 21 marks you as a word player; and 26 is remarkable.

Answers on page 474

1. Conform strictly to standard _____

2. Poet who wrote *Man with the Hoe* _____

3. It tells you where to start
    reading again _____

4. Abstract expressionist artist who died
    in 1970 leaving a contested estate _____

5. Expression used when you're sure
    what you're saying will be proved _____

6. Creator of Tom Sawyer _____

7. Impression on paper _____

8. Colored pen used by artists
    and children _____

9. American Olympics swimming
    star, 1972 _____

10. Official stamp of purity or
    genuineness _____

11. English prima ballerina _____

12. Condition of heavy supply,
    causing lower prices _____

13. Skill at hitting the target _____

14. Amount added to cost to set the price _____

15. Noted female Irish revolutionary _____

16. Up for sale _____

17. Fall short; fail _____

18. She played Jane to Elmo K. Lincoln's
    Tarzan of the Apes in 1918 _____

19. Sign of exclusive ownership _____

20. Monetary unit of Finland _____

21. Gathering information about
    consumer preferences _____

22. Punishment meted out in Genesis I:15 _____

23. Reduce the price _____

24. Noted hotel with a hilltop view of
    San Francisco _____

25. Call to get ready for a race _____

26. Notice; state _____

27. Mrs. Strong's meddling mother in
    David Copperfield

28. Cleopatra's lover _____

ON ICE

Below, you will find 32 words and expressions. Each one should suggest to you another expression which contains the three letters ICE. The dashes indicate missing letters. For example: *gaming cubes* are *d*ICE.

A score of 18 is fair; 25 is very good; 30 ices the cake.

Answers on page 474

1. __ ICE   Vermin

2. ICE __ __ __ __ __   Nation in North Atlantic

3. __ __ ICE __ __ __ __ __ __   Dinosaur

4. __ __ ICE   __ __

   __ __ __ __ __ __ __ __ __ __   Lewis Carroll favorite

5. __ ICE __ __   Finer point

6. __ ICE   Food staple

7. __ ICE   __ __ __ __ __ __ __ __ __ Second in command

8. __ __   __ ICE   __ __ __

   __ __ __   John Steinbeck novel

9. _ _ ICE   Flavoring

10. _ _ ICE   Cost

11. ICE _ _ _ _   Floe

12. _ _ ICE   Instant

13. _ _ _ _ _   _ _ _   ICE   To put at ease

14. _ ICE _ _ _ _ _ _ _   200th birthday

15. _ ICE _ _ _   Official permission

16. _ _ _   ICE _ _ _ _ _ _ _ _   Eugene O'Neill play

17. _ _ _ ICE   Mechanical contraption

18. _ _ ICE _ _   Muscle of upper arm

19. ICE _ _ _ _ _ _ _   Winter sport

20. _ _ _ _ _ ICE   Black candy

21. _ _ ICE   Sliver

22. _ _ _ ICE   Option

23. _ _ _ _ _ _ ICE   Cliff

24. _ ICE   City in the South of France

25. _ ICE _ _ _ _ _   Police division

26. _ _ _ ICE   Counsel

27. _ _ _ ICE   Lure

28. _ _ _ ICE _ _   Seldom speaking

29. _ _ ICE _ _ _ _   Invaluable; irreplaceable

30. _ _ _ _ _ _ _ _   _ _ ICE   Met diva from Mississippi

31. _ ICE _ _ _ _ _ _   Lascivious

32. _ _ _   _ _ ICE   _ _ _ _ _   _ _ _ _ _ _   Play by Van Druten

OF THEE I SING

Below are 30 clues, each of which should suggest a word or phrase containing the letters THE. See how many you can provide.

A score of 20 is good; 24 is excellent; 26 makes you the cream of the crop.

Answers on page 474

1. Instrument to indicate temperature   THE _ _ _ _ _ _ _

2. Greek letter   THE _ _

3. Flat stringed instrument   _ _ THE _

4. Sad; pitiable   _ _ THE _ _ _

5. Margaret Mitchell novel of 1936   _ _ _ _   _ _ _ _

        THE   _ _ _ _

6. Larceny   THE _ _

7. Bird's coat   _ _ _ THE _ _

8. Machine for turning something   _ _ THE

9. Cinema or playhouse   THE _ _ _ _

10. Husband of Desdemona; Shakespeare play   _ THE _ _ _

11. Wash oneself   _ _ THE

12. Topic; written composition   THE _ _

13. Actor   THE _ _ _ _ _

14. Oedipus' city   THE _ _ _

15. Study of religion   THE _ _ _ _ _

16. Pagan; uncivilized   _ _ _ THE _

17. Animal skin   _ _ _ THE _

18. Bounteous giver   _ _ THE _

        _ _ _ _ _ _

19. One of Christ's 12 apostles   _ _ _ THE _

20. Algebra, geometry, etc.   _ _ THE _ _ _ _ _ _

21. 1941 Noel Coward comedy   _ _ _ THE

_ _ _ _ _ _

22. Capital of Greece   _ THE _ _

23. Boil; be furious   _ _ _ THE

24. Despise   _ _ _ THE

25. Supposition; speculation   THE _ _ _ _

26. Curved harvesting implement   _ _ _ THE

27. Jar for storing hot or cold liquids   THE _ _ _ _ _

28. O'Neill masterpiece of 1946   THE   _ _ _ _ _ _ _

_ _ _ _ _ _

29. Tsarina with strange tastes   _ _ THE _ _ _ _ _

30. Squirm; twist oneself in pain   _ _ _ THE

175

MIGHTIER THAN
THE SWORD

The 35 definitions below should each suggest a word or phrase which contains the letters PEN. For example: a *porker's home* is a *pig*PEN.
A score of 17 is fair; 24 is excellent; 32 is stuPENdous.

Answers on page 474

1. American one-cent piece   _____

2. Ali Baba's command   _____

3. Without funds   _____

4. Suspended ornament or jewel   _____

5. Rooftop apartment   _____

6. One living on a fixed income   _____

7. Flightless Antarctic bird   _____

8. Five-sided figure   _____

9. Colorado resort; tree   _____

10. Banner or flag   _____

11. Outlay of funds   _____

12. Federal prison (e.g. Leavenworth)   _____

13. Prudent in small matters but not in large ones   _____

14. Indians, river, and bay in Maine   _____

15. Sheer chance or serendipity   _____

16. Be contingent upon   _____

17. British one-cent piece   _____

18. Become profound; make lower in tone   _____

19. Writing implement using lead   _____

20. First books of Old Testament   _____

21. Italian mountain range   _____

22. Fleming's wonder drug   _____

23. The *Thoughts* of Pascal   _____

24. Regret one's sins   _____

25. She thought the sky was falling   ———————————

26. Roman household gods;
    Lares' partners   ———————————

27. Dear; costly   ———————————

28. Hone or make acute   ———————————

29. Tarkington hero   ———————————

30. Used up; exhausted   ———————————

31. Upright   ———————————

32. Make allowances for   ———————————

33. Wasted, "_____ youth"   ———————————

34. Song from "Sweet Charity"   ———————————

35. Revolutionary War battle site
    in South Carolina   ———————————

TRIPLE-HEADER

Each of the words defined below contains three sets of double letters. Can you identify these words?

A score of 4 is above average; 5 is excellent; 6 is noteworthy; and 7 is—well, perfect is perfect.

Answers on page 474

1. Person in charge of business records   ———————————

2. State whose capital is Jackson   ———————————

3. Person to whom mail is sent   ———————————

4. Home state for Andrew Jackson and
    Andrew Johnson   ———————————

5. Bird whose name reflects its call   ———————————

6. In a way that achieves what is desired   ———————————

7. A river in Georgia   ———————————

177

RHYMING EXPRESSIONS

Below are definitions for 45 words or expressions which are composed of rhyming syllables. Can you supply the answers? For example: a *Chinese gambling game* is FAN-TAN.

A score of 25 is good; 30 proclaims you a poet; 40 is superduper.

Answers on page 474

1. Dumbbell; vehicle riding empty   _____

2. TV set   _____

3. Card game; bludgeon   _____

4. Candied fruit and the like   _____

5. Barrel organ   _____

6. Trash; stuff and nonsense   _____

7. Helplessly; by compulsion   _____

8. Show-off; skillful,
   aggressive performer   _____

9. Guileful trickery; illicit amour   _____

10. Disorderly confusion; Beatles song
    made infamous by Charles Manson   _____

11. Ice cream flavor containing
    candied fruit   _____

12. Lavish party; spree   _____

13. Sinuous, suggestive carnival dance   _____

14. Derisive term for large
    political contributor   _____

15. Magic incantation   _____

16. Ritualistic gibberish   _____

17. The masses (Greek)   _____

18. Fussbudget; stuffed shirt   _____

19. Insipid; unmanly   _____

20. Heedlessly; (with different spelling) Presley film   _____

21. To show obsequious deference; fawn   _____

22. Deterioration through use   _____

23. Indiscriminately; headlong   _____

24. Pal around with; chat with   _____

25. Expletive; opener of a song extolling a young lady's eyes   _____

26. Cheap dance hall; part of a Rolling Stones song title   _____

27. Precursor of stereo recording   _____

28. What the big bad wolf threatened to do   _____

29. Haitian black magic   _____

30. Noisy confusion of sound; excitement   _____

31. A stew of various ingredients; mixture   _____

32. Slang superlative of the 1920s   _____

33. Close relatives and friends   _____

34. Very loyal   _____

35. Completely just and honorable   _____

36. Promise of utopian fulfillment   _____

37. Eighty   _____

38. The jitters   _____

39. Simple, unpretentious girl   _____

40. Best TV viewing slot   _____

41. The London press   _____

42. The sound of crying   _____

43. Nocturnal rendezvous   _____

44. When airfare is often cheaper   _____

45. Labor holiday   _____

A PLACE IN THE SUN

The clues below should suggest to you words or phrases containing the letters SUN. For example: *An egg fried on one side only* would be SUN*ny-side up*.

A score of 19 is reasonable; 25 is very good; 30 means the SUN has broken through the clouds.

Answers on page 475

1. An ice-cream extravaganza   _____

2. Prostration from extreme heat   _____

3. Optimist's thoroughfare   _____

4. To have fun while you can   _____

5. American evangelist (1863-1935)   _____

6. Notions or miscellaneous items   _____

7. Hemingway novel set in Spain   _____

8. Beatles song from "Abbey Road" album   _____

9. Ski resort in Idaho   _____

10. Florida   _____

11. Orthodox Moslems   _____

12. Astronomical phenomena, capable of disrupting communications on earth   _____

13. Movie starring Newman and Redford _____

14. Turn-of-the-century Chinese leader _____

15. British cocktail party; Aussie tramp _____

16. Broadway musical, a spoof of
    Eddy-MacDonald films _____

17. Ancient instrument for
    measuring time _____

18. Where children receive
    religious instruction _____

19. Louis XIV _____

20. Neil Simon play and film _____

21. Nocturnal phenomenon visible in
    arctic regions _____

22. Kansas _____

23. Novel by Kate Douglas Wiggin and
    film with Shirley Temple _____

24. Arizona State U. athletic team _____

25. Song from *Fiddler on the Roof* _____

26. A painting by Van Gogh _____

27. TV detective show with "Kookie"
    Byrnes and Efram Zimbalist, Jr. _____

28. Japan _____

29. Melina Mercouri film _____

30. Apart, in pieces _____

31. Lorraine Hansberry play, made
    into film with Poitier _____

32. Song from *Hair*, recorded by the
    Fifth Dimension _____

33. Classic film with Holden
    and Swanson _____

34. Quarrel; disagreement _____

35. The season of Pentecost _____

36. Japanese manufactured car _____

37. Petty officer on a ship _____

38. Not honored or celebrated
    in literature _____

181

THE GOLD GAME

All 40 of the clues below should suggest to you a word or phrase which contains the letters GOLD. For example: *a famous proverb* would be *All that glitters is not* GOLD.

A score of 20 is good; 27 is excellent; and 34 is as good as GOLD.

Answers on page 475

1. "Do unto others. . ." _____
2. James Bond book and movie _____
3. California _____
4. Famous speech by
   William Jennings Bryant _____
5. Mass immigration to California,
   late 1840s _____
6. Woman after a man's money _____
7. American wildflower _____
8. Source of great wealth _____
9. King Midas' affliction _____
10. Uninvited guest of the three bears _____
11. Fifty years of wedded bliss _____
12. Petroleum _____
13. What's at the end of the rainbow _____
14. What Hercules sought from
    the Hesperides _____
15. The harbor of Istanbul _____
16. Short story by Poe _____
17. Era of great comfort, great art, etc. _____
18. Shirker or deadbeat _____
19. Italian dramatist of the 18th century _____
20. Object of Jason's search _____
21. Entrance to San Francisco Bay _____
22. Major Hollywood studio _____

23. Author of *Lord of the Flies* _____

24. Roman novel by Apuleius, 2nd century A.D. _____

25. Former British colony in West Africa _____

26. American cartoonist, known for zany invention of intricate contraptions _____

27. Symbol of unworthy worship; that which caused Moses to smash the tablets _____

28. Noted female American anarchist _____

29. Flower _____

30. Jewish humorist, author of *Only in America*, etc. _____

31. Work by James G. Frazer, anthropological study of magic and religion _____

32. Small songbird _____

33. British author of *The Deserted Village, She Stoops to Conquer, The Vicar of Wakefield* _____

34. Motto for a good listener _____

35. Arizona senator, unsuccessful Presidental candidate, 1964 _____

36. American beer _____

37. Living conditions offering no privacy _____

38. Decoration for some picture frames, furniture, etc. _____

39. Euphemistic expression for greying hair _____

40. Inseparable pair, from old soap powder ad _____

SIBILANTS

Ever since the snake caused mankind's expulsion from the Garden of Eden, the sound of the hiss has had limited popularity. Below are definitions of words that each contain three "s" sounds. Can you hiss them out?

A score of 5 is average; 7 is excellent; 8 is outstanding; and 9 is brilliant!

Answers on page 475

1. A female tailor _____

2. A dried leaf used for
   tea and medicines _____

3. A skin disease involving scaly,
   red patches _____

4. Means of livelihood _____

5. Favorable outcome _____

6. The combining of separate elements
   into wholes _____

7. The state that gave us Paul Revere _____

8. Severe mental illness _____

9. Not trustful _____

10. A student of Greek and
    Roman culture _____

I.R.S. CONFRONTATION

Feel overtaxed? Here's a way to beat the I.R.S. The definitions below should bring to mind words that contain these three ominous letters in the positions indicated. The rest of the dashes need to be filled in appropriately.

A score of 13 is an honest return; 17 shows superior form-filling ability; and 22 indicates you can talk your way out of any situation.

Answers on page 475

1. _ I R S _   To begin with

2. _ _ I R S _ _   In need of liquid

3. _ I R _ _ S   Spectacular show with human
                                and animal feats

4. _ _ I _ _ R S _   The entire cosmic system

5. I _ _ _ R _ S _   Charge for borrowing money

6. _ I _ _ R _ S _   What an SOS signals

7. I _ _ R _ _ _ S _   To compose without preparation

8. I R _ _ _ S _ _ _ _ _   Brilliantly colored, as a rainbow

9. I _ _ R _ _ S _   Gain in size

10. _ I R _ S _ _ _   Hearth

11. _ I R _ S   Culprit blamed for many illnesses

12. _ I R _ S _ _ _   Greek seer who predicted
                                Oedipus's doom

13. I R _ S _ _ _ _ _ _   Easily made angry

14. _ _ I _ R _ _ _ S   She works in a restaurant

15. _ I _ R _ S _   Stray from the main point

16. _ I R _ _ _ _ S   Port of Athens

17. _ I _ _ _ R _ S _ _ _   Quaint; charming

18. I _ _ _ _ R S _ _ _ _   Meet and cross; overlap

19. _ I R _ _ _ _ S _ _   Disease of the liver

20. _ _ _ _ _ I _ R _ S   Greenish-blue deposit on metal

21. _ I R S _ _ _ _   Hairy

22. _ I R _ _ _ _ S _ _ _ _   Cautious; prudent

185

PARDON THE STUTTER

The reduplicated syllable may be the first words to appear in children's beginning speech, as in *mama, papa, cuckoo,* but this proclivity seems short-lived. Not too many words continue this echoic habit.

However, the clues below should inspire you to identify words in which there is a duplicated syllable. Stutter away.

A score of 8 is okay; 10 is really good; 12 is outstanding; and 14 is worth an ovation.

Answers on page 475

1. The sound of ringing bells _____

2. A goody; often cream-filled chocolate _____

3. The city that gave us the Reds _____

4. Low, continuous sound of a voice, a stream, or leaves _____

5. Automatic antiaircraft gun used in World War II _____

6. Primitive; wild; cruel _____

7. Surgical operation for research or study _____

8. North African dish of semolina and meat _____

9. French dance immortalized by Toulouse-Lautrec _____

10. A songbird _____

11. Disease caused by lack of vitamin B1 _____

12. A simple drum _____

13. Ballerina's skirt _____

14. To bring to life _____

15. Moslem people living in North Africa _____

16. Copy; ape _____

EARNED INCREMENT

Each of the 20 definitions below should bring to your mind a word, name, or title somewhere within which may be found the letter sequence URN. For example: *a producer of heat* is a f*URN*ace.

A score of 10 is nice; 13 is grand; and 17 says you're a star.

Answers on page 475

1. Hair that's reddish-brown   _____

2. Scottish poet, penned *Auld Lang Syne*   _____

3. Himalayan peak scaled by Herzog   _____

4. The way into the subway   _____

5. English landscape painter   _____

6. In the daytime   _____

7. Ballet movie with Anne Bancroft and Shirley MacLaine   _____

8. Describes someone who believes silence is golden   _____

9. Julius Caesar's wife   _____

10. Bandage to control bleeding   _____

11. Drama about World War I by Robert C. Sherriff   _____

12. Reject disdainfully   _____

13. Styron's novel about famous slave   _____

14. Gloomy; born under the sign of 2nd largest planet   _____

15. Henry James novel about two scary kids   _____

16. Tonsorial style now back in favor   _____

17. Famous TV comedienne   _____

18. Renegade   _____

19. Former slave who became an effective abolitionist   _____

20. Lighthearted play by Christopher Fry   _____

187

ALL IN GOOD FUN

Below you will find 20 expressions, phrases, or names. Each one of these should suggest to you another expression that contains the word GOOD. For example: *A would-be reformer* is a DO-GOODER.

A score of 11 is good; 14 is *very* good; 19 means you've really got the goods!

Answers on page 476

1. Someone who thinks only of having fun   _____

2. Famous jazz clarinetist   _____

3. What deserves another   _____

4. Best-selling novel by Judith Rossner   _____

5. Novel about an English schoolmaster   _____

6. Prissy individual; sentimentally virtuous   _____

7. Commercial name of a certain frozen confection   _____

8. The Bible   _____

9. African promontory   _____

10. Pearl Buck's novel about family life in China   _____

11. Novel by Ford Madox Ford   _____

12. What Charley Brown always says in the comic *Peanuts*   _____

13. Play by Bertolt Brecht   _____

14. Handsome; comely   _____

15. To secure damaging evidence against   _____

16. Nickname for the United States   _____

17. Tire manufacturer   _____

18. To be chosen over riches   _____

19. Pre-Easter holiday   _____

20. Neil Simon movie   _____

BOTTOMS UP

Below, you will find 20 words, phrases, or expressions. Each should suggest an expression or word which contains the word UP. For example: *To honor or support* is to UP*hold.*

A score of 11 is fair; 14 is above average; and 18 is outstanding.

Answers on page 476

1. A junior or senior in college   _____

2. Evening meal   _____

3. Vehement expression meaning "Go to Hell!"   _____

4. Violent social commotion or agitation   _____

5. Good times and bad times   _____

6. Surrender   _____

7. The Uncola   _____

8. Famous Mae West expression   _____

9. To stuff furniture and cover with decorative fabric   _____

10. Author of *The Centaur* and *Marry Me*   _____

11. Pep pill   _____

12. Rounded roof or dome   _____

13. Big Bird and Kermit the Frog   _____

14. Author of *The Jungle*   _____

15. Conspiracy or plot to incriminate someone on false evidence   _____

16. Famous 1960s Fifth Dimension song   _____

17. Enjoy greatly; have a good time   _____

18. Snobbish; fresh   _____

19. Broadway and television takeoff on *The Princess and the Pea*, starring Carol Burnett   _____

20. Mentally distressed or perturbed   _____

100 PERCENT

Each of the 46 definitions below should suggest to you a word, name, or expression containing the letters PER. How many of them can you identify?

A score of 27 is proPER; 35 is suPER; 40 or better is bordering on PERfection!

Answers on page 476

1. Scornful; haughty _____

2. Tyrannical; overbearing _____

3. Literary exaggeration _____

4. It's always just around the corner _____

5. Banter; raillery; repartee _____

6. Border; outlying area _____

7. Nickname for a helicopter _____

8. Latin expression meaning "in and of itself" _____

9. Infant's loincloth _____

10. Ingmar Bergman film _____

11. Rabbit featured in Disney's *Bambi* _____

12. Heat, measured in Fahrenheit or Celsius _____

13. Nero, Hirohito, or Haile Selassie, e.g. _____

14. Upright; opposite of parallel _____

15. Punish; vex; harass _____

16. City in New York, site of Baseball Hall of Fame _____

17. The Beatles' Lonely Hearts Club Band was his _____

18. Recklessness; utter lack of hope or scruples _____

19. Trial; scientist's undertaking _____

20. Character in Shakespeare's *The Tempest* _____

21. Silent film series about a young heroine's hair-raising adventures _____

22. Water-based paint   _____

23. Type of long-distance phone call   _____

24. Pair of geometric shapes which were the symbol of the 1939 World's Fair   _____

25. Long-lasting or durable   _____

26. Capricious; used of actresses and prima donnas   _____

27. In Greek mythology, the maidens who guarded the Golden Apples   _____

28. What you can't get a job without, and you can't get without a job   _____

29. Sweet yellow fruit   _____

30. &   _____

31. 1967 film starring Dame Edith Evans   _____

32. Pervade; saturate; penetrate   _____

33. 50s sitcom featuring Leo G. Carroll and two ghosts   _____

34. Trailing evergreen with pale blue blossoms   _____

35. Roman poet who wrote verses to his beloved Cynthia   _____

36. Theater for musical drama   _____

37. Novel by Smollett   _____

38. Pre-dinner drink   _____

39. Long-lasting   _____

40. Prank; escapade; pickled condiment   _____

41. Brand of suntan lotion   _____

42. Urgent; compelling   _____

43. All-powerful hero   _____

44. Abusive   _____

45. One of the polltakers   _____

46. It often replaces buttons   _____

TONS AND TONS

Every one of the 43 terms defined below contains the letters TON. For example, "a musical note" would be TONE. How many of them can you identify?

A score of 23 is good; 30 is excellent; 37 means you're a glutTON for word games.

Answers on page 476

1. Muscular organ in the mouth; a language _____

2. Genteel seaport city in South Carolina _____

3. Program hosted by Johnny Carson _____

4. Radioactive chemical element _____

5. The kind of love that is spiritual and not physical _____

6. An elixir; quinine water _____

7. A Soviet Socialist Republic _____

8. To surprise or confound _____

9. Box; crate; hero of *A Tale of Two Cities* _____

10. Crisp pieces of bread garnishing soups and salads _____

11. Capital of Massachusetts _____

12. Shaved spot on monk's head _____

13. Rock superstar ("Crocodile Rock," "Philadelphia Freedom") _____

14. Cleopatra's lover and Julius Caesar's eulogist _____

15. Superman's home planet; element #36 _____

16. Welsh-born actor (*Equus, Who's Afraid of Virginia Woolf?*) _____

17. Texas's largest city _____

18. Long-running TV series set in the Virginia mountains _____

19. Founder of the International Red Cross _____

20. Crop which dominated Southern agriculture through the Civil War   _____

21. Capital of New Brunswick   _____

22. Personal freedom; community right of self-government   _____

23. First U.S. Treasury Secretary, killed in duel with Aaron Burr   _____

24. Ivy League university in New Jersey   _____

25. Explode; blow up   _____

26. Play about a celebrated draft-resistance incident   _____

27. Capital of Jamaica   _____

28. Chant or recite in a singing voice   _____

29. Jai alai arena   _____

30. Capital of Louisiana   _____

31. Buxom blonde country singer ("Here You Come Again")   _____

32. Sliding plunger within a cylinder   _____

33. City in Ohio and in China   _____

34. Irresponsible; capricious; licentious   _____

35. Novel by Willa Cather   _____

36. Survivor-take-all investment group   _____

37. South Pacific island nation, neighbor of Fiji   _____

38. Famous British boarding school   _____

39. Texas city, home of the Alamo   _____

40. In Roman mythology, mother of Apollo and Diana   _____

41. Small organs in the throat, often removed in childhood   _____

42. Author of *Paradise Lost*   _____

43. Capital of New Jersey   _____

QUESTIONABLE THINGS

Below are 40 questions about questions. Fill in the blanks to complete the familiar interrogatory expression. For example: "*Is everybody* HAPPY?"

A score of 20 is fair; 28 is excellent; 35 is an unquestionable success.

Answers on page 476

1. How are things in _____ _____?

2. Who killed _____ _____?

3. What is so rare as a _____ _____ _____?

4. What hath God _____?

5. Am I my brother's _____?

6. Does your chewing gum lose it's flavor _____

   _____ _____ _____?

7. Pardon me, boy, is this the _____ _____ _____?

8. Why can't a woman be _____ _____ _____

   _____?

9. Et tu, _____?

10. Where have all the _____ gone?

11. I wonder who's kissing _____ _____?

12. Why did the chicken _____ _____ _____?

13. Where are the _____ of yesteryear?

14. Was this the face that launched a _____ _____?

15. Is there a doctor _____ _____ _____?

16. Guess who's coming to _____?

17. Bill Bailey, won't you please _____ _____?

18. Brother, can you spare a _____?

19. What light through yonder _____ _____?

20. They shoot _____, don't they?

21. What's in a _____?

22. What is this thing called _____?

23. What kind of _____ _____ _____?

24. How do I _____ _____?

25. How much is that _____ _____ _____ _____?

26. Are you sleeping, _____ _____?

27. Do I hear _____ _____?

28. Do you think the rain will _____ _____ _____?

29. Do you know the way to _____ _____?

30. Is Paris _____?

31. Is there no balm _____ _____?

32. Can a leopard _____ _____ _____?

33. Do you know the muffin man that lives _____ _____

_____?

34. Baa baa, black sheep, have you _____ _____?

35. Death, where is _____ _____?

36. Oh, say can _____ _____?

37. Wherefore art thou, _____?

38. Ah, but a man's reach should exceed his grasp, or what's _____

_____ _____?

39. Did you ever see a _____?

40. To be or _____ _____ _____?

LONG LIVE THE KING

Each of the 42 clues below should suggest to you a term containing the letters KING. Put on your thinking cap and see how many of them you can come up with.

A score of 25 is noble; 32 is regal; 38 or better shows you have the makings of a monarch.

Answers on page 477

1. Nursery rhyme character;
   a merry old soul   _____

2. American author, Penrod series, etc.   _____

3. Idiom meaning a vast sum of money   _____

4. Capital of China   _____

5. Proper speech, correct grammar   _____

6. Author of *Water Babies* and
   Westward Ho!   _____

7. Kipling story, made into film with
   Michael Caine and Sean Connery   _____

8. Character in *Amos and Andy*   _____

9. Nickname for Benny Goodman   _____

10. Capital of Jamaica, West Indies   _____

11. Eminent civil rights leader,
    slain in 1968   _____

12. Merle Miller's biography of
    Harry S. Truman   _____

13. Section of Grieg's *Peer Gynt Suite*   _____

14. World's best-known ape   _____

15. Famous offer of exchange in
    Shakespeare's *Richard III*   _____

16. Black American popular singer
    (1919-1965)   _____

17. Original name of Columbia
    University   _____

18. Term, taken from the Lord's Prayer,
    meaning the hereafter   _____

19. Legendary monarch of Camelot _____

20. Large bed and linens _____

21. British author who continued the
    James Bond series _____

22. 1950s TV series about a ranch pilot _____

23. Large and delicious shellfish _____

24. Idiom meaning a berating or
    dressing-down _____

25. Harper Lee's prize-winning book and
    film starring Gregory Peck _____

26. Rodgers and Hammerstein play and
    movie starring Yul Brynner
    as the ruler of Siam _____

27. Early Scandinavian seafarers _____

28. 1977 film starring Diane Keaton _____

29. British national anthem when a male
    is on the throne _____

30. Idiom for improving; researching _____

31. *Star Trek* episode; a quote
    from *Hamlet* _____

32. Nickname for the lion _____

33. The mighty oak _____

34. Hiding, concealing; kind of tape _____

35. 1949 Oscar-winning Best Picture
    starring Broderick Crawford _____

36. Nickname for John Philip Sousa _____

37. Nickname for Richard Strauss _____

38. Bowling piece; most important
    member of a group _____

39. Nonmoving driving violation _____

40. Early Hollywood director _____

41. Film starring Jack Nickolson,
    set in Atlantic City _____

42. Well-known edition of the Bible _____

THE LADY IN THE CASE

Each of the 50 virile words in this quiz has a feminine counterpart. It's a matter of "Cherchez la femme!"

A score of 30 is good; 38 is very good; 42 is excellent.

Answers on page 477

1. Executor   _____

2. Master   _____

3. Masseur   _____

4. Tiger   _____

5. Marquis   _____

6. Rooster   _____

7. King   _____

8. Chairman   _____

9. Drake   _____

10. Earl   _____

11. Bullock   _____

12. Couturier   _____

13. Patriarch   _____

14. Fox   _____

15. Chamberlain   _____

16. Groom   _____

17. Usher   _____

18. Buck   _____

19. Lord   _____

20. Abbot   _____

21. Dog   _____

22. Guy   _____

23. Peacock   _____

24. Monk   _____

25. Monsieur   _____

26. Aviator   _____

27. Sire   _____

28. Ram   _____

29. Sultan   _____

30. Duke   _____

31. Colt   _____

32. Maharaja   _____

33. Host   _____

34. Boar   _____

35. Lad   _____

36. Nephew   _____

37. Stallion   _____

38. Tsar   _____

39. Fiancé   _____

40. Best man   _____

41. Cob   _____

42. Hero   _____

43. Stag   _____

44. Señor   _____

45. Pierrot   _____

46. Billy goat   _____

47. Baronet   _____

48. Gander   _____

49. Sannup   _____

50. Bull   _____

HOW TO SOLVE CRYPTOGRAMS

To some people a cryptogram is nothing less than one of the milder forms of self-torture; but a lot of people think cryptograms are a lot of fun. If you thrill to tales of espionage and fantasize yourself a secret agent, you will find decoding cryptograms a fascinating pastime.

A cryptogram is a secret message in which one letter has been systematically substituted for another letter. To break the code, you have to figure out what each letter in the message really stands for.

This might seem altogether arbitrary and virtually impossible. But not so. Linguists have come up with information about the English language that is very helpful to crytographers. They tell us, for example, that all English words include one or more vowels, and that the five vowels—A, E, I, O, U—comprise 40 percent of all written communications. The letters L, N, R, S, and T comprise 30 percent of usage; and J, K, Q, X, and Z comprise but 2 percent. The remaining 11 letters comprise 28 percent of words commonly used in written English.

Armed with this information, you are ready to tackle any cryptogram. You might want to write each letter of the alphabet, followed by an equal sign, on a piece of paper. One-letter words are, of course, likely to be "I" or "A." Examine the coded message to see how often each letter appears. It is a good hypothesis that the letter which appears most often stands for E. Examine especially the three-letter words. If the same three-letter combination appears frequently, and the third letter is also the letter that appears most frequently throughout, the chances are the word is THE. For example, if A B Z appears four or five times, and Z appears most frequently throughout, it is a fairly safe bet that A B Z stands for THE. Write T under A wherever it appears in the message; H under B; and E under Z.

Now examine the coded words again. If there are any two-letter words beginning with A standing for T, the chances are the word is TO. Continue making educated guesses, changing your hypothesis whenever that becomes necessary, until you break the code.

Don't forget to time yourself. If you are a novice in cryptography, you're doing well to solve the cryptogram in Par time. As you become more proficient, aim for Medal time.

PREVARICATION AS AN ART

PAR TIME: 28 minutes
MEDAL TIME: 19 minutes

Solution on page 477

GAB PLLI EGA SNII SQN
——— ———— ——— ———— ———

SVZSQ, FZS TS VNOZTVNR
—————— ——— —— ————————

G DGA LP RLDN RNARN SL
— ——— —— ———— ————— ——

XALH QLH SL ITN HNII.
———— ——— —— ——— ————

A̅ B̅ C̅ D̅ E̅ F̅ G̅ H̅ I̅ J̅ K̅ L̅ M̅

N̅ O̅ P̅ Q̅ R̅ S̅ T̅ U̅ V̅ W̅ X̅ Y̅ Z̅

BRAT AT A BALL

PAR TIME: 40 minutes
MEDAL TIME: 20 minutes

Solution on page 477

AGUFFQ AYRAUGUV AXTTQ
_____ _____ _____

AUUOKNLTQ AXIFUV,
_____ _____

AGKNNKTQ AIF XC LUG
_____ ___ __ ___

AIGATU AXR-AXR, YCV
_____ ___-___ ___

AUFFKNLTQ AUGYRWITYFUV
_____ _____

YF Y ATXVVKCM AYDU.
__ _ _____ ____

A	B	C	D	E	F	G	H	I	J	K	L	M

N	O	P	Q	R	S	T	U	V	W	X	Y	Z

ABSOLUTELY!

PAR TIME:　15 minutes
MEDAL TIME:　　8 minutes

Solution on page 477

DRJ NMKW DRSMQ DRFD DRJ
___ ____ _____ ____ ___

FBDSCD HFMMND CJJ
_____ _____ ___

SC DRJ NGZSNEC
__ ___ _____

DRJ NMKW DRSMQ
___ ____ _____

DRFD DRJ OEGKSH HFM CJJ
____ ___ _____ ___ ___

SC DRJ NGZSNEC.
__ ___ _____

A B C D E F G H I J K L M
‾ ‾ ‾ ‾ ‾ ‾ ‾ ‾ ‾ ‾ ‾ ‾ ‾

N O P Q R S T U V W X Y Z
‾ ‾ ‾ ‾ ‾ ‾ ‾ ‾ ‾ ‾ ‾ ‾ ‾

THE POWER OF MUSIC

Solution on page 477

PAR TIME: 20 minutes
MEDAL TIME: 17 minutes

LRBU MR LRR NRBNDNH MR
———— —— ——— ——————— ——

LRRUINRB RER. NRREL
———————— ——— —————

LOOLRNRB, CZN LRBURNH
———————— ——— ———————

MR MLD.
—— ———

$\overline{A}$ $\overline{B}$ $\overline{C}$ $\overline{D}$ $\overline{E}$ $\overline{F}$ $\overline{G}$ $\overline{H}$ $\overline{I}$ $\overline{J}$ $\overline{K}$ $\overline{L}$ $\overline{M}$

$\overline{N}$ $\overline{O}$ $\overline{P}$ $\overline{Q}$ $\overline{R}$ $\overline{S}$ $\overline{T}$ $\overline{U}$ $\overline{V}$ $\overline{W}$ $\overline{X}$ $\overline{Y}$ $\overline{Z}$

ERSE PHILOSOPHY

PAR TIME: 20 minutes
MEDAL TIME: 12 minutes

Solution on page 477

X HYT'R RVXTI RVOJO'M WTK
— ———— —————— ———— ———

AYXTR XT ZOXTU XJXMV XP
————— —— ————— ————— ——

KYS HYT'R ITYB RVWR RVO
——— ———— ———— ———— ———

BYJNH XM UYXTU RY ZJOWI
———— —— ————— —— ————

KYSJ VOWJR OCOTRSWNNK.
———— ————— ——————————

$\overline{A}$ $\overline{B}$ $\overline{C}$ $\overline{D}$ $\overline{E}$ $\overline{F}$ $\overline{G}$ $\overline{H}$ $\overline{I}$ $\overline{J}$ $\overline{K}$ $\overline{L}$ $\overline{M}$

$\overline{N}$ $\overline{O}$ $\overline{P}$ $\overline{Q}$ $\overline{R}$ $\overline{S}$ $\overline{T}$ $\overline{U}$ $\overline{V}$ $\overline{W}$ $\overline{X}$ $\overline{Y}$ $\overline{Z}$

205

THE CULT OF
INCOHERENCE

PAR TIME: 20 minutes
MEDAL TIME: 15 minutes

Solution on page 478

UNMG N EIYBRI ARRUA BL
‗‗‗‗ ‗ ‗‗‗‗‗‗ ‗‗‗‗‗ ‗‗

BZYMW ZR YA MLB KILSLCMQ
‗‗‗‗‗ ‗‗ ‗‗ ‗‗‗ ‗‗‗‗‗‗‗‗

CMVRAA ZR ZYUARVS PNM'B
‗‗‗‗‗‗ ‗‗ ‗‗‗‗‗‗‗ ‗‗‗‗ ‗

CMQRIABNMQ EZNB ZR ZNA
‗‗‗‗‗‗‗‗‗‗ ‗‗‗‗ ‗‗ ‗‗‗

KCB QLEM LM KNKRI.
‗‗‗ ‗‗‗‗ ‗‗ ‗‗‗‗‗

A B C D E F G H I J K L M
‾ ‾ ‾ ‾ ‾ ‾ ‾ ‾ ‾ ‾ ‾ ‾ ‾

N O P Q R S T U V W X Y Z
‾ ‾ ‾ ‾ ‾ ‾ ‾ ‾ ‾ ‾ ‾ ‾ ‾

TALISMAN

PAR TIME: 18 minutes
MEDAL TIME: 12 minutes

Solution on page 478

V OGGJ YRPWP BVZ VHQ RP
_ ____ _____ ___ ___ __

IVQP RSZ MWVEPW YG V
____ ___ _____ __ _

WVN VHQ V UGHP VHQ V
___ ___ _ ____ ___ _

RVHF GO RVSW.
____ __ ____

A B C D E F G H I J K L M

N O P Q R S T U V W X Y Z

RUBBING IT IN

PAR TIME: 50 minutes
MEDAL TIME: 30 minutes

Solution on page 478

MQ SBB XUG UMPPVF,
__ ___ ___ _____

UVFGMWY ZMXGY MQ KMG,
_____ _____ __ ___

YSFFGP XUSZ MKB-YMZRY
_____ ____ ___ _____

MP XUG AVFZVRUX TBSYX,
__ ___ _____ _____

VY XUSX NMPXGZXMWY
__ ____ _____

NUPSYG "V XMBF IMW YM."
_____ _ ____ ___ __

208

$\overline{A}$ $\overline{B}$ $\overline{C}$ $\overline{D}$ $\overline{E}$ $\overline{F}$ $\overline{G}$ $\overline{H}$ $\overline{I}$ $\overline{J}$ $\overline{K}$ $\overline{L}$ $\overline{M}$

$\overline{N}$ $\overline{O}$ $\overline{P}$ $\overline{Q}$ $\overline{R}$ $\overline{S}$ $\overline{T}$ $\overline{U}$ $\overline{V}$ $\overline{W}$ $\overline{X}$ $\overline{Y}$ $\overline{Z}$

ONE-TRACK MIND

PAR TIME: 15 minutes
MEDAL TIME: 12 minutes

Solution on page 478

YRL IBXCI GHHA FOHAL
___ _____ ____ _____

YRL FEGA HM YRL
___ ____ __ ___

FHHAALLILO VRH
_____ ___

DLWLOYRLBLZZ ALIY
_____ ____

EZAQDN MHO GHMMLL.
_____ ___ _____

A B C D E F G H I J K L M
N O P Q R S T U V W X Y Z

SOUND PERCEPTION

PAR TIME: 24 minutes
MEDAL TIME: 18 minutes

Solution on page 478

PQG AMPB VQXPLV WP DWKS,

‾‾‾ ‾‾‾‾ ‾‾‾‾‾‾‾ ‾‾ ‾‾‾‾

MPL W WPODXLS MDD XFNMP

‾‾‾ ‾ ‾‾‾‾‾‾‾ ‾‾‾ ‾‾‾‾

MPL MDD FXFMD VQXPLV,

‾‾‾ ‾‾‾ ‾‾‾‾‾ ‾‾‾‾‾‾

SCOSSL WP WPGSFSVG M

‾‾‾‾‾‾ ‾‾ ‾‾‾‾‾‾‾‾ ‾

IPQOI MG GJS LQQF.

‾‾‾‾‾ ‾‾ ‾‾‾ ‾‾‾‾

A B C D E F G H I J K L M

N O P Q R S T U V W X Y Z

FOLLY! FOLLY!

PAR TIME: 32 minutes
MEDAL TIME: 19 minutes

Solution on page 478

M EXT TDJ FMLV SDK JIV
_ ___ ___ ____ ___ ___

WDGQKYX WDG HKEEVHH,
_____ ___ _____,

UKJ M EXT FMLV SDK JIV
___ _ ___ ____ ___ ___

WDGQKYX WDG WXMYKGV—
_____ ___ _____—

ZIMEI MH "JGS JD
_____ __ ___ __

BYVXHV VLVGSUDAS."
_____ _____.

A̅ B̅ C̅ D̅ E̅ F̅ G̅ H̅ I̅ J̅ K̅ L̅ M̅
N̅ O̅ P̅ Q̅ R̅ S̅ T̅ U̅ V̅ W̅ X̅ Y̅ Z̅

ADVICE TO
THE STRIFE-TORN

PAR TIME: 30 minutes
MEDAL TIME: 20 minutes

Solution on page 478

J F P   C F X Q H Q W T   P E I F
___   _____   ____

M Q K U,   U N U W   Q K   Q J   A E U H
____   ____   __   __   ____

K F Q T G J U W   G U F   X J   K Q F H J.
_____   ___   __   _____.

A B C D E F G H I J K L M

N O P Q R S T U V W X Y Z

AH CHOO!

PAR TIME: 35 minutes
MEDAL TIME: 20 minutes

Solution on page 478

W QELLOLU H QELLOL
— ——————— — ——————

WERT RVL HWP,
———— ——— ———

HEU ET TEL XELA KPTD
——— —— ——— ———— ————

AVLEIL TP AVLPL;
—————— —— ——————

GYR FTEJ HEU VHPU ALPL
——— ———— ——— ———— ————

RVL FTTXQ TK RVTQL,
——— ————— —— ——————

WE AVTQL CWIWEWRS
—— ————— ————————

W QETOL!
— —————

A	B	C	D	E	F	G	H	I	J	K	L	M

N	O	P	Q	R	S	T	U	V	W	X	Y	Z

213

YOUTH IS UNQUALIFIED

PAR TIME: 35 minutes
MEDAL TIME: 20 minutes

Solution on page 478

R V X   T B Y W X   Q V Z B A Y   E Z R   H X
___   _____   _____   ___   __

L Z B E W ;   V X   Q V Z B A Y   V I C X
_____   __   _____   ____

A X I P E X Y   R Z   S E Z F   X C U A ,
_____   __   ____   ____

E Z R   J P Z D   V U Q   Z F E   Q Z B A
___   ____   ___   ___   ____

H B R   J P Z D   A Z E W
___   ____   ____

Z H Q X P C I R U Z E .   S E Z F A X Y W X
_____   _____

Q V Z B A Y   H X   V U Q   W B U Y X ,
_____   __   ___   _____

E Z R   K X P Q Z E I A   X M K X P U X E G X .
___   _____   _____

A B C D E F G H I J K L M
N O P Q R S T U V W X Y Z

THE SUPREME JUDGMENT

PAR TIME: 35 minutes
MEDAL TIME: 18 minutes

Solution on page 478

MAS OM SGI BKELAQ AD
___ __ ___ _____ __

SGI BQAVCIC RSQIIS,
___ _____ _____

MAS OM SGI RGAYSR EMC
___ __ ___ _____ ___

NKEYCOSR AD SGI SGQAMF,
_____ __ ___ _____

TYS OM AYQRIKZIR EQI
___ __ _____ ___

SQOYLNG EMC CIDIES.
_____ ___ _____

A B C D E F G H I J K L M
___ ___ ___ ___ ___ ___ ___ ___ ___ ___ ___ ___ ___

N O P Q R S T U V W X Y Z
___ ___ ___ ___ ___ ___ ___ ___ ___ ___ ___ ___ ___

215

ULTIMATE JUSTICE

PAR TIME: 35 minutes
MEDAL TIME: 25 minutes

Solution on page 478

UI UCCBUW RN ZQBI EFP
—— ——————— —— ————— ———

UNT FIB HFPMO OF NQFZ
——— ——— ————— —— ————

RON HFIOBXCO AFM
——— ———————— ———

UIFOQBM HFPMO.
——————— —————

216

A B C D E F G H I J K L M
N O P Q R S T U V W X Y Z

INESCAPABLE
DEDUCTION

PAR TIME: 32 minutes
MEDAL TIME: 21 minutes

Solution on page 478

VIGX JHN VZ SIVA GKUTP
____ ___ __ ____ _____

   HRQ SGHV YHUA QH YHUA;
   ___ ____ ____ __ ____

I QJHRPIUB DGKQKDP
_ _____ _____

   PJHRQKUT: "JA'P RUXUHNU!"
   _____ ___ _____

A	B	C	D	E	F	G	H	I	J	K	L	M

N	O	P	Q	R	S	T	U	V	W	X	Y	Z

LAMENT

PAR TIME: 20 minutes
MEDAL TIME: 10 minutes

Solution on page 478

JOWM XR WVK OW XVDIWLDY

‾‾‾‾ ‾‾ ‾‾‾ ‾‾ ‾‾‾‾‾‾‾‾

GOIMRJ, "O ZX EIVTR!

‾‾‾‾‾‾ ‾ ‾‾ ‾‾‾‾‾

KVV XZWP JUYDIMRJ!"

‾‾‾ ‾‾‾‾ ‾‾‾‾‾‾‾‾

A B C D E F G H I J K L M

N O P Q R S T U V W X Y Z

PLOY

PAR TIME: 35 minutes
MEDAL TIME: 29 minutes

Solution on page 478

IQKZ, JGDORZP AZ YT LRZK

‾‾‾‾ ‾‾‾‾‾‾‾ ‾‾ ‾‾ ‾‾‾‾

FAYYDZJ AL XDZPMDPK,

‾‾‾‾‾‾‾ ‾‾ ‾‾‾‾‾‾‾

R HDRJ ZAIQRZP.

‾ ‾‾‾‾ ‾‾‾‾‾‾

A B C D E F G H I J K L M

N O P Q R S T U V W X Y Z

DISDAIN

PAR TIME: 30 minutes
MEDAL TIME: 20 minutes

Solution on page 478

LT WFFQTH VM AT VO KJ
__ _____ __ __ __ __

K CVO V OKHT HKOL LT
_ ___ _ ____ ____ __

LVHX'M FDHTDTH.
_____ _____.

A B C D E F G H I J K L M

N O P Q R S T U V W X Y Z

PRAGMATISM

PAR TIME: 35 minutes
MEDAL TIME: 20 minutes

Solution on page 479

TN IHW GDFFHU GDUGS D
__ ___ _____ _____ _

ETPL HN KDPDLTRM,
____ __ _____,

EMUUMP UDXM D BMU SMF.
_____ ____ _ ___ ___.

A B C D E F G H I J K L M

N O P Q R S T U V W X Y Z

COMIC DICTIONARY

ACOUSTIC   An instrument used in shooting pool.

ACQUAINTANCE   A person whom we know well enough to borrow from, but not well enough to lend to.

AD LIBBER   A man who stays up all night to memorize spontaneous jokes.

ADOLESCENCE   The age between puberty and adultery.

ADULT   A person who has stopped growing at both ends and started growing in the middle.

ADVERTISING   A technique that makes you think you've longed all your life for something you've never heard of before.

AFTERNOON   That part of the day spent figuring how we wasted the morning.

ALARM CLOCK   A device for awakening childless households.

ALCOHOL   A liquid good for preserving almost anything except secrets.

ALIBI   A legal way of proving that you couldn't possibly have been at a place where you really were.

ALIMONY   The high cost of leaving.

AMBASSADOR   An honest man sent abroad to lie for the commonwealth.

AMERICANS   People who insist on living in the present tense.

ANATOMY	Something everybody has—but it looks better on a girl.
ANECDOTE	A revealing account of an incident that never occurred in the life of some famous person.
ANGEL	A pedestrian who forgot to jump.
ANT	A small insect that, though always at work, still finds time to go to picnics.
AUGUST	The month you can't open the car window you couldn't close in February.

BABY	An alimentary canal with a loud voice at one end and no responsibility at the other.
BACHELOR	A man who never makes the same mistake once.
BANJO	Let's not invite Joseph.
BANK	An institution where you can borrow money if you can present sufficient evidence to show that you don't need it.
BARBER SHOP	A clip joint.
BARGAIN	A transaction in which each party thinks he has cheated the other.
BASSO PROFUNDO	A deep-thinking fish.

BATHING BEAUTY   A girl who has a lovely profile all the way down.

BEACH   A place where a girl goes in her baiting suit.

BEAUTY CONTEST   A lass roundup.

BIGAMIST   An Italian fog.

BIGAMY   One wife too many. Monogamy is the same.

BOASTER   A person who, every time he opens his mouth, puts his feats in.

BORE   A guy with a cocktail glass in one hand, and your lapel in his other.

BOSS OF THE
   FAMILY   Whoever can spend ten dollars without thinking it necessary to say anything about it.

BRASSIERE   An invention designed to make a mountain out of a molehill, and vice versa.

BRAT   A kid that displays his pest manners.

BRIDGE   A card game in which a good deal depends on a good deal.

222

BRIDGE EXPERT	One who can keep a kibitzer quiet all evening.
BROADWAY	New York's main artery—the hardened artery.
BUDGET	A mathematical confirmation of your suspicions.
BUREAUCRAT	A man who shoots the bull, passes the buck, and makes seven copies of everything.
BUST TRUSTER	A man who is sure his girl doesn't wear falsies.
BUSYBODY	One who burns a scandal at both ends.
CADDY	A lad who stands behind a golfer and didn't see the ball either.
CAMELOT	A place where they park camels.
CARBUNCLE	An auto collision.
CAREER GIRL	One who'd rather bring home the bacon than fry it.
CAULIFLOWER	A cabbage with a college education.
CHAFING DISH	A pretty girl who has been stood up on a date.
CLASSIC	A book which people praise and don't read.
CLASSICAL MUSIC	The kind that we keep hoping will turn into a tune.
COINCIDE	What you do when it starts to rain.
COMMITTEE	A body that keeps minutes and wastes hours.
COMMUNITY CHEST	An organization that puts all its begs in one ask it.

COMMUTER — A traveling man who pays short visits to his home and office.

CONCEIT — A form of I-strain.

CONSCIENCE — A little gimmick inside you that makes you tell your wife before somebody else does.

CONSERVATIVE — One who believes that nothing should be done for the first time.

CONSULT — To seek another's approval of a course already decided upon.

COUNTER-IRRITANT — A woman who looks at everything and buys nothing.

CRIMINAL — A person with predatory instincts who has not sufficient capital to form a corporation.

CROOK — A business rival who has just left the room.

CYNIC — One who knows the price of everything and the value of nothing.

DACHSHUND — Half a dog high and a dog and a half long.

DARKROOM — A place where many a girl with a negative personality is developed.

DEBATE   It lures de fish.

DENIAL   A river in Egypt.

DENTIST   A man who lives from hand to mouth.

DESK   A trash basket with drawers.

DETOUR   The roughest distance between two points.

DEUCE   The unkindest cut of all.

DINER   A restaurant where you can eat dirt cheap . . .
                but who wants to eat dirt?

DIPLOMACY   To do and say the nastiest things in the nicest
                way.

DIPLOMAT	A fellow who has to watch his appease and accuse.
DOGMA	A puppy's mother.
ECONOMY	A way of spending money without getting any fun out of it.
EDUCATION	The knowledge that a chorus girl gets by stages and that a college girl gets by degrees.
EFFICIENCY EXPERT	A guy smart enough to tell you how to run your business and too smart to start his own.
EGOTIST	A person of low taste, more interested in himself than me.
ELDERLY WOLF	One who's not gonna lust much longer.
EPIGRAM	A wisecrack that has played Carnegie Hall.
ETIQUETTE	Learning to yawn with your mouth closed.
EUNUCH	One who is cut off from temptation.
EXCHEQUER	A retired supermarket employee.
EXPERT	One who knows more and more about less and less.
FALSIES	Hidden persuaders.
FIRMNESS	That admirable quality in ourselves that is detestable stubbornness in others.
FISH	The animal that seems to go for a vacation about the same time most fishermen do.

FLASHLIGHT   A case in which to carry dead batteries.

FORGER   A man who gives a check a bad name.

FREE COUNTRY   One in which there is no particular individual to blame for the existing tyranny.

GARDENING   A labor that begins with daybreak and ends with backbreak.

GENEALOGY   Tracing yourself back to people better than you are.

GENIUS   One who can do almost anything except make a living.

GENTLEMAN   A worn-out wolf.

GIRDLE   A device to keep an unfortunate situation from spreading.

GLADIATOR   What the cannibal said after he ate the female explorer.

GOLD-DIGGER   A girl with a gift of grab.

GOLFER   A man who hits and tells.

GOOD-BYE   What money says when it talks.

GOSSIP   A woman with a nice sense of rumor.

GRADE CROSSING   The meeting place of headlights and light heads.

GRANDMOTHER   The person you bring the baby to for an over-mauling.

GUEST TOWEL   A small square of absorbent linen completely surrounded by useless embroidery.

GUILLOTINE   A french chopping center.

HANGOVER   The wrath of grapes.

HAPPINESS   A peculiar feeling you acquire when you're too busy to be miserable.

HEREDITY   Something you subscribe to wholeheartedly when your son's report card shows all As.

HIGHBROW   A person who enjoys a thing until it becomes popular.

HOLLYWOOD   A place where you live happily and get married forever afterward.

HOME   A place to go when all the other joints are closed.

HONEST POLITICIAN   One who when he is bought will stay bought.

HORSE-SENSE   A degree of wisdom that keeps one from betting on the races.

HOSPITAL ROOM   A place where friends of the patient go to talk to other friends of the patient.

HOSPITALS	Places where people who are run-down wind up.
HOTEL GUEST	A person who leaves his room only because he can't get it into his bags.
HUSBAND	What's left of a sweetheart after the nerve has been killed.
HYPOTHENUSE	The washroom upstairs is occupied.
IGLOO	An icicle built for two.
INDIAN RESERVATION	The home of the brave.
INFLATION	Something that cost $10 to buy a few years ago and now costs $20 to repair.
INTOXICATION	To feel sophisticated and not be able to pronounce it.
INTUITION	The inner voice that tells you to do the right thing after you decided that the wrong thing was too risky.
JACKET BLURB	Fable of contents.
JAYWALKING	An exercise that brings on that run-down feeling.
JURY	A group of 12 people selected to decide who has the better lawyer.
KINDERGARTEN TEACHER	One who should know how to make the little things count.
KNOB	A thing to adore.
LAMB STEW	Much ado about mutton.

LAS VEGAS	The land of the spree and the home of the knave.
LINGUIST	One who has the ability to describe a beautiful girl without using his hands.
LITTER	The result of literary efforts.
LOS ANGELES	Six suburbs in search of a city.
MADAM	For whom the belle toils.

MARRIAGE	An institution that starts with billing and cooing, but only the billing lasts.
MAYFLOWER	A small ship on which several million Pilgrims came to America in 1620.
METEOROLOGIST	A man who can look into a girl's eyes and tell whether.
MINISKIRT	Hemme fatale.
MINOR OPERATION	One performed on somebody else.
MISTRESS	A cutie on the Q.T.
MOLASSES	Additional girls.

MONEY	Jack of all trades.
MONOLOGUE	A conversation between a real estate promoter and a prospect.
MUMMY	An Egyptian who was pressed for time.
NEUROTIC	A person who has discovered the secret of perpetual emotion.
NEW YORKERS	A group of people who feel rich because they charge each other so much.
NIGHT-CLUB DANCING	Merely lifting one's eyebrows in time to the music.
NUDIST	A person who goes coatless and vestless, and wears trousers to match.
OBOE	An ill woodwind that nobody blows good.
OFFICER	A cop whom you can talk out of giving you a ticket.
OILY	The opposite of late.
OPERATOR	An employee who takes the padding out of his shoulders and puts it in his expense account.
OPTIMIST	The optimist sees the doughnut; the pessimist, the hole.
OUT OF BOUNDS	A pooped kangaroo.
OVEREATING	An activity which will make you thick to your stomach.
PASTEURIZE	Something you see moving.

PESSIMIST   A man who's always building dungeons in the air.

PETITION   A list of people who didn't have the nerve to say no.

PETTING   A study of anatomy in braille.

PHARMACIST   Man in a white coat who stands behind a soda fountain and sells ball-point pens.

PHILOSOPHICAL   The cheerful attitude assumed by everybody not directly involved in the trouble.

POLYGON   A dead parrot.

POPULAR GIRL   One who has been weighed in the balance and found wanton.

PRACTICAL NURSE   One who marries a rich, elderly patient.

PROCRAS-TINATION   Putting off problems for a brainy day.

PROCRASTINATOR   Man with a wait problem.

232

PRUNE   A plum that has seen better days.

PSYCHOLOGY   The science that tells you what you already know in words you can't understand.

PUBLIC-SPEAKING   The art of diluting a two-minute idea with a two-hour vocabulary.

PUNCTUALITY   The art of guessing how late the other fellow is going to be.

RACEHORSE   An animal that can take several thousand people for a ride at the same time.

RADICAL   A conservative out of a job.

RAMSHACKLE   A chain used to tie up a he-goat.

REGULAR DRINKING   Drinking between drinks.

RENO	The city of otherly love.
REPARTEE	An insult with its dress-suit on.
RESORT	A place where the tired grow more tired.
RUMMAGE SALE	A place where you can buy stuff from somebody else's attic to store in your own.
SALES RESISTANCE	The most fun you can have without laughing.
SHOTGUN WEDDING	A case of wife or death.
SILLY GAME	One at which your wife can beat you.
SKELETON	A man with his insides taken out and his outsides taken off.
SLANG	Language that takes off its coat, spits on its hand, and goes to work.
SMALL FRY	A one-dollar steak.
SMART COOKY	A girl who starts out with a little slip and ends up with a whole wardrobe.
SNEEZING	Much achoo about nothing.
SPECIMEN	An Italian astronaut.
STRENGTH OF MIND	The ability to eat one salted peanut.
SUNBATHER	A fry in the ointment.
SUPER SALESMAN	One who can sell a double-breasted suit to a man with a Phi Beta Kappa key.

SWIMMING POOL   A small body of water completely surrounded by other people's children.

SYMPATHY   That which one person offers another in exchange for the details.

SYNTAX   A levy on brothels.

TACT   The ability to make your guests feel at home when you wish they were.

TAXIDERMIST   A man who knows his stuff.

TEUTONIC   Not enough gin.

THEORY   A hunch with a college education.

TITIAN   The color a poor red-headed girl's hair becomes as soon as her father strikes oil.

TOOTHACHE   A pain that drives you to extraction.

TRAFFIC LIGHT   A little green light that changes to red as you car approaches.

TRIANGLE   A figure invented by Euclid, tested by Don Juan, and brought to perfection by scenario writers.

UNTOUCHABLES   People you can't borrow money from.

USED CAR   A car in first crash condition.

VACATION — A period during which people find out where to stay away from next year.

VIOLIN — A bad hotel.

WALLFLOWER — A girl without a gent to her name.

WASHINGTON — The only place in the world where sound travels faster than light.

WIFE — A person who can look in a bureau drawer and find the husband's tie clasp that isn't there.

WINDOW SCREEN — A device for keeping flies in the house.

WOLF — A man who invites a girl for a scotch and sofa.

YESMEN — Fellows who hand around the man that nobody noes.

HOW TO SOLVE ALFABITS

The idea is to try to form as many words of five letters or more as possible from the letters which comprise the given title.

There are only a few rules to observe:

1. You may not form a new word simply by adding *s*, unless adding the *s* involves a change in the spelling. For example: *books* and *looks* are not acceptable, but *calves* and *tries* are permitted.

2. You may use all other variations of a word if the letters are available. For example: *react, reacted, reacting, reactor, reaction.*

3. Proper names and obsolete or archaic words are taboo. Reformed spellings are not acceptable. For example: *nite, thru.*

4. Contractions are not allowed. For example: *can't, aren't.*

ARCHITECT

There are at least 36 words of five letters or more which can be formed from the letters in the word ARCHITECT. How many of them can you construct?

A score of 20 is good; 24 is excellent; 29 makes you a real wordsmith!

Answers on page 479

1. _____
2. _____
3. _____
4. _____
5. _____
6. _____
7. _____
8. _____
9. _____
10. _____
11. _____
12. _____
13. _____
14. _____
15. _____
16. _____
17. _____
18. _____
19. _____
20. _____
21. _____
22. _____
23. _____
24. _____
25. _____
26. _____
27. _____
28. _____
29. _____
30. _____
31. _____
32. _____
33. _____
34. _____
35. _____
36. _____

STEREOTYPE

There are at least 29 words of five letters or more to be found in the word STEREOTYPE.

A score of 19 is passing; a score of 21 is above average; and a score of 23 is exceptional. If you get 27 or more you deserve huge applause.

Answers on page 479

1. _____ 11. _____ 20. _____
2. _____ 12. _____ 21. _____
3. _____ 13. _____ 22. _____
4. _____ 14. _____ 23. _____
5. _____ 15. _____ 24. _____
6. _____ 16. _____ 25. _____
7. _____ 17. _____ 26. _____
8. _____ 18. _____ 27. _____
9. _____ 19. _____ 28. _____
10. _____   29. _____

CIGARETTE

There are at least 30 words of five letters or more that can be formed from the letters in CIGARETTE. How many of them can you come up with?

Finding 15 is good; 20 is excellent; and 25 would really light up your life.

Answers on page 479

1. _____ 11. _____ 21. _____
2. _____ 12. _____ 22. _____
3. _____ 13. _____ 23. _____
4. _____ 14. _____ 24. _____
5. _____ 15. _____ 25. _____
6. _____ 16. _____ 26. _____
7. _____ 17. _____ 27. _____
8. _____ 18. _____ 28. _____
9. _____ 19. _____ 29. _____
10. _____ 20. _____ 30. _____

PLATITUDES

There are at least 53 words of five letters or more to be found in the word PLATITUDES.

Finding 27 constitutes a passing grade; 35 declares you're way out front. If you get 42, you are entitled to an award; and if you score 48, then for you huzzahs and hosannas.

Answers on page 479

1. _____
2. _____
3. _____
4. _____
5. _____
6. _____
7. _____
8. _____
9. _____
10. _____
11. _____
12. _____
13. _____
14. _____
15. _____
16. _____
17. _____
18. _____

19. _____
20. _____
21. _____
22. _____
23. _____
24. _____
25. _____
26. _____
27. _____
28. _____
29. _____
30. _____
31. _____
32. _____
33. _____
34. _____
35. _____

36. _____
37. _____
38. _____
39. _____
40. _____
41. _____
42. _____
43. _____
44. _____
45. _____
46. _____
47. _____
48. _____
49. _____
50. _____
51. _____
52. _____
53. _____

MELANCHOLIC

No less than 37 words of five letters or more can be formed out of the letters in the word MELANCHOLIC.

If you find 17, you've topped the hurdle. If your score is 24, you're way, way up in front; and if by dint of effort you score as many as 31, you've really won the bronze tomato.

Answers on page 479

1. _____   13. _____   26. _____
2. _____   14. _____   27. _____
3. _____   15. _____   28. _____
4. _____   16. _____   29. _____
5. _____   17. _____   30. _____
6. _____   18. _____   31. _____
7. _____   19. _____   32. _____
8. _____   20. _____   33. _____
9. _____   21. _____   34. _____
10. _____ 22. _____   35. _____
11. _____ 23. _____   36. _____
12. _____ 24. _____   37. _____
                25. _____

DEPOSIT

There are at least 14 words of five letters or more to be made from the letters in DEPOSIT.

A score of 8 is pretty good; 10 is lovely; and 12 is superb.

Answers on page 480

1. _____   6. _____   10. _____
2. _____   7. _____   11. _____
3. _____   8. _____   12. _____
4. _____   9. _____   13. _____
5. _____   14. _____

MONASTERY

There are at least 54 words of five letters or more that can be found in the word MONASTERY. How many can you come up with?

A score of 33 is excellent; 40 is splendid; and 47 puts you in the very, very top of the class.

Answers on page 480

1. _____
2. _____
3. _____
4. _____
5. _____
6. _____
7. _____
8. _____
9. _____
10. _____
11. _____
12. _____
13. _____
14. _____
15. _____
16. _____
17. _____
18. _____

19. _____
20. _____
21. _____
22. _____
23. _____
24. _____
25. _____
26. _____
27. _____
28. _____
29. _____
30. _____
31. _____
32. _____
33. _____
34. _____
35. _____
36. _____

37. _____
38. _____
39. _____
40. _____
41. _____
42. _____
43. _____
44. _____
45. _____
46. _____
47. _____
48. _____
49. _____
50. _____
51. _____
52. _____
53. _____
54. _____

PHANTASMAGORIA

At least 55 words of five letters or more can be found in the word PHANTASMAGORIA.

If you find 25, you're doing fine; while a score of 35 catapults you into the upper brackets. If you wind up with 45, you deserve a medal; and it is safely asserted that if you come up with as many as 52, you're one in ten thousand.

Answers on page 480

Answers on page 480

1. _____
2. _____
3. _____
4. _____
5. _____
6. _____
7. _____
8. _____
9. _____
10. _____
11. _____
12. _____
13. _____
14. _____
15. _____
16. _____
17. _____
18. _____
19. _____
20. _____
21. _____
22. _____
23. _____
24. _____
25. _____
26. _____
27. _____
28. _____
29. _____
30. _____
31. _____
32. _____
33. _____
34. _____
35. _____
36. _____
37. _____
38. _____
39. _____
40. _____
41. _____
42. _____
43. _____
44. _____
45. _____
46. _____
47. _____
48. _____
49. _____
50. _____
51. _____
52. _____
53. _____
54. _____
55. _____

PENULTIMATE

At least 33 words of five letters or more can be formed from the word PENULTIMATE.

If you find 16, you have a passing grade. A score of 22 puts you in an entirely different class; while if you can deliver as many as 26, you can consider that a real achievement.

Answers on page 480

1. _____	12. _____	23. _____
2. _____	13. _____	24. _____
3. _____	14. _____	25. _____
4. _____	15. _____	26. _____
5. _____	16. _____	27. _____
6. _____	17. _____	28. _____
7. _____	18. _____	29. _____
8. _____	19. _____	30. _____
9. _____	20. _____	31. _____
10. _____	21. _____	32. _____
11. _____	22. _____	33. _____

MOUNTAINOUS

There are at least 21 words of five letters or more to be found in the word MOUNTAINOUS.

A score of 12 is passing; 14 is good; 16 is excellent; 18 is very special. If you come up with 20, you must be a lexicographer.

Answers on page 480

1. _____	8. _____	15. _____
2. _____	9. _____	16. _____
3. _____	10. _____	17. _____
4. _____	11. _____	18. _____
5. _____	12. _____	19. _____
6. _____	13. _____	20. _____
7. _____	14. _____	21. _____

MANIPULATION

There are at least 51 words of five letters or more to be found in the word MANIPULATION.

A score of 25 is average; 30 is very good; and 40 makes you a winner. If you score 45 or more, you are entitled to be enshrined in a Hall of Fame.

Answers on page 480

1. _____	18. _____	35. _____
2. _____	19. _____	36. _____
3. _____	20. _____	37. _____
4. _____	21. _____	38. _____
5. _____	22. _____	39. _____
6. _____	23. _____	40. _____
7. _____	24. _____	41. _____
8. _____	25. _____	42. _____
9. _____	26. _____	43. _____
10. _____	27. _____	44. _____
11. _____	28. _____	45. _____
12. _____	29. _____	46. _____
13. _____	30. _____	47. _____
14. _____	31. _____	48. _____
15. _____	32. _____	49. _____
16. _____	33. _____	50. _____
17. _____	34. _____	51. _____

CHAPLAIN

We found only seven words of five or more letters in CHAPLAIN. How many can you spot?

Anything over 5 is commendable.

Answers on page 481

1. _____	3. _____	6. _____
2. _____	4. _____	7. _____
	5. _____	

DICTIONARY

There are at least 43 words of five letters or more which can be made from the letters in the word DICTIONARY. How many of them can you supply?

A score of 20 is good; 27 is excellent; 35 means you must be a lexicographer!

Answers on page 481

1. _____	15. _____	30. _____
2. _____	16. _____	31. _____
3. _____	17. _____	32. _____
4. _____	18. _____	33. _____
5. _____	19. _____	34. _____
6. _____	20. _____	35. _____
7. _____	21. _____	36. _____
8. _____	22. _____	37. _____
9. _____	23. _____	38. _____
10. _____	24. _____	39. _____
11. _____	25. _____	40. _____
12. _____	26. _____	41. _____
13. _____	27. _____	42. _____
14. _____	28. _____	43. _____
	29. _____	

CHARACTERIZE

There are at least 48 words of five letters or more that can be made out of the letters contained in the word CHARACTERIZE.

A score of 23 is good; 30 is excellent; and 40 characterizes you as a word expert.

Answers on page 481

1. _____	17. _____	33. _____
2. _____	18. _____	34. _____
3. _____	19. _____	35. _____
4. _____	20. _____	36. _____
5. _____	21. _____	37. _____
6. _____	22. _____	38. _____
7. _____	23. _____	39. _____
8. _____	24. _____	40. _____
9. _____	25. _____	41. _____
10. _____	26. _____	42. _____
11. _____	27. _____	43. _____
12. _____	28. _____	44. _____
13. _____	29. _____	45. _____
14. _____	30. _____	46. _____
15. _____	31. _____	47. _____
16. _____	32. _____	48. _____

TOGETHER

There are at least 14 words to be made from the letters in TOGETHER.

A score of 8 is passing; 10 is surpassing; and anything more shows you've got it all together.

Answers on page 481

1. _____	6. _____	10. _____
2. _____	7. _____	11. _____
3. _____	8. _____	12. _____
4. _____	9. _____	13. _____
5. _____		14. _____

CONCENTRATE

There are at least 53 words of five letters or more that can be formed from the letters in CONCENTRATE.

A score of 28 is fair; 38 is excellent; and 48 shows you can really concentrate.

Answers on page 481

1. _____
2. _____
3. _____
4. _____
5. _____
6. _____
7. _____
8. _____
9. _____
10. _____
11. _____
12. _____
13. _____
14. _____
15. _____
16. _____
17. _____
18. _____

19. _____
20. _____
21. _____
22. _____
23. _____
24. _____
25. _____
26. _____
27. _____
28. _____
29. _____
30. _____
31. _____
32. _____
33. _____
34. _____
35. _____

36. _____
37. _____
38. _____
39. _____
40. _____
41. _____
42. _____
43. _____
44. _____
45. _____
46. _____
47. _____
48. _____
49. _____
50. _____
51. _____
52. _____
53. _____

POMEGRANATE

There are at least 93 words of five letters or more that can be formed from the letters in POMEGRANATE.

A score of 50 is passing fair; 65 shows endurance; and 80 earns you a place in the Garden of Eden.

Answers on page 481

1. _____   30. _____   59. _____
2. _____   31. _____   60. _____
3. _____   32. _____   61. _____
4. _____   33. _____   62. _____
5. _____   34. _____   63. _____
6. _____   35. _____   64. _____
7. _____   36. _____   65. _____
8. _____   37. _____   66. _____
9. _____   38. _____   67. _____
10. _____   39. _____   68. _____
11. _____   40. _____   69. _____
12. _____   41. _____   70. _____
13. _____   42. _____   71. _____
14. _____   43. _____   72. _____
15. _____   44. _____   73. _____
16. _____   45. _____   74. _____
17. _____   46. _____   75. _____
18. _____   47. _____   76. _____
19. _____   48. _____   77. _____
20. _____   49. _____   78. _____
21. _____   50. _____   79. _____
22. _____   51. _____   80. _____
23. _____   52. _____   81. _____
24. _____   53. _____   82. _____
25. _____   54. _____   83. _____
26. _____   55. _____   84. _____
27. _____   56. _____   85. _____
28. _____   57. _____   86. _____
29. _____   58. _____   87. _____

88. _____   90. _____   92. _____
89. _____   91. _____   93. _____

DEMONSTRATE

Some 66 words of five letters or more can be formed out of the letters in the word DEMONSTRATE.

A score of 35 is average; a score of 45 puts you in the upper echelon; while a score of 55 testifies to your having a wide vocabulary. If you deliver 60 words, you must be a teacher of English, or a writer.

Answers on page 482

1. _____   23. _____   45. _____
2. _____   24. _____   46. _____
3. _____   25. _____   47. _____
4. _____   26. _____   48. _____
5. _____   27. _____   49. _____
6. _____   28. _____   50. _____
7. _____   29. _____   51. _____
8. _____   30. _____   52. _____
9. _____   31. _____   53. _____
10. _____   32. _____   54. _____
11. _____   33. _____   55. _____
12. _____   34. _____   56. _____
13. _____   35. _____   57. _____
14. _____   36. _____   58. _____
15. _____   37. _____   59. _____
16. _____   38. _____   60. _____
17. _____   39. _____   61. _____
18. _____   40. _____   62. _____
19. _____   41. _____   63. _____
20. _____   42. _____   64. _____
21. _____   43. _____   65. _____
22. _____   44. _____   66. _____

FRIENDSHIP

There are at least 27 words of five letters or more to be found in the word FRIENDSHIP.

A score of 18 puts you across the line; a score of 20 declares you're a winner; while a score of 25 or more marks you as a word maven.

Answers on page 482

1. _____	10. _____	19. _____
2. _____	11. _____	20. _____
3. _____	12. _____	21. _____
4. _____	13. _____	22. _____
5. _____	14. _____	23. _____
6. _____	15. _____	24. _____
7. _____	16. _____	25. _____
8. _____	17. _____	26. _____
9. _____	18. _____	27. _____

TRIUMVIRATE

There are at least 32 words of five letters or more that can be made out of the letters of the word TRIUMVIRATE.

A score of 15 is good; 20 is super; and 25 says you are way above average.

Answers on page 482

1. _____	12. _____	22. _____
2. _____	13. _____	23. _____
3. _____	14. _____	24. _____
4. _____	15. _____	25. _____
5. _____	16. _____	26. _____
6. _____	17. _____	27. _____
7. _____	18. _____	28. _____
8. _____	19. _____	29. _____
9. _____	20. _____	30. _____
10. _____	21. _____	31. _____
11. _____		32. _____

MASTERFULLY

There are at least 50 words of five letters or more which can be made out of the letters in the word MASTERFULLY.

If you can deliver 27, you've achieved a normal score. If you find as many as 35, you're far above average. A score of 40 is super-duper; while a score of 45 makes you worthy of a crown.

Answers on page 482

1. _____ 18. _____ 34. _____
2. _____ 19. _____ 35. _____
3. _____ 20. _____ 36. _____
4. _____ 21. _____ 37. _____
5. _____ 22. _____ 38. _____
6. _____ 23. _____ 39. _____
7. _____ 24. _____ 40. _____
8. _____ 25. _____ 41. _____
9. _____ 26. _____ 42. _____
10. _____ 27. _____ 43. _____
11. _____ 28. _____ 44. _____
12. _____ 29. _____ 45. _____
13. _____ 30. _____ 46. _____
14. _____ 31. _____ 47. _____
15. _____ 32. _____ 48. _____
16. _____ 33. _____ 49. _____
17. _____   50. _____

EXECUTIVE

We found a mere five words of five letters or more that can be made from the word EXECUTIVE.

If you can equal or top this, you are clearly of executive rank.

Answers on page 482

1. _____   3. _____   4. _____
2. _____   5. _____

VOCABULARY

There are at least 18 words that contain five letters or more which can be formed from the letters in VOCABULARY. How many of them can you come up with?

A score of 9 is good; 12 is excellent; 16 means vocabulary is your strong point.

Answers on page 483

1. _____   7. _____   13. _____
2. _____   8. _____   14. _____
3. _____   9. _____   15. _____
4. _____   10. _____   16. _____
5. _____   11. _____   17. _____
6. _____   12. _____   18. _____

BASEMENT

There are at least 12 words—made up of five letters or more—to be found in BASEMENT.

A score of 7 is very nice; 9 or more puts you on top.

Answers on page 483

1. _____   5. _____   9. _____
2. _____   6. _____   10. _____
3. _____   7. _____   11. _____
4. _____   8. _____   12. _____

DOG JOKES

ONE EVENING a man entered a bar, and, after a brief glance around the room, his eye was caught by a dog sitting on a barstool. His master, sitting next to him on another stool, was deep in thought, studying the checkerboard which lay on the bar between them.

The dog suddenly lifted his paw and moved a black counter from one square to another.

The newcomer gaped in astonishment, approached the players, and, unable to conceal his wonderment, said to the dog's owner, "Gee, that dog's pretty smart."

"Oh, he's not so smart," answered the owner. "I beat him two out of three."

■

The boy was delighted when, after months of prodding, his father agreed to let him keep a dog. When a fox terrier on the block had a litter, the father brought home one of the pups, but insisted that the new pet be kept in the basement at night.

The first night, not surprisingly, the puppy howled until dawn, keeping the entire neighborhood awake. The second night, he again disturbed the neighbors with his mournful cries.

The next morning, the boy's mother heard a pawing at the front door. She opened it to find the pup's mother standing on the porch. The terrier walked in, picked up her puppy by the scruff of the neck, and, leaving the woman aghast, walked back out the door and returned home.

253

For a month, a mongrel pup maintained a lonely vigil above an old well near Rockford, Illinois. The townspeople, fearing that the dog's master had fallen down the 100-foot well, insisted that the water in it be drained. Thousands of curious onlookers watched as the ten-day, $1,000 pumping job was completed. At the bottom of the pit, the rescuers found only an ancient, five-inch bone.

■

Postal authorities in Texas received a telephone call from a woman who complained about the substitute mailman on her route. "The regular carrier gets along fine with our dog," she explained irately, "but whenever the substitute makes the rounds, he upsets the dog."

"Oh? Where is your dog now?" the postal official asked.

"He's out in the yard, under a tree," the woman replied.

"And where's the mail carrier?"

"He's up in the tree. He's upsetting my dog and making him bark."

■

A female mongrel was stretched out before the living-room fireplace as the woman of the house sat knitting nearby. The bored animal woke up, yawned, and looked around absently. Her eyes fell on a plate of chocolates in a dish on a low table.

The pet was very fond of sweets, but she had been taught never to help herself. Furtively, she sauntered over to the low table, picked up a piece of chocolate, and dropped down before the hearth with the candy between her paws.

There she nuzzled her prize for a while, avoiding the woman's eyes, then gave a long, sad sigh of resignation. As the woman watched, the dog took the chocolate in her mouth again, returned to the table, and dropped the candy back into the dish.

The great inventor, Thomas A. Edison, never a man to enjoy publicity, was once persuaded by his wife to attend a gala social function in New York. After trying for most of the evening to escape the well-wishers who surrounded him, the inventor at last managed to find a place to sit alone in a corner. But Edison continually glanced at his watch with a look of resignation on his face. When a friend edged near to him unnoticed, he heard the inventor sigh to himself: "If there were only a dog here!"

■

Stories about bravery of St. Bernards in saving snow-bound people are generally very touching. Here is a favorite that treats the whole thing with a light touch.

Two men, stranded in a snow storm for some 12 hours had just about resigned themselves to freezing to death and were intoning their last prayers, when one of them suddenly looked up and spotted a St. Bernard approaching with the proverbial brandy barrel under the dog's chin. Excitedly, the man poked his partner who was still kneeling in the snow, "Mike, Mike, we're saved! Look! Here comes a dog with man's best friend!"

■

The unmitigated love dog-owners have for their pets remains a mystery to the uninitiated. Mrs. Foster was chatting with the neighbor who had just moved in, "Our dog is just like a member of the family."

"Oh, really," came the polite answer. "Which one?"

■

At the counter of an exclusive clothing shop, a woman with a toy poodle on a leash was standing next to a man who was also waiting to be served. The dog hovered around the man's legs, and the man continually drew back from the animal. Finally, the annoyed woman said, "For goodness sakes, my poodle won't bite you."

"Madam, I'm not afraid that your dog is going to bite me," replied the gentleman, "but as he keeps lifting his leg, I'm afraid he's going to kick me."

Two DOGS met in the street one afternoon for their usual romp. "Say, Terry, what's wrong with you?" asked the little poodle. "You look terrible today."

"I feel terrible," the terrier replied. "I'm on edge, I can't sleep, and I have no appetite."

"Then you should see a good vet."

"I've seen a half dozen already, and they all say I'm in fine shape."

"Maybe what you really need is a good psychiatrist."

"That's impossible," the terrier sighed, "I'm not allowed on couches."

■

Little Ann arrived home one day with a mongrel bitch, but try as she might, she could not convince her mother that they should keep the dog.

About a week later, Ann arrived home from school and found the mongrel running about the yard, pursued by a pack of male dogs. Her eyes gleaming with pride, she burst into the house. "Mommy," she called out, "come to the window! My dog is just a natural-born leader!"

A man once went hunting with a pointer he had borrowed from a friend. While the friend was a crack shot, the man himself was a very poor shot, and each time he missed his target the pointer would look up at him in bewilderment.

After an unrewarding afternoon, the dog finally set a pheasant out in an open field, and glanced back at the hunter as if to say, "You can't miss this one."

The man shot and missed. The pheasant rose and flew off, and again the man missed. The pointer sat down, raised his nose to the sky, and howled long and woefully. Then, without another look at the disappointed huntsman, he turned and trotted home.

Pueblo, Colorado, is justly proud of its own version of "The Odd Couple." Charlie the Cat and Daisy the Dog set up joint residence in a doghouse owned by Jeff Anderson. Each critter has its own entrance to the house and, according to Mr. Anderson, both eat, sleep, and play in perfect harmony. What makes this story doubly amazing is that Charlie and Daisy did not grow up together; they are both strays.

Mrs. Arlene Higuera's pooch had had that hangdog look for a couple of days, and just wasn't the playful pet it had always been. So, naturally, Mrs. Higuera rushed her darling to the vet. After a simple operation to extract the 267 marbles in the dog's stomach, Fido was soon romping around the house with his accustomed panache.

Rip was one of several dogs employed at major airports around the country to sniff out drugs that might be concealed in incoming cargo or luggage. Rip was the star of Miami International Airport's customs inspections team, but officials began to doubt Rip's sense of smell when he commenced to bark at some crates containing massive concrete pedestals for lawn statues.

But Rip's past record induced the officials to check out the cargo. Each pedestal was five feet tall and weighed 400 pounds. After drilling through 1½" of steel-reinforced concrete on the first pedestal, the customs men discovered a sealed, galvanized steel container which held 80 pounds of marijuana! The other nine pedestals yielded the same trove. The street value of this haul was $160,000.

It will be a long time before anyone questions the super schnozzola of Canine Agent Rip.

HOT POTATO

This is a good ice-breaker which requires no props except for a plain, ordinary handkerchief. The handkerchief is rolled and knotted into a ball.

All the guests, except one, sit in as even a circle as can be managed. The less distance between chairs, the better. Choose someone to be IT. He stands in the middle of the circle.

The players then proceed to toss the handkerchief from one to the other, around and across the circle. IT tries to grab the handkerchief.

If he succeeds, he changes places with the player who touched the "hot potato" last.

The essence of this game is speed—the faster the funnier!

DEAD PAN

This game is the quintessence of something or other. Play it, and you'll know what we mean. If this doesn't get a laugh out of your company, send them all back to the cleaners.

Seat your guests in what is more or less of a circle.

The first player says "Ha!" The second player must say "Ha! Ha!" The third says "Ha! Ha! Ha!" Each player adds one "Ha!"

The idea is—first, to be accurate (which is unimportant) and second, to keep a straight face (which is very important). If you laugh, you're out!

If you smile, grin, or smirk, you're sort of playing it sharp; that may count as a foul Not calling an accurate number of Ha! Ha!s is also a foul. In this game, fouls don't count.

However, good sportsmanship decrees that you must call the "Ha! Ha!"s fast and furious, and without hesitation.

The one holding out the longest wins a lemon, as Champion Sourpuss.

MATCH IT

A great game for a sophisticated party. You will have to do a little advance preparation for this game.

You pair the guests off into couples by one means or another. Each couple is now a team, and the team works together to solve the puzzles. You give each team the same list. The list consists of 15 phrases. Each of these phrases is a clever hint that defines some object in the room or rooms where the game is played. For example, the hint may say, "A member of a baseball team." Somewhere in the room, the team will run across a pitcher and recognize it as the answer.

The team that is first to solve all 15 clues, runs to the Umpire (the host who wrote the clues) and claims the victory.

To prepare this list, look around your house for objects whose names have double meanings, or lend themselves to wordplay. Type the 15 phrases you are going to use on a sheet of paper and duplicate it (by xerox) so that each team (pair) in the party has the list.

Here is a sample list of clues and of the objects described:

ON THE LIST	THE OBJECT
1. A member of a baseball team	A pitcher
2. The swimming match	A used match that you placed in water in an ashtray
3. The light that failed	A burned out candle, or one of your bulbs that's no longer working
4. Adam's undoing	An apple
5. An extra foot	A 12-inch ruler
6. Sweet sixteen	Sixteen lumps of sugar in a bowl
7. The seasons	Salt and pepper shakers, or other spices
8. Something to adore	A door knob
9. Origin of Burns	An iron
10. Of absorbing interest	Cotton balls
11. What everyone wants on New Year's Eve	A date
12. With this, you hold the world in your hand	An atlas, map, or globe
13. A place to reflect	A mirror
14. Painless blows	A pair of socks
15. One that sounds like two	A pear

HOLDING THE BAG

This is a game of wits. In every game you play, there is a picture with a three-line setup. The top line consists of five shopping bags, the middle line consists of four laundry bags, and the bottom line consists of three paper bags.

The players decide who goes first. Each player gets one turn in order. The player whose turn it is must cross out one or more of the containers. He does this by making a large "X" right on the face of the bag with his pencil.

He may cross out as many containers in any one line as he wishes, but he must confine all his crossing out to just one line. For example, a player may cross out one, two, three, four, or five shopping bags, or as many shopping bags as there happen to be left on the line.

Or he may elect to cross out the three paper bags on the bottom line, or perhaps only two of them, or even one of them, but all his activity must be confined to the one single line he has chosen.

The object of the game is to leave your opponent "holding the bag," that is, you make him cross out *the last bag*. The one who crosses out the very last container in the diagram loses the game.

Here are a few setups, so that you can play a few games. Of course, you can duplicate these on blank sheets of paper.

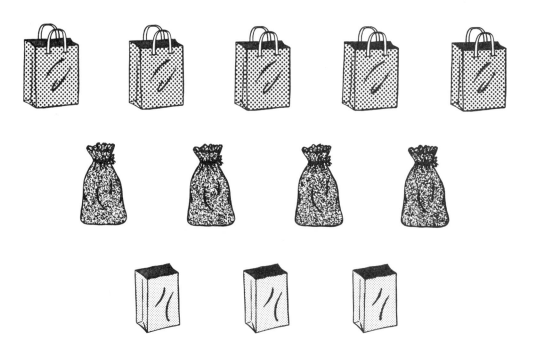

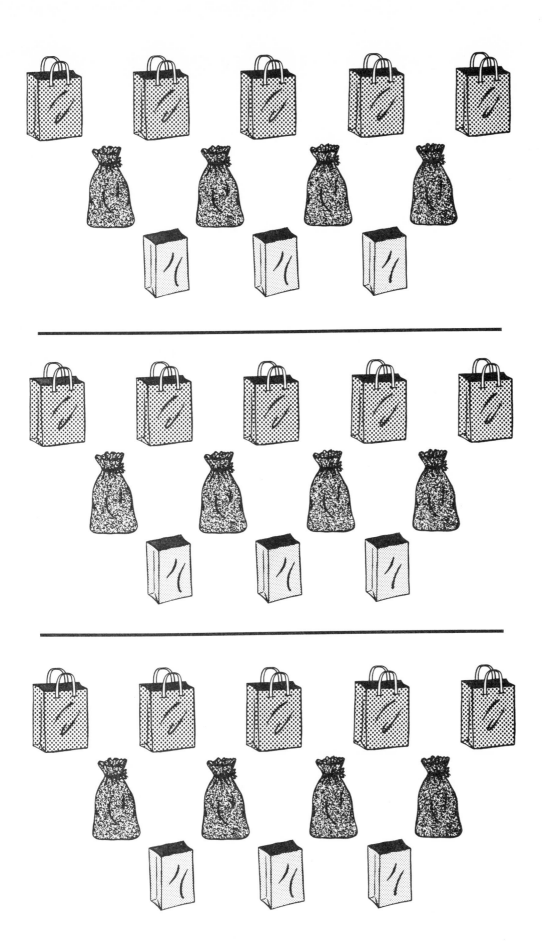

TABLE SHUFFLEBOARD

DIAGRAM 1

Here's a wonderful game you can play at home. It can be played by two players, or by four players, as two teams of two. Anybody from eight years up can play; you can even include Grandma or Grandpa. The only must is a table that's at least six feet long and two and one-half feet wide. And be sure the table has a flat surface.

Now take a piece of white shelf paper, or a piece of white wrapping paper, and spread it over the entire length of the table. With Scotch Tape, secure the paper under one end of the table. Now draw the paper tight. And tape the paper under the other end of the table.

Now you are ready to draw the shuffleboard court. Here's how this is done:

Using a ruler, draw two triangular forms on the paper, one at each end of the table. (See Diagram 1).

Copy this diagram on the white paper, making sure that the triangles point toward each other. Each triangular form should be the same distance from the ends of the table, and from the sides of the table. The base of the triangle should be at least five inches away from the end of the table.

Here's how you play TABLE SHUFFLEBOARD:

Each player gets two checkers. One player uses black checkers; the other, red checkers.

The object of the game is to land your checkers in the scoring sections of the diagram at the other end of the table. If your checker lands on a line, it does not score; the checker must land entirely within a box. The owner of the checker scores the number of points which that box counts. If a player's checker remains in the very top box—*the death slot*—he *loses* 10 points.

How do you get your checkers into the box? You do it by snapping your index finger against the checker, and by propelling it across the table. *(See Diagram 2).*

DIAGRAM 2

Each player gets one turn. Choose for who goes first. After the first player shoots one black checker, his opponent shoots one red checker. Then the first player shoots his last black checker, and then his opponent shoots his last red checker.

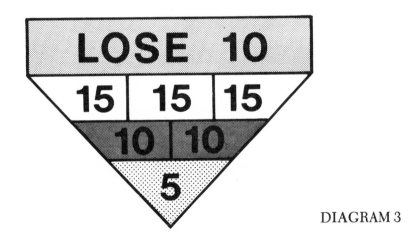

DIAGRAM 3

After the four checkers have been shot, you examine the scoring box to see who scored. Each player records his score on the tally sheet. *(See Diagram 3).*

The game consists of nine innings. The one who scores the highest for the nine innings wins the game.

TABLE SHUFFLEBOARD is lots of fun, and provides much excitement. The first checker might land in a box marked "15," but then be knocked out by the opponent whose own checker, lands in a box which scores 10. Now the first player, on his last chance, may hit his opponent's checker into *The Death Slot*, thus giving his opponent *minus ten* and dramatically turning the game around.

WHO AM I?

This is a fun game for a party. It is especially good for a group that doesn't know each other very well because it gets people milling around. Before you know it, everyone has warmed up to everybody else and whether they succeed in this game or not, your party is sure to be successful.

Give each person an 8½ x 11 sheet of paper and a pencil. Instruct them to print the name of a well-known personage on the paper, but not to let anyone see what they have written. Collect all the papers. While your guest are having hors d'oeuvres, tie string through two holes **at** the top of each paper to make a loop that will enable you to hang the paper over each guest's head. Circulate about the room and hang a sheet of paper over each person's head so that the name is on the person's back.

When everyone has been tagged, instruct your guests about the rules of the game. Tell them they have 10 minutes to circulate about. Each person may ask each other person one question which can be answered with Yes or No. The object, of course, is to find out as quickly as you can who's hanging around your neck.

When the 10 minutes are up, everyone sits down. One at a time, they stand up and say who they think is on their paper. Right or not, they can't help but enjoy themselves.

BE REASONABLE

This game challenges guests to be on their mental toes. They have to try to detect a logical pattern from rather confusing data. Once they get it, they'll love it and will start improvising variations of their own.

First, be sure everybody is comfortably relaxed; then you can introduce the game. Explain that there's a verbal trick to the game that they should be able to figure out. Here goes: announce "Mr. Magoo is making a tea party. What do you suppose he'll serve? Ask me questions to figure out Mr. Magoo's system."

Your guests are invited to ask one question at a time, which you will simply answer with "yes" or "no." Pretty soon someone will catch on to the system and ask a series of questions. Next, everyone will be jumping up and down with a question to see if they got the idea.

For example:

Will he serve toast? Yes.

Will he serve cookies? No.

Will he serve fruit? No.

Will he serve nuts? No.

How about some tarts? Yes.

Cheese? No.   Fritos? No.   Potato chips? No.

Tomatoes? Yes.   Turnips? Yes.   Tapioca pudding? Yes.

You got it! Anything that begins with the letter T.

Obviously, there are many, many variations possible. A favorite one is: "I'm making a party. You can come if you bring the right thing." As each guest asks a question and gets an answer, it becomes apparent that the right thing is anything that begins with the same initial as the name of the host. And so on. Be reasonable!

SCOUTING FOR WORDS

Anyone who has played this game once will keep calling for repeat performances.

The paraphernalia is a set of 49 "alphabet cards," which you can easily make. Draw large capital letters—heavy enough to be visible several feet away—on heavy file cards. (4" × 6" is a convenient size.) Make two cards for each letter except X, Y, and Z. One apiece will do for these. Mix the cards up so they are not in sequence.

The hostess picks a certain classification of objects—let us say FISHES. She stands in front of the guests with the pack of letter cards held in front of her. Let's suppose the top card is P. The first person who calls out "Pickerel" or "Pike" wins the card. The hostess tosses it to him, thus exposing the next card. Now, she calls out the letter which next appears, and the first person to name a fish beginning with *that* letter gets the *second* card.

This is continued until 12 cards are distributed. Then a *new* classification is begun.

If no one succeeds in calling a name for a particular card, it is placed at the back of the pack.

This is a fascinating game, calling for alertness and quick thinking.

The following classifications are surefire:

AUTOMOBILES	CITIES
ANIMALS	VEGETABLES
MAGAZINES	SPORTS
FLOWERS	ARTISTS
BEVERAGES	COLORS

266

MISFITS

Here's a game to test the powers of observation of your guests.

Before the guests arrive, the hostess places various common objects in spots where they don't belong. These should not be placed in an obvious position. For example: a box of crackers might be sandwiched in between books on a bookshelf; a round baking tin might be stacked up with the phonograph records; a kitchen dishcloth might be neatly folded in with the pretty guest towels in the bathroom, etc. The idea is have the objects in a place where they don't belong and yet in a place which a guest might easily overlook.

Divide the guests into teams. Give each team a pad and a pencil, and tell them to walk through the rooms, jotting down the "misfits" they run across. They should silently write down what they find, and not become over-jubilant, for it would be against their own interest to call attention to any of their finds.

A time limit of 10 or 15 minutes is set. The team who finds the most misfits wins the game.

WISECRACKS

There are two reasons why some people don't mind their own business. One is that they haven't any mind, the other that they haven't any business.

The bigger the summer vacation, the harder the fall.

Don't question your wife's judgment—look whom she married!

Let us be happy and live within our means, even if we have to borrow money to do it with. *(Artemus Ward)*

Try praising your wife, even if it does frighten her at first. *(Billy Sunday)*

The well-bred man steps on his cigarette so it won't burn the rug.

Courtship is the period during which the girl makes up her mind whether or not she can do any better.

Seven days in a jeep makes one weak.

The man who enters a bar very optimistically often comes out very misty optically.

Half the lies they tell about me aren't true.

What can one expect of a day that begins with getting up in the morning?

The food in this hotel is absolutely poison—and such small portions!

A great many prominent family trees were started by grafting.

In Hollywood success is relative. The closer the relative, the greater the success. *(Arthur Treacher)*

After a divorce, a woman feels like a new man.

It was just a platonic friendship—play for him, tonic for her!

Lend your neighbor a garden rake and he'll come back for mower.

Marriage is popular because it combines the maximum of temptation with the maximum of opportunity. *(G.B. Shaw)*

Marriage is a romance in which the hero dies in the first chapter.

Getting the baby to bed is hardest when she's about 18 years old.

When people go to summer hotels for a change and a rest, the bellboys get the change and the hotel gets the rest.

Brother started off working for peanuts until he proved he was worth his salt. Now he gets salted peanuts.

A diplomat? He's the man who can convince his wife that a woman looks stout in a fur coat.

The average man is an irrational creature who's always looking for home atmosphere in a hotel, and hotel service at home.

He reminds me of the man who murdered both his parents and then when sentence was about to be pronounced, pleaded for mercy on the grounds that he was an orphan. *(Lincoln)*

Every woman likes to be taken with a grain of assault.

Thirty is a nice age for a woman—especially if she happens to be forty.

After two days in the hospital, he took a turn for the nurse.

HOW TO SOLVE
PICTURE PUZZLES

The picture puzzle is a cartoon which illustrates a particular title. The title may be the name of a famous person, book, movie, play, song, or geographical locality. Under each picture puzzle you will find a choice of titles. You, of course, have to figure out which one is the correct title.

To detect the correct title you will have to examine the cartoon very carefully and use many different kinds of clues. You will find some clues in the picture that will fit each of the suggested choices. But a title is the correct one *only when every single letter can be accounted for* by some object, syllable, definition, sound, or inference in the picture puzzle. When you have accumulated enough clues, you will be able to string them together in the right order so that reading them aloud will give the exact sound of the title.

Here are some of the ways in which you may gather individual clues from elements in the picture puzzle:

1. You may use the name of any object which appears in the picture. However, you may not use an intrinsic part of an object. For example, if there is a coat in the cartoon, you may use that word; but you may not use *sleeve*, which is an intrinsic part of the coat—if the word *sleeve* were needed for the solution, then the picture would have to be there in isolation, or the word would have to be derived in some other way.

2. Any individual letter which appears in the picture puzzle may be used to represent a letter in the title. However, individual letters may not be taken out of whole words and used in isolation. You may, on the other hand, use an individual letter, if it appears, to represent a whole word. For example, if the letter R appears in isolation, it may be used to represent the word *are;* the letter B may be used to represent the word *be;* the letter C may be used to represent the word *see.* In addition, you may use two single letters if they appear in the picture puzzle, to represent a word for which it is homophonous. For example, you may use CC to represent the word *seize.*

3. A word from the picture puzzle cartoon may be used to represent a word or a syllable in the title. It may be used just as it is; or a homophone for the word may be used. For example, the word *hymn* in the picture puzzle may be used to represent the word *him* in the title; *knight* in the picture may represent *night* in the title. Note, however, that a syllable within a word may be used *only* if it is separated from the body of the word by a hyphen. For example, if the word *mantle* were in the picture puzzle, the syllable *man* could not be extracted

from it for use in the title; but if the word *man-made* were in the picture puzzle, the syllable *man* could be used in the title.

4. A synonym of any word found in the puzzle may be used to form a part of the title. For example, *present* may suggest *gift*.

5. A definition found in the puzzle may be compressed to a single word to yield a clue for the title. For example, if there is a reference in the picture puzzle to an American coin worth five cents, the word *nickel* is a proper clue for the title.

6. Anything which may be definitely inferred from a situation or from a spoken word in the puzzle may be used as a clue. For example, if a male addresses a lady as "Mother," he, of course, must be her son. Therefore, the word *son* is a clue which may be used.

To complete a solution, juggle your clues around until they are in the right order to sound out the title. The same consonant may be used at the end of one syllable and the beginning of another syllable. For example, if you got the following elements out of a puzzle, IN DEEP PEN DEN T LAID E, these elements would form the title INDEPENDENT LADY. The P used at the end of the word DEEP and the beginning of PEN does not disturb the flow of sound in reading the winning title. Elision of syllables is very common in the more difficult type of puzzle. Don't let this baffle you. Just look out for syllables hidden within a protective maze of strange orthography.

The clues you extract must be congruous with the scene in the cartoon. You may not place an archaic or obsolete word in the mouth of a modern schoolboy. Nor can Egyptians be made to talk Shakespearean English. Nor can Victorian ladies be made to speak slang.

PICTURE-PUZZLE NO. 1

One, and only one, of the following is the correct title for this picture:

EDWARD JULIUS   SEA SERPENTS
MECCA   HOUDINI
MOUNT CLEMENS   ALPHONSUS DRESS
ROMEO AND JULIET   RICARDO MALTHUS
YOU KNOW ME, AL!   HIGH ADVENTURE

Solution on page 483

PICTURE-PUZZLE NO. 2

One, and only one, of the following is the correct title for this picture:

LEAVES OF GRASS   REGINALD BARKER
DIDO   SITTING PRETTY
DIOCLETIAN   THE RED AND THE BLACK
RED GRANGE   THE BLACK ARROW
DARK ANGEL   ON A STEAMER COMING OVER

Solution on page 483

PICTURE-PUZZLE NO. 3

One, and only one, of the following is the correct title for this picture:

TICK-TACK-TOE   SACRAMENTO
OUT ON A LIMB   TACOMA
THE TAXIDERMIST   TONY WONS
SHEEPSHEAD BAY   NEWFOUNDLAND
CHARING CROSS   HAVELOCK ELLIS

Solution on page 483

PICTURE-PUZZLE NO. 4

One, and only one, of the following is the correct title for this picture:

MALCOLM COWLEY   HOUNDS OF SPRING
OLD FORGE   BULLDOG DRUMMOND ESCAPES
MEN ARE NOT GODS   MATE IN TWO MOVES
STEPHEN DOUGLAS   YE DRUNKEN DAMOZEL
EX-HUSBAND   DRUMS ALONG THE MOHAWK

Solution on page 483

PICTURE-PUZZLE NO. 5

One, and only one, of the following is the correct title for this picture:

ADAM SMITH
BEFORE MORNING
ADAMS EXPRESS CO.
MYRON SHAPLEY
PICKING WINNERS

LAWRENCE SPELLMAN
BABY MINE
ADAM BEDE
GABRIEL HEATTER
BEAUTY ON THE RUN

Solution on page 483

PICTURE-PUZZLE NO. 6

One, and only one, of the following is the correct title for this picture:

THE JAFFA ROAD   KATHARINE HEPBURN
JOSIE MANSFIELD   MARLENE DIETRICH
LORETTA YOUNG   THE WONDER EYE OF ABDUL
JEAN HARLOW   THE FORTY DAYS OF MUSA DAGH
CLARA BOW   THE FAIR WEATHER MAN

Solution on page 483

PICTURE-PUZZLE NO. 7

One, and only one, of the following is the correct title for this picture:

MARC ANTHONY
KARL MARX
THE OPEN SESAME
RIPTIDE
WIDE OF THE MARK

THE SCARLET LETTER
SCHNOZZLE DURANTE
HIGH, WIDE, AND HANDSOME
ERSKINE CALDWELL
CORNELIUS S. VAN RIPER

Solution on page 483

PICTURE-PUZZLE NO. 8

One, and only one, of the following is the correct title for this picture:

TEMPLES OF AN EARLY PERIOD   MONTGOMERY SCHUYLER
IN A CHINESE TEMPLE   WELLESLEY P. CODDINGTON
BECAUSE I LOVE YOU   A TOURIST IN CHINA
CHINA SEAS   THE MYSTERY OF TOMORROW
REELING IT OFF   ON A STEAMER COMING OVER

Solution on page 483

PICTURE-PUZZLE NO. 9

One, and only one, of the following is the correct title for this picture:

JANE EYRE
BUCK JONES
BOB GOODHUE
SISTER CARRIE
HIGH FINANCE

THIS IS MY MOTHER
THE COIGN ON THE HILL
JEANETTE MACDONALD
BENJAMIN CARDOZO
ROBERT W. SILVER

Solution on page 484

PICTURE-PUZZLE NO. 10

One, and only one, of the following is the correct title for this picture:

OWEN MOORE   OZONE PARK
SONJA HENIE   O, NO, JOHN
CEILING ZERO   MEAN TO ME
CODDINGTON   UNDER THE DOUBLE EAGLE
ANYTHING GOES   THE SILVER LINING

Solution on page 484

PICTURE-PUZZLE NO. 11

One, and only one, of the following is the correct title for this picture:

FRANCES STARR

REX BEACH

HOLY NIGHT

STARK YOUNG

CECIL RHODES

STARS AND STRIPES FOREVER

FOREIGN LEGION

STARS OF THE SUMMER NIGHT

HEART TO BE WON

WHY GIRLS LEAVE HOME

Solution on page 484

PICTURE-PUZZLE NO. 12

One, and only one, of the following is the correct title for this picture:

CORSAIRS ON THE SEA   FIORELLO LAGUARDIA
GIBRALTAR   EIGHT TRAILS FORWARD
GUSTAVE L. BECKER   TOO WELL DONE
"FLAGPOLE" KELLY   ABOUT A QUARTER TO NINE
ANTHONY EDEN   THE MUSIC GOES ROUND AND ROUND

Solution on page 484

PICTURE-PUZZLE NO. 13

One, and only one, of the following is the correct title for this picture:

SURGEON PARRAN
KENSINGTON GARDENS
LADY IN DISTRESS
PIERCE BUTLER
ICHABOD BARTLETT

CAB CALLOWAY
COLE L. BLEASE
ONLY NINE IN HELP
LORD JOHN CARSTAIRS
HUGH JOHNSON

Solution on page 484

HOW TO SOLVE STEPLADDERS

A STEPLADDER is a word puzzle based on two key letters. The words that you are looking for always contain five letters. You're given two of these letters. The two letters that you're given are the same in all words of the STEPLADDER.

Next to the two letters there's a definition. From this definition, you solve the other three letters. For example: Suppose the two letters were LO, and the definition was *a flower*. The word would be LOTUS. If the first two letters were LO and the definition was *to hate*, the word would be LOATH.

In a STEPLADDER, the two letters are placed in various positions. For example: LO might be the last two letters and the definition be *a greeting*. The word would then be HELLO.

PE

Below, you will find definitions for 25 five-letter words. Two letters, PE, are contained in each word in the positions indicated. Can you identify the words?

A score of 14 is peaceable; 18 is perspicacious; and 25 is perfection itself.

Answers on page 484

1.	P	E				Danger
2.	P	E				A tea
3.	P	E				Part of a flower
4.	P	E				Discoverer of North Pole
5.	P	E				A fish
6.		P	E			Velocity
7.		P	E			Plural of opus
8.		P	E			Particle
9.		P	E			Set upside down
10.		P	E			Lance
11.			P	E		Push; force
12.			P	E		Venomous snake
13.			P	E		Mature
14.			P	E		The man who does polls
15.			P	E		Cause distaste
16.				P	E	Run off to marry
17.				P	E	Food that comes from the stomach of an ox
18.				P	E	Contour
19.				P	E	Range; extent
20.				P	E	Complain
21.	P				E	Money bag
22.	P				E	Demonstrate conclusively
23.	P				E	Glue
24.	P				E	Principal; main
25.	P				E	Cut away leaves or branches

LO

Each of the phrases below defines a word that contains the letters LO in the position indicated. Can you complete the words by filling in the remaining letters?

A score of 13 is somewhat low; 17 is lots better; and 22 must mean you're loquacious.

Answers on page 485

#	col1	col2	col3	col4	col5	Clue
1.	L	O				Free from confinement
2.	L	O				Small magnifier used by jewelers
3.	L	O				Gorgeous Italian actress
4.	L	O				Science of reasoning
5.	L	O				Confined to a particular place
6.		L	O			Lowness of spirits
7.		L	O			Pull; influence
8.		L	O			American painter, "Ashcan" school
9.		L	O			Obstruct passage
10.		L	O			Scorn; disregard contemptuously
11.			L	O		A wispy flower
12.			L	O		A mixture of metals
13.			L	O		Athenian lawgiver
14.			L	O		Underneath
15.			L	O		Spartan serf
16.				L	O	Salutation
17.				L	O	Star of TV show *That Girl*
18.				L	O	Low calorie dessert
19.				L	O	Site of Edison's lab, _____ Park
20.				L	O	Musical instrument
21.	L				O	Lariat
22.	L				O	Grassy plain in South America
23.	L				O	Slow movement in musical composition
24.	L				O	A print made from a stove or metal plate
25.	L				O	A game of chance popular with children

287

SE

The two letters, S E, appear in each of the five-letter words in this vocabulary quiz. The position of S E within the word is indicated, and the definition is given next to each word. Fill in the blanks to identify each word. Then check your answers.

A score of 16 is good; 19 is excellent; and 22 is exceptional.

Answers on page 485

1.	S E _ _ _	To wait on; meet the needs of
2.	S E _ _ _	Car for four or more persons
3.	S E _ _ _	To divide; separate; disjoin
4.	S E _ _ _	To feel; understand; perceive
5.	S E _ _ _	Brown pigment used in monochrome drawing
6.	S E _ _ _	Plan; arrangement
7.	_ _ S E _	Wooden frame to support a painting
8.	_ _ S E _	Avaricious person; hoarder of wealth
9.	_ _ S E _	To overturn; disturbed
10.	_ _ S E _	Something put within something else
11.	_ _ S E _	Inquisitive; prying
12.	_ _ S E _	Something with value; positive quality
13.	_ _ _ S E	To lift up; elevate; increase
14.	_ _ _ S E	Slip of memory, tongue, or pen; slight mistake
15.	_ _ _ S E	Apathetic; indifferent; bored
16.	_ _ _ S E	Thick; impenetrable
17.	_ _ _ S E	To rub out; obliterate
18.	_ _ _ S E	Outdated
19.	_ _ _ S E	Concise
20.	S _ _ _ E	Sword with a curved blade
21.	S _ _ _ E	Horny plate; balance; instrument for weighing
22.	S _ _ _ E	To move on ice; shoe with blade or roller
23.	S _ _ _ E	To screen from light; make dark; cool place
24.	S _ _ _ E	Large nail; sharp point; add liquor to a drink
25.	S _ _ _ E	Move stealthily

AN

The two letters, AN, appear in each of the five-letter words which are defined below. The position of AN within the word is indicated. Can you fill in the blanks with the appropriate missing letters?

A score of 13 is fine; 18 is dandy; and 23 is incandescent.

Answers on page 485

No.	Grid	Clue
1.	A N _ _ _	Cancel; invalidate
2.	A N _ _ _	Caper
3.	A N _ _ _	Point of view; go fishing
4.	A N _ _ _	Wrath
5.	A N _ _ _	Positive electrode
6.	_ A N _ _	Sweets
7.	_ A N _ _	Scope
8.	_ A N _ _	Mansion
9.	_ A N _ _	Asian bear
10.	_ A N _ _	Male who primps
11.	_ _ A N _	Mark of ownership
12.	_ _ A N _	Simple song
13.	_ _ A N _	Slope
14.	_ _ A N _	Empty
15.	_ _ A N _	African antelope
16.	_ _ _ A N	Unsoiled
17.	_ _ _ A N	Huge, powerful person
18.	_ _ _ A N	Moslem Bible
19.	_ _ _ A N	Cry of pain or distress
20.	_ _ _ A N	Central American Indian
21.	A _ _ _ N	Once more
22.	A _ _ _ N	Source of a great oak
23.	A _ _ _ N	Capital of Jordan
24.	A _ _ _ N	Chef's apparel
25.	A _ _ _ N	Foreigner

CE

Each of the five-letter words defined below contains the letters C E in the positions indicated. Complete the words by supplying the missing letters.

A score of 13 is decent; 18 is certainly better; and 23 is exceptional.

Answers on page 485

#	1	2	3	4	5	Clue
1.	C	E				Stop
2.	C	E				Tree
3.	C	E				Musical instrument
4.	C	E				Goddess of agriculture
5.	C	E				Pertaining to whales
6.		C	E			Setting
7.		C	E			Large body of water
8.		C	E			Upward pitch of a ship
9.		C	E			Sour, bitter
10.		C	E			Aroma
11.			C	E		Disease of the stomach
12.			C	E		To be superior
13.			C	E		Kitchen utensil
14.			C	E		French prep school
15.			C	E		Ran in competition
16.				C	E	Cessation of war
17.				C	E	Chop up
18.				C	E	Food dressing
19.				C	E	Colorful Utah canyon
20.				C	E	Elbow room
21.	C				E	Boat steered with paddles
22.	C				E	Greek island
23.	C				E	Routine task
24.	C				E	Imprecation
25.	C				E	Plant of the onion family

TH

Each of the 25 definitions below should bring to mind a word that contains the letters TH in the indicated positions. It's up to you to complete the word.

A score of 15 shows thought; 20 or more is thoroughly knowledgeable.

Answers on page 485

#						Definition
1.	T	H				Toss
2.	T	H				The unpleasant part of a rose
3.	T	H				A kind of shoe
4.	T	H				Ponder
5.	T	H				Crook
6.		T	H			Anesthetic
7.		T	H			Moral principles
8.		T	H			Chemical base of alcohol
9.		T	H			One of the Three Musketeers
10.		T	H			Different
11.			T	H		Flexible and graceful
12.			T	H		Wash; swim
13.			T	H		Contribution of a tenth part
14.			T	H		Concise; cogent
15.			T	H		Machine for shaping wood or metal
16.				T	H	Merriment
17.				T	H	Ire
18.				T	H	Contemporary American writer; author of *Giles Goat Boy*
19.				T	H	Demise
20.				T	H	Lincoln's assassin
21.	T				H	Feel; handle
22.	T				H	Junk
23.	T				H	Molar, for example
24.	T				H	Jewish holy scriptures
25.	T				H	Difficult

ME

The 25 words defined below all contain the letters ME in the positions indicated. Fill in the missing letters.

A score of 13 is merely fair; 18 is meritorious; and 22 shows mental agility.

Answers on page 485

#	C1	C2	C3	C4	C5	Clue
1.	M	E				Award for achievement
2.	M	E				Compassion
3.	M	E				Gourd eaten as a fruit
4.	M	E				Iron, for example
5.	M	E				Nuclear particle
6.		M	E			Refine ore
7.		M	E			Change; improve
8.		M	E			Smudge
9.		M	E			Last letter of Greek alphabet
10.		M	E			Coarse substance used for grinding
11.			M	E		Bearing weapons
12.			M	E		Gem carved in relief
13.			M	E		Female adults
14.			M	E		Greek poet, author of *Iliad*
15.			M	E		Dromedary or Bactrian
16.				M	E	Fire
17.				M	E	Chief; best part
18.				M	E	Topic; melody
19.				M	E	Feather
20.				M	E	Poetry
21.	M				E	Syrup that goes with waffles
22.	M				E	American inventor of the telegraph
23.	M				E	Popular entertainment
24.	M				E	Free-for-all fist fight
25.	M				E	Purple

RO

Each of the 25 words defined below contains the letters RO as indicated. Can you fill in the blanks?

A score of 13 is not rotten; 18 is a robust score; and 23, a rousing one.

Answers on page 485

#						Clue
1.	R	O				Red-breasted bird
2.	R	O				Wanderer
3.	R	O				Perch
4.	R	O				Scoundrel
5.	R	O				Highway
6.		R	O			Conclusive evidence
7.		R	O			Penniless
8.		R	O			A small wood
9.		R	O			Sarcasm
10.		R	O			Pleasant smell
11.			R	O		Fortune-telling cards
12.			R	O		Evergreen tree
13.			R	O		Directional mark
14.			R	O		Rhythmic beat
15.			R	O		A fish often seen on menus
16.				R	O	French subway
17.				R	O	Prefix for iron
18.				R	O	Mr. Agnew
19.				R	O	Large; gross
20.				R	O	A castle on a promontory
21.	R				O	Love-sick lad
22.	R				O	Proportion
23.	R				O	Musical form
24.	R				O	Cowboy show
25.	R				O	Wireless communication

FUNNY EPITAPHS

On the tombstone of an orator:
Here lies the body of Cynthia Near
Whose mouth it stretched from ear to ear.
Tread softly, stranger, o'er this wonder,
For if she yawns, you're gone by thunder!

In Bath Abbey:
Here lies Ann Mann; she lived an old
Maid and she died an old *Mann*.

In Burlington, Mass.:
Here lies the body of Susan Lowder
Who burst while drinking Seidlitz powder;
Called from this world to her Heavenly rest—
She should have waited till it effervesced!

At Fosbrooke, in Northumberland:
Here lieth Matthew Hollingshead,
Who died from cold caught in his head.
It brought on fever and rheumatiz,
Which ended me—for here I is!

In Boot Hill Cemetery, Kansas:
Shoot-'em-up Jake—
Ran for sheriff, 1872;
Ran from sheriff, 1876;
Buried, 1876.

In Medway, Mass.:
>Beneath this stone, a lump of clay,
>>Lies Uncle Peter Daniels,
>Who too early in the month of May
>>Took off his winter flannels!

In Hollis, N.H.:
>Here lies Cynthia, Steven's wife,
>She lived six years in calm and strife.
>Death came at last and set her free,
>I was glad and so was she.

In Winslow, Maine:
>Here Betsy Brown her body lies,
>Her soul is flying to the skies.
>While here on earth she oft-times spun
>Six hundred skeins from sun to sun,
>And wove one day, her daughter brags,
>Two hundred pounds of carpet rags.

In Canaan, New Hampshire:
>He heard the angels calling him
>>From the Celestial Shore,
>He flapped his wings and away he went
>>To make one angel more.

In Sargentville, Maine:
>Beneath these stones do lie,
>Back to back, my wife and I!
>When the last trumpet the air shall fill,
>If she gets up, I'll just lie still.

Epitaph for Paul Scarron, written by himself:
    Traveller, let your step be light,
       So that sleep these eyes may close,
    For poor Scarron, till tonight,
       Ne'er was able e'en to doze.

Epitaph for John Camden Hotten:
    Hotten,
    Rotten,
    Forgotten

In Skaneateles, New York:
    Underneath this pile of stones
       Lies all that's left of Sally Jones.
    Her name was Briggs; it was not Jones,
       But Jones was used to rhyme with stones!

In Lee, Mass.:
    Open wide ye heavenly gates
       That lead to the heavenly shore;
    Our father suffered in passing through
       And mother weighs much more.

In Lincoln, Maine:
    SACRED TO THE MEMORY OF JARED BATES
    WHO DIED AUG. THE 6TH, 1800

    His widow, aged 24, lives at 7 Elm Street,
    has every qualification for a good wife, and
    yearns to be comforted.

Over the grave of a dentist:
    Stranger! Approach this spot with gravity!
    John Brown is filling his last cavity.

From an English village cemetery:
> Here lies a miser who lived for himself,
> And cared for nothing but gathering pelf,
> Now where he is or how he fares,
> Nobody knows and nobody cares.

In a 17th-century English churchyard:
> Here lies the body of Ethan Bevan,
> Killed by lightning sent from heaven
> For trading horses on Sunday, June eleven,
> In the year Eighteen Hundred Twenty-seven.

And here are a few final inscriptions—fictitious, of course—that might fittingly adorn the gravestones of some famous personalities.

"Gentleman Jim" Corbett:
> Excuse me for not rising.

Lionel Barrymore:
> Well, I've played everything but a harp.

Walter Winchell:
> Here lies Walter Winchell in the dirt he loved so well.

Ilka Chase:
> I've finally gotten to the bottom of things.

Benedict Arnold:
> Involved in a plot.

Dorothy Parker:
> Excuse my dust.

THE MONEY PIT OF OAK ISLAND

Here's the story of an unhidden treasure. There are no secret clues, no lost maps, no ghastly murders. The location is known.

The exact spot has been worked over by picnickers, adventurers, a doctor, a salvage company, a college professor. All attempts to reach gold have met with dismal failure. Yet there is ample proof that there is hidden treasure.

These are the facts: Oak Island, lying just off the coast of Nova Scotia, is washed by a deep inlet called Mahoni Bay. Beyond the Bay, there is a tiny, picturesque cove. Here, in the year 1795, three young men came to picnic.

McGinnis, Smith, and Vaughan little knew that what they were to discover that day on their pleasant outing, would tantalize treasure hunters for the next century and a half. Walking through a grove into a clearing beyond, the men spied an enormous oak. One huge arm of the tree had been sawed off, apparently for use as a derrick. On the trunk were marks and nicks caused by the friction of a block and tackle.

Suddenly, they beheld at their feet a hollow in the turf which looked like an old filled-in well. While they were examining this, they came upon a rusty ring-bolt attached to a moss-covered stone, which had just been uncovered by the receding tide. Looking about with

increasing interest, they found an old boatswain's whistle. And how their excitement mounted when they discovered a copper coin dated 1713!

Now the search started in earnest. Digging down into that "old well," they found that it was, in reality, a circular shaft where the marks of pick and spade were still visible. Two feet, four feet, eight feet—down and down they dug into the soft loam . . . At 10 feet, they struck a heavy floor of oak planking. After this, nothing but more dirt! Yet strangely enough, the structure of the shaft continued on.

Twenty feet, and another layer of planking was hit and removed. Thirty feet down and they had to give up! The tired men had reached a bulkhead which they could not budge. The men returned that day from their picnic, but the intriguing challenge of Oak Island had taken root in their minds. For years they dreamed about the treasure trove that lay beyond the wooden buttresses.

But it was 1801 before they succeeded in interesting a Dr. Lynds of Truro, Nova Scotia, in forming a company to conduct real excavations. This time the shaft was excavated to a depth of 95 feet. At every 10 feet, just as before, some new obstruction was met. Once it was a layer of coconut matting; another time it was wood; and still another time it was putty.

When they had probed down to a depth of 90 feet, one of the diggers struck a stone which seemed to bear an inscription. But somehow it was lost, never to be found again. That may have been the only clue to the secret of Oak Island.

When, at the end of a full day of digging, they reached a wooden platform at a depth of 95 feet, the excavators were dead tired. They decided to let things go till morning . . . While they slept, 70 feet of water seeped into the shaft and filled it to within 25 feet of the mouth.

They sank another shaft, *and still another shaft*, but it was just no go! No matter how early they started, they could never reach the treasure through the work they did in any one long day and the shaft always filled up with water during the night . . . The men, foiled in every effort and broken with disappointment, had to abandon the quest.

It was all of 101 years after the treasure of Oak Island had first been spotted that a new company of adventurers began an elaborate attempt to secure the hidden treasure. This crew sank a number of shafts *at the same time*, with the idea of draining off the water from the central well, where, it was supposed, the treasure was hidden.

In the course of their work, some soft metal was hit but it somehow wouldn't stick to the bore bits. Though they only got the feel of it and never saw the real thing, they concluded that the soft metal was gold. They redoubled their efforts, but the relentless seepage of water mocked their drainage system; and in time, they too had to admit that they were beaten by Oak Island.

In 1910, the Bath Wrecking and Salvage Association of New York thought to take a crack at the hidden gold. They drilled through to the amazing depth of 170 feet. They drilled through every obstacle, even drilling through what seemed to be solid cement. But the maddening, vicious, ever-present water licked the best engineers the company could muster.

In 1913, Professor Welling of the University of Wisconsin made an intensive study of the problem, bringing to bear the full power of his scientific knowledge. Welling came upon an airshaft that had been used by the original builders. It appeared that the men who built the money pit of Oak Island bored a tunnel from a small inlet on the nearby shore

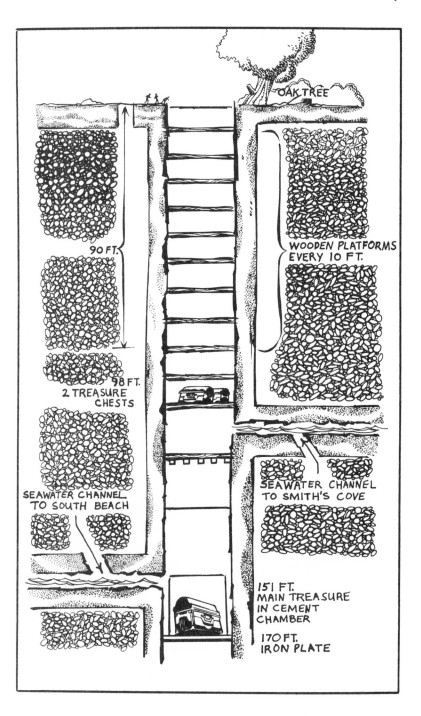

to their cache. The Professor conclusively demonstrated that this tunnel connected the pit with the broad sea.

Welling dissolved a red dye in the water of the central pit. Strangely enough, this colored water did not drift out to sea through the tunnel, but remained in the *treasure shaft*. Since the tunnel leading out to sea and the treasure shaft were connected, this seemed to offer still a new mystery.

The Professor concluded that somewhere in the airshaft the hiders of the treasure had constructed a shut-off valve which held the water in the pit. The valve must have been constructed in such a way that the men in on the secret could release the water from the shaft whenever they wished, and so reach their gold. But how the shut-off valve worked—*and where it was*—was a secret that had eluded all search for 200 years.

Here's the most tantalizing treasure mystery of all time! It's hard to believe that anyone would have gone to such lengths to build a vault, if they had not wished to hide a fortune of fabulous proportion. How these men, 200 years ago, were able to construct a system of tunnels which has foiled some of the best engineering brains of modern times, is indeed a baffling poser.

SUGGESTED SOLUTIONS:

(1) The men constructed a trap door which was reached by a rope worked on a pulley. This pulley was placed in the airshaft; but during a storm, a strong sea had washed away the contraption, making it practically impossible for anyone to find the location of the door.

(2) The men who hid the treasure were pirates who had looted the Spanish Main. The leaders of the expedition, with the help of a number of sailors, hid the treasure on Oak Island. They had the sailors construct the planking, the cement, the coconut matting, and all the other different layers of obstruction. In order that the secret location might abide with them alone, they left the sailor-laborers on Oak Island to die of hunger and exposure while they sailed away. The abandoned men knew they were doomed to die. They also knew that they did not have the tools to dig down through the several obstructions and reach the treasure and destroy it. In their intense thirst for vengeance, they hit upon the diabolically clever idea of keeping the treasure forever from the hands of their betrayers. They dug a shaft from the sea to lead into the bottom of the money pit. The result was that the treasure was flooded beyond hope of recovery.

(3) By one of these strange quirks of Fate, the hiders of the treasure had the misfortune to sink their shaft on top of a subterranean well. When they sank their treasure, the well just happened to be dry. It is well known that wells function with fickle periodicity. Every time a search was made, the well was active and filled the shaft.

SALO FINKELSTEIN

Some few years before World War II, the Treasury Department of the Polish Government began an economy drive by hiring Dr. Salo Finkelstein of Warsaw. Dr. Finkelstein merely replaced some 40-odd people. The incredible man, all by himself, did the work of 40 calculating machines, each of which had formerly been manned by a trained employee.

And the Polish Government vouches for the fact that during those five years in which Dr. Finkelstein tossed huge columns of figures around in the most agile mathematical mind in the world, he did not make a single mistake.

For Salo Finkelstein is a genius if there ever was one. You can give him a large number like 3108 and in less than one minute he reduces it accurately to the following squares: 52^2, 16^2, 12^2, and 2^2—just a simple little maneuver that would take most of us half an hour or more to work out, if we could do it at all.

The Doctor looks at an arithmetical problem like 6894 x 2763 and in just seven seconds, without benefit of paper and pencil, he comes up with the right answer.

Soon after Finkelstein came to the United States, he was hired by the Democratic National Committee to tally the presidential election returns. They sat Dr. Finkelstein next to the telephone. They read him all the figures that came in that way and handed him all the telegrams, and in less time than it takes to actually write down a column of figures, he mentally made the addition and computed the results.

No matter how fast one's brain clicked, no one could do the stunts that Finkelstein performs without the use of a pencil and paper. Even a mathematical wizard has to *see* what he is doing. What makes Finkelstein the baffling mystery that he is, is his superhuman and utterly inexplicable memory.

The fact is that is is really *more* than a memory. Some people call it a photographic mind. You call out two five-digit numbers to Finkelstein and tell him to multiply one by the other. Remembering the two given numbers is not what makes Finkelstein a phenomenon; it is his ability to carry in his mind *all the numbers he is working with*—just as if they were written down on a huge slate before him.

Finkelstein, in his public performances, does use a blackboard. He draws a square containing five rows of five spaces, or twenty-five spaces in all. Then he turns his back to the board.

Folks in the audience come up and fill in the spaces with numbers. Finkelstein turns around and take one quick glance at the blackboard. Then, either blindfolded or with his back turned to the board, he recites the 25 numbers, going from left to right, then going from top to bottom, then moving diagonally, then spirally, or in fact, in any way that you might ask him to juggle his figures . . . And an hour later, after his mind has been filled with every conceivable sort of calculation, he will repeat those 25 numbers for you to perfection.

You see, the numbers have been engraved on that photographic mind of his just as if they had been impressed on a gelatin plate. He remembers *pi* to 300 decimal places. He can recite logarithms from 1 to 100 to the seventh decimal and from 101 to 150 to the fifth decimal. He can conjure up, without a second's hesitation, thousands of square roots, cubic roots, products, quotients, and number combinations. These numbers never fail him. They are there in his mind, and they stick!

Dr. Finkelstein himself was completely unconscious of his talent until he was 20 years old. Somehow he chanced to learn that his mind was really an adding machine. Yet the genius himself cannot explain just how that machine works.

SUGGESTED SOLUTIONS:

(1) Circus giants have grown to their great height because their pituitary glands have been hyperactive. In somewhat the same way, in Dr. Finkelstein's case, the nerves connected with the brain cells which control memory are developed to a highly abnormal degree. This is merely saying that Dr. Finkelstein was born with a colossal memory.

(2) Judged as an abstraction, television existed in this world long before it was actually discovered and used. In the same way, photo cells exist in the brains of each and every human being. If these cells were developed, we all would exhibit powers none of us could even imagine. These cells happen to be developed in the individual case of Dr. Salo Finkelstein. In other words, he of all men, sees with his mind in just the same way that we see with our eyes.

303

THE FIRE WALKERS
OF INDIA

The Hindu land of India is full of many strange things—of religious penitents standing in one spot for twenty years, of snake-charmers who pipe the deadly cobra into harmlessness, of fakirs who lie on a bed of nails—but none more strange or inexplicable than the fire walkers of India. Whether this strange rite is performed as a Yogi demonstration of the power of mind over matter or whether in expiation of sin, the sight is no less confounding.

The Hindus prepare a bed of hot ashes approximately twenty by forty feet. The heat is intense, the coals glow, the ashes hiss, but all this holds no terror for the Hindus. Some with complete calm and others in religious ecstasy walk slowly over the blazing coals—walk barefoot the full forty feet, and mystery of mysteries—come out unscathed; no scars, no blisters, no burns, nothing to bear witness to the fact that these men have verily walked through a living furnace.

These astounding feats of physical endurance have been ascribed by some of the gullible to magic. But even coldly scientific persons watch in amazement as the fire walkers perform their incredible demonstrations. Fire walking is a sight, once seen, that can never be forgotten.

Many European scientists have examined the fire walkers' feet before the ordeal and directly after the performance of the rite. It appears that there is no application of salve, no special treatment of any sort. The soles of their feet are not even extraordinarily calloused.

It was thought for a time, that the fire walkers took opiates which made them insensible to pain, but a few of the Hindus submitted themselves to the complete custody and observation of the doubters, and the scientists found no indication at all that any drugs were taken.

Others offered the opinion that by some trick or illusion the appearance of a fire was created, whereas in fact the coals were harmless; but tests proved that the coals were actually red-hot.

Some Europeans have dared to do the fire-walk themselves and, strangely enough, some of them have come through unscathed. In most cases, the foolhardy suffered terrible burns.

How do these Hindus walk over living coals without searing their flesh? Here is a baffling mystery indeed!

SUGGESTED SOLUTIONS:

(1) The Hindus have a secret solution which they have succeeded in keeping from the world. This solution has an asbestos-like property which renders the skin impervious to heat. The solution is colorless and

therefore cannot be detected. It can be applied weeks in advance and retains its strength.

(2) Just as certain Yogis, by an act of will power, can cut down their breathing to less than half the normal rate and so accomplish the feat of suspended animation (and thus, lay entombed underground for days and yet live), so by a similar act of will power, these Hindus can suspend all sensation.

(3) The feet of these religious performers have become toughened in a peculiar way. They have been conditioned to heat and so can be exposed to fire without actually being burned. In the same way, certain African savages can swallow whole bowls of poison without succumbing to the potion. This is because they have drunk a little bit of poison when they were young and have increased the dose until they were immune to its effects. Similarly, these Hindus have undergone years of training, exposing their legs to heat and thus can withstand what would be certain destruction to other men.

(4) This is a matter of self-hypnosis. Under hypnosis, doctors have been able to perform operations and to make a person completely impervious to pain. Similarly, the Hindu firewalker is so thoroughly convinced that the coals will not burn him, that the flesh becomes resistant to heat.

KASPAR HAUSER

It is May, 1928. Two men are standing in the village square of the city of Nuremburg in Bavaria. They notice an outlandish peasant moving about in uncertain bewilderment. This man—or is he a boy?—stares dazedly about him. His manner is *so strange!* The two men ask him whom he is looking for. For answer he holds out a letter. The letter is addressed to the Captain of the cavalry regiment stationed at Nuremburg.

The boy is brought to the Captain's house and questioned. Can it be that this goof of a peasant does not understand German? To all questions, he has this single reply: "I want to be a soldier like my father was." But he pronounces these words too as if he does not know what they mean, and as if they were learned by rote. Otherwise, he can utter only incomprehensible sounds. The strange lad keeps pointing to his feet and weeps as if he were suffering great pain.

The good people of Nuremburg offer him food but the boy can stomach nothing other than black bread and water . . . But what is this! Strangest thing of all! This clodhopper *can write his name.* In a firm and legible hand, he traces the words *"Kaspar Hauser."* Since no one can make head nor tail of the situation, he is lodged in the city jail.

Had his jailer not been a really intelligent man, the story of Kaspar Hauser would have ended here. But there was something about the boy which convinced the man that Kaspar Houser had a keen intelligence, but was the victim of some great villainy. Secretly observing the boy, when he was unaware of being watched, the jailer soon realized that he had judged correctly—that here was a youth of about 17 years, who was in full possession of his mental faculties, but who, through some strange mystery, was somehow still an undeveloped child . . . How did such a strange thing come to pass?

When the Mayor of the town, the Chief of Police, and the other bigwigs became interested in the case, they tried to get some facts from the boy by use of sign language. This was rather difficult at first; but Kaspar caught on to words quickly, and with his new vocabulary and an apt use of pantomime he was able to tell the following story:

Until the day when he was found in the village square of Nuremburg, and for as long as he could remember, he inhabited a cell—a small, dark cell approximately six feet long, four feet wide, and five feet high. In this restricted world, he had no companions save two wooden horses which he was given to play with. His life was always dark. He knew no difference between night and day. He always sat on an earthen floor, with a little straw under him. A woolen blanket lay next to him with which he might cover himself when it got cold.

Whenever he was tired, he lay down and slept. When he got up, he always found a jug of water and a piece of black bread at his right hand. Sometimes, he awoke to find that his clothes had been changed, or his nails had been trimmed.

He never heard any noise. Betimes, a man came to take care of him. His guardian was never unkind and in all the years only struck him once, when he happened to make too much noise with his horses. Yet he never saw the man's face. In fact, in the twilight world in which he lived, there was really nothing to see.

Some little time before he was found in Nuremburg, his keeper visited him more frequently. The man put a board across his lap, placed a

pencil in his fingers, and then guided his hand across a paper. After several lessons, the boy learned how to write the words, *"Kaspar Hauser."*

Then the same man came and taught him how to walk. He lifted him up from the floor, put him on his feet, stood behind him, and pushed his feet forward one before the other. This lesson in walking was repeated several times before Kaspar Hauser learned how to propel himself forward like a human being.

A few days later, the man came and took him out of the cell—took him out to a new, wondrous world which he had never seen, or heard about, or even imagined. When, after living in a confined space for some 14 years, Kaspar felt the fresh open air for the first time, the sheer shock of it made him faint. Fresh air was altogether too pulsating for Kaspar.

It seemed to him that it took a few days to reach Nuremburg, but his recollections of the journey were very confused. This whole new world was an experience of such overpowering force that his nerves snapped.

It took many weeks to get this story from Kaspar Hauser. During this time, after contact with human beings, his facial expression, which had been dull and slack, changed markedly. He responded eagerly to the thrilling new world about him and learned quickly. The town of Nuremburg was all agog with his strange story.

Some six weeks later, the Mayor of Nuremburg issued a public statement regarding Kaspar Hauser: "His clear open glance, his high broad forehead, his perfect innocence of soul which knows no difference of sex, and his wonderful gentleness, his childlike confidence in all who approach him, his remarkable eagerness to learn, all these traits show conclusively that he was endowed by nature with the noblest capacities of mind and heart; and lead inevitably to suspicion that the inhuman treatment he received was founded upon a criminal suppression of his family rights, whereby he was robbed of parents, fortune, and high social position. It is our duty to use every means in our possession to bring to justice the miscreants who have committed this crime against the human soul in order that the truth may be brought to light and the victim of such cruel injustice may be restored to his lost rights."

The publication of this statement created great excitement throughout the length and breadth of Europe. People suggested all sorts of motives for the kidnapping and hiding of Kaspar Hauser. In an effort to learn more about the mysterious foundling, the most noted criminal lawyer of Germany, Anselm von Feurbach, was consulted. After visiting the boy, the eminent jurist publicly stated, that in his opinion, the story that Kaspar Hauser told was true.

However, von Feurbach pointed out that Kaspar Hauser was learning so rapidly and under such great nervous tension, that he would undoubtedly succumb to a serious brain fever unless he were removed to a calm atmosphere where his intense desire to learn might be properly governed and supervised. At his suggestion, the young man was removed from jail and placed under the tutelage of Professor Daumer, who was given the duty of restoring to this unfortunate boy the lost years of his life.

And then, into the newly peaceful existence of Kaspar Hauser crept the shadow that had lurked over his whole life. Came a new outrage to substantiate the story of the first villainy. Here in Nuremburg, while living in the tranquil bosom of the kindly Professor's home, Kaspar Hauser was foully attacked by a blackguard who sought to stab him. *The assailant escaped!* Fortunately, the would-be murderer had only succeeded in wounding Kaspar in the head.

Yet Fate had decreed that Kaspar Hauser was doomed! Four years later, the very same villain managed to successfully execute the deed he had once before attempted. Done to death with a mortal stab, Kaspar Hauser, as he lay dying, identified his murderer as the same man who had attempted to kill him four years earlier.

The story of Kaspar Hauser is one of the most incredible tales that this incredible world has ever known. Though it be hard to believe, Kaspar had reached the age of 17 years *without growing up!*

Shut up in a dungeon, living in eerie half-light, he sat crowded on a floor of earth all his long days and years, hearing no human voice, speaking to no one, seeing no one. His jailer provided him with bread and water, and on this simple and meager diet, he subsisted for the full length of his days.

When he was discovered, the soles of his feet were soft as a baby's. His face was expressionless and pale. He had not developed any muscles. He was ignorant of the uses of even the most common everyday objects. He was an infant—aged 17 years!

Why was Kaspar Hauser put in a dungeon? Who was his jailer? Why was he kept alive? Why was he released, a babe grown nigh to manhood? Who placed him in the village square at Nuremburg? Why was he given the letter to the Captain? Why was his innocent life taken?

These questions are shrouded in mystery—a mystery as deep and black as the identity of the man who murdered him.

SUGGESTED SOLUTIONS:

(1) Kaspar Hauser was the rightful heir to the throne of Bavaria. He was kidnapped when three or four years old. Conspirators had already succeeded in poisoning his older brother. The succession to the throne was thereby assured to the children of his father's morganatic wife. His half-brother actually ascended the throne. Why was Kaspar not killed, too, as his brother was? Because the conspirators knew that the rightful heir, kept alive, would be the most powerful way of exacting blackmail from the Royal Family. They could always threaten exposure. The Royal Family never felt safe until they had Kaspar Hauser murdered.

(2) Kaspar Hauser was the son of an impoverished nobleman who lived in a country outside of Germany, perhaps Hungary or the Balkans. He was kidnapped and held for ransom. His father could not raise the money to pay the ransom, but the kidnappers did not believe that a man with a castle could have no ready funds. In constant hope of prying money out of the bereaved parents, they kept the boy alive for years. A kindhearted jailer released Kaspar when he was 17. The kidnappers, frustrated after a crime prolonged for many years, were violent in their hate and vented their chagrin upon the innocent boy.

(3) Kaspar Hauser was the illegitimate son of a Hungarian Countess. To protect her social standing, she gave the child out to board. But the unconscionable foster parents, cruel beyond belief, in order to save clothes, schooling, food, etc., put the young boy in a dungeon and kept him there while they pocketed the large sums allotted to them for his safekeeping. They lied all the time to the Countess and so kept her tranquil. The boy was released by some kindhearted person who learned the secret. He was killed by the people to whom he had been entrusted when they felt that their terrible crime might be revealed.

THE MARY CELESTE

"She looks mighty queer," thought Captain Morehouse as he leaned over the deck of the *Dei Gratia* and in the distance spied a trim brigantine stumbling over the ocean. "For all the years I've been sailing, I've never seen a ship navigated like that. Looks as if she were drunk!"

A short while later, Captain Morehouse drew near the *Mary Celeste* and sent Deveau, his first mate, to board her.

It was December 3, 1873. *Since that day, no ship more strange has ever sailed the seas.*

When Deveau got aboard, his eyes popped! The captain's cabin was in good order. His clothing, furniture, charts, and books were all in their proper places. The mate's cabin, too, was spic and span. The seamen's quarters were just as one might expect to find them: oilskin boots, sou'westers, pipes, all in their proper places. The galley was stored with plenty of preserved meats, flour, etc. . . . Yes, everything was just so—except that there wasn't any captain, or any mate, or any steward, or any seamen—*or anyone at all!*

The *Dei Gratia* towed the *Mary Celeste* into Gibraltar where, according to the laws of the Admiralty, a hearing was held to determine the amount of salvage compensation the owners of the *Mary Celeste* would be obliged to pay. At the hearing held before Sir James Cochran, the following facts were brought to light:

The *Mary Celeste*, a ship of 228 tons, had left New York harbor on November 7th. She carried a cargo of raw alcohol. She was manned by a crew of seven men who took orders from Captain Briggs. The captain had taken along his wife, Sarah, and his daughter, Sophia, aged two.

The *Mary Celeste* was bound for Genoa, Italy.

When the derelict was found, the ship's slate-log was on the captain's table. According to its records, the *Mary Celeste* held its course for 17 days out of New York. On November 25th, she passed six miles north of Santa Maria Island in the Azores. Here the record breaks off.

From that day until she was sighted by the *Dei Gratia*, the ship had traveled 507 miles—*holding her own course!* Here is a mystery indeed! For when Deveau came aboard, the wheel was found to be loose!

On that fateful day of November 25th, the *Mary Celeste* was on a port tack, bound for Gibraltar. In the interval, the wind had shifted. When the ship was discovered, she was on a starboard tack. Someone had shifted her sails! It would thus seem that the ship was not deserted as of the day of the last log recording; but it must have been a very strange and portentous circumstance that would cause a captain to neglect his log entries.

When the *Mary Celeste* was brought into Gibraltar, she was in excellent condition, seaworthy in every respect; but the chronometer, the sextant, the ship's papers, *and her lone lifeboat* were gone! Deveau testified that when he got on the *Mary Celeste*, its hatch was open. One of the barrels of alcohol appeared to have been tampered with.

Yes, here's "a ship which haunts the seas, her tale a mystery that deepens with time." For there is no sound explanation of just what happened to Captain Briggs, his wife and child, and to the seven other souls that sailed along with him. The decks and the cabins revealed no evidence of violence. Apparently, the ship was not pirated because valuable

clothing and six months' provisions were found on the *Celeste*. According to the log and to the reports of other seamen, the weather had been fine. The vessel was seaworthy, without sign of a leak. There was even an unfinished letter lying in the mate's cabin.

What force could have lured these men from the ship? What hidden hand could have guided the *Mary Celeste* on its course? "Drowned and sea-locked is the key to the mystery" of the Ghost Ship of the Atlantic.

SUGGESTED SOLUTIONS:

(1) The crew got to the alcohol and became intoxicated. They seized the captain and his family and cast them overboard, thinking to run off with the ship. Then, in fear they would be brought to justice, they lowered the lifeboat and abandoned ship with the idea that they would allege that the *Mary Celeste* had been lost in a storm.

(2) The alcohol in the hold generated gases and a slight explosion occurred. The captain was afraid that the whole ship would blow up. He ordered the lifeboat to be lowered, and they all rowed off a short distance. When they attempted to get back to the boat, a wind came up which blew the ship out of their reach. Without sufficient provisions, they all perished and were lost at sea.

(3) A creature from the sea overcame the boat, or travellers on a UFO took them off to the unconfirmed regions of space.

THE PARKED-CAR MURDERS

The crimes known as the Parked-Car Murders might have come from the bottom drawer of a writer for the more volatile pulps. There were messages in code, a rape, a secret international society, a clandestine love affair, and a killer of cavalier courtesy.

But the Parked-Car Murders are notable in the annals of crime not because they were compounded of these melodramatic ingredients; the events are engaging because *the criminal himself* deliberately plied the police with a constant stream of clues—and the police ended up as puzzled as ever!

Here's a case unique in the history of criminology: the murderer sends the police letters; he provides them with the cartridge shells with which he has committed the crime; he tells them what he is after and who will be his next victims; he practically does everything but mail in his photograph and address. Yet, though at least two adults have seen and can identify the murderer, the Parked-Car Murders prove a dead end for detectives. The murderer has never been brought to bay.

It was one of those balmy June nights—Wednesday the 11th, 1930, to be exact—one of those soft June nights when swains pitch woo under the tent of a sedan. In a quiet lane in the Borough of Queens, New York City, Miss Catherine May was snuggled close in the arms of Joseph Mozynski. Mozynski worked as a grocery clerk in College Point. Bored with his job and his wife, Mozynski was doing his best to convince Miss May that she alone really understood him. While the sale was going on, a stranger appeared at the rear door of the car, whipped out a gun, and shot Mozynski dead.

The murderer ordered the terrified Miss May from the car and ravished her. And then, with unimaginable *sangfroid*, he gallantly escorted her to a trolley line and put her on a car to her home. Before she left, he gave her a note which read: "Joseph Mozynski 3X 3X-097." Though Miss May was sick with terror and shock, the fear of scandal shut her lips. She was mortally afraid her family would find out that she had been mixed up with a married man. But she was tracked by the police through the bloodstained coat she had left in the car. Brought to Headquarters, she described the murderer and gave full details of the crime.

Two days later, the City Editor of the *New York Evening Journal* received a very strange letter. In the envelope, the writer enclosed a communication in code. He entreated the editor of the *Journal* to print the code message in the newspaper *"to save lives."* The next day the *Journal* received a still longer letter penned by the same hand. The writer referred to the Mozynski killing and alleged that Miss May was innocent. The dead man, he averred, was a rascal unworthy of pity.

And then the writer identified himself as the murderer! He described himself as a member of a secret international society, and claimed he was trying to get certain documents in Mozynski's possession. He went on to inform the police that he was going to kill fourteen more of Mozynski's gang, or as many more as would be necessary to get the enumerated documents.

The murderer even described the murder weapon, identifying the fatal bullet by its caliber. The damning letter, written on stationery of the College Point Civil Service Bureau where Miss May had been working, was signed AV3X . . .The editor of the *Journal* turned the letter over to the baffled police.

A short time later, Noel Sowley, a radio repairman, was making love to Miss Betty Ring in a car parked near a desolate auto dump in Creedmore, Queens. Suddenly, out of the night, a shadow walked over to the car, and at the point of a gun, demanded that Sowley produce his registration. Sowley complied. The stranger then went to the rear of the car and inspected the license plate to make sure it agreed with Sowley's registration. Then, returning to the young couple, he cold-bloodedly fired two shots into Sowley's head. He then searched Sowley's pockets. Miss Ring escaped criminal attack by pleading with the assassin and showing him a religious medal. And then, as before, the murderer, always the gallant, escorted her to a nearby bus line.

The following morning, the police and the *Journal* each received letters. This time the murderer's audacity exceeded anything that had gone before: he sent the police the two empty cartridges from the gun that had killed Noel Sowley. The incredible man threatened to wreak vengeance on "thirteen more men and one woman if they do not make peace with us and stop bleeding us to death."

When the police examined Sowley, they found in his pocket a newspaper clipping telling about the murder of Mozynski. Over the clipping, in pencil scrawl, appeared the words: "Here's how!" On June 19th, the police received still another letter written by the same hand, promising a new murder soon. But for some reason the killer changed his mind. A few days later, he wrote the police that his work was done. He had been representing the Red Diamond Secret Society, he said, and his mission was now ended. The documents he had been seeking had now been returned. The dead men, the letter went on to say, had broken the rules of the Society, and so they had to die. This letter was signed: HP12WA . . . The killings stopped!

Now let's review the situation: Two capital crimes are committed in the largest city in the world. The deeds are done by a murderer who goes to the trouble to furnish the police again and again with all kinds of tangible clues. The laboratories of the New York Detective Bureau have at their disposal the paper, the handwriting, and the bullets mailed by the criminal himself. There are two eyewitnesses to the crimes. Yet with all this evidence at hand, and with all its scientific apparatus for crime detection, modern criminology cannot lay its hand upon the criminal.

The baffling questions remain unanswered. Who was this fantastic man? To what secret order, if any, did he belong? What was the real motive for these strange killings?

SUGGESTED SOLUTIONS:

(1) The murderer was just a plain crook and blackguard. He shot the men to rob them and to get to the girls without interference. Because of his religious background, he softened in the case of Miss Ring when she struck a chord to which his better nature responded. The letters were not written by him at all. They were the work of some nut who concocted a weird story. The cartridges just happened to be the same caliber as the bullets used by the criminal.

(2) Mozynski, Sowley, and the murderer were all members of some racketeering gang. Mozynski and Sowley had threatened either to squeal to the police, or sell out to some rival racket, or to start a competitive ring of their own. They were bumped off with the usual cold-bloodedness of gangsters. The secret society angle was just so much bunk to throw the police off the scent.

(3) Mozynski and Sowley were agents for the Russian Government. They had been sworn to secrecy by a branch of the OGPU. They were murdered because the OGPU believed they had betrayed their trust.

THE BORDEN MURDER CASE

Undoubtedly, the most baffling mystery in the annals of American crime is the Borden Murder Case.

Although two respectable burghers were hacked to death in a most brutal and violent manner in the heart of a busy American city, no one has been able to determine just how the crime was committed, who was the criminal, or what was the motive.

The crime was so sensational that the newspapers of the day fairly reeked with its bloody details; and though investigation piled on investigation, the circumstances of the case were so perplexing that every theory ended up a blind alley and left what has come down to us as the great Borden Murder Mystery.

On the morning of August 4, 1892, Mrs. Abbie Borden said good-bye to her houseguest and went upstairs to the second floor. Their guest, Mr. John V. Morse, who had been staying with them for a while, had gone to visit some friends for the day and was not expected back till dinner... This was the last time Mrs. Borden was ever seen alive.

The very comfortable middle-class frame house was tenanted by the Bordens' two daughters and a maid. On the fatal day, Emma Borden, the elder daughter, was visiting friends in Fairhaven, Massachusetts.

The younger girl, Lizzie, who was then 32, was deemed to be of a retiring nature. Although quite active in church and charitable affairs, she had few personal friends and was at home. The only other person in the house was Bridget Sullivan, the maid-of-all-work.

It appears that when Mrs. Borden went upstairs to her death at 9:30 that morning, Bridget and Lizzie were in the kitchen. About one-half hour later, Mr. Borden came home. He had left early that morning for business. Bridget admitted him by the front door which she *opened* for him and *locked* after him. In the Borden home, it was the practice to lock all doors. Mr. Borden came in and lay down on the sofa in the sitting room on the ground floor.

At 10:45, Lizzie and Bridget were doing housework in the dining room.

At 11:00, Bridget interrupted her work to go to her room on the third floor. At about this same time, Lizzie went to the stable.

At 11:15, Bridget heard a piercing shriek. Lizzie had discovered the body of her father lying slashed and hacked in a pool of blood which flooded the sofa where he had lain down to nap.

Bridget, with the futility born of hysteria, dashed across the street to call Dr. Bowen . . . The police were on the scene by 11:30.

Then suddenly someone thought of asking where Mrs. Borden was. When Bridget Sullivan, the maid, and Mrs. Churchill, a neighbor, went upstairs to break the terrible news to her, they found Abbie Borden hacked most hideously about the head and lying stark naked in a welter of her life's blood.

The police searched the house from cellar to garret. They found everything in its usual order. Nothing was disturbed nor was there anything extraordinary. Though several axes were found in the cellar, none of them carried any traces of blood.

Now, in reviewing this case, the first thing to be considered is *how* were the murders committed? If the murderer was some stranger, how did he get into the house? The doors were locked all morning. He would have had to climb in through some window unobserved by any passers-by, or jimmy one of the locks without being heard or seen. He would have had to commit the murders just at the fortuitous moment when Lizzie and Bridget were both occupied. Bridget went up to her room at about 11:00. Lizzie stated that she left the house a few minutes later to go the stable to get something. The murderer would have been obliged to have either hidden himself in the house for a long period of time and come out of his hiding place at just that minute, or he would have been obliged to have made his entrance and exit during this short interval.

The coroner reported that Mrs. Borden had been dead about two hours before Mr. Borden met his fate. Mrs. Borden was last seen at 9:00. Mr. Borden was found dead at 11:15. Did the murderer have the outrageous audacity to do away with the wife and then hide himself for a full two hours in a house occupied by other people—in a house made desperately dangerous by the presence of a corpse? Could any murderer have the *sangfroid* to slink about a house that any minute would be invaded by police? Where could he have hidden? How is it that he did not leave a trail of blood from Mrs. Borden's room on the second floor to the living room on the ground floor?

If the murderer was a stranger, how did he manage to elude detection leaving the house in broad daylight—a house situated near the main thoroughfare of Fall River, just one block away from constant traffic?

Where did the murderer hide the axe—the axe which was never found? Could he have made his getaway carrying it with him without its being noticed? Could he have carried it away without its dripping even a single drop of telltale blood?

Could an outsider have possibly contrived to commit a violent crime such as this—chopping away at the bodies of his victims no less than 40 times—without giving alarm to the other people in the house? Nothing was stolen from the house nor was the person of Mr. Borden despoiled of valuables. If the crimes were committed by some outsider, would not gossip, investigation, and time have turned up some motive?

No, none of these questions have been satisfactorily answered; and the combination of paradoxes they pose has led general opinion to conclude that no outsider could have committed the Borden double murder. And so, suspicion led directly to the two other people who were in the house at the time, Lizzie and Bridget.

But suspicion was immediately deflected from Bridget. No reason could be found why she would have perpetrated the deed; also the police and all other questioners were unanimous in their conclusion that

Bridget's personality and make-up were anything but homicidal.

When Lizzie Borden was brought to trial, there were equally cogent reasons for disbelieving that she committed the murders. All the evidence against Lizzie was based solely on implication. The real reason for suspecting Lizzie was that no one else was there to be suspected. There was no positive evidence of any sort adduced at, before or after the trial, that Lizzie Borden murdered her father and step-mother. No one ever came forward and sustained and proved a motive showing why she would have wished to commit the crimes.

Abbie Borden was Lizzie's stepmother, and it is true that Lizzie was anything but fond of her. It is true that on cross-examination there were flaws in the testimony of the accused. But, bereft of her parents and tense under accusation, could she not have been confused as to the details of that horrible morning?

It is true that a drug clerk stepped forward and said that Lizzie tried to purchase some hydrocyanic acid a few days previous. This same clerk stated that he had refused to sell her the deadly potion. Yet this testimony was uncorroborated and no one can say whether or not the witness was telling the truth or was merely seeking to bask in the sensationalism of a front-page story.

It is true that the police insisted that when they examined the stable, there were no footprints or marks in the dust which covered the floor, such as Lizzie might have left had she in fact been there at the time of the crime. Here too, there are veins of vagueness which streak the alleged facts.

If it is difficult to assume that the crime was committed by an outsider, it is equally difficult to assume that Lizzie was the criminal. In the first place, there were no bloodstains discovered anywhere on her clothing. Had she murdered her mother, she would have had to do the deed and change her clothes all within a few minutes so as not to be detected by Bridget. Then again, where did she hide the axe—the axe that was never found? How could she have avoided leaving a trail of blood some place, somewhere in the house? How could she, a fairly frail woman, have had the strength to deal 40 mighty blows with a heavy steel weapon? How could she have committed two murders in the space of such a short time without revealing her agitation to Bridget? She certainly would have had to move quickly and deftly from one crime to the other, changed her clothes and disposed of the fatal weapon and of her stained clothing, and contined to work with Bridget, all during this short fateful interval.

After Lizzie was acquitted, neither the police, the penny-a-liners, nor the sensation-mongers could conjure up any solid reason why Lizzie would have wanted to hack her own father to death; and reams of imaginative theory have left us nothing more than what is still one of the world's most baffling murder mysteries.

SUGGESTED SOLUTIONS:

(1) Lizzie and Bridget conspired to do away with Mr. and Mrs. Borden. Lizzie promised to give part of her inheritance to Bridget, who assisted her in the crimes.

(2) Lizzie hated her stepmother with a violent, demoniacal hatred. At first she hoped to poison her, but, having been frustrated, hacked her to death in a moment of hysterical anger. She wielded the weapon with a strength born of mortal madness. When she descended the staircase with the weapon, her father saw her and, having gone insane with fear, she struck him unconscious and hauled him over to the sofa where, in her frenzy, she hacked him to death.

(3) The murders were committed by a homicidal maniac who gained access to the house during the night. He hid in the cellar and got hold of an axe. On the morning of the murders, he sneaked up to Mrs. Borden's room, hid in the closet, and murdered her when she came up at 9:00. He then crept downstairs and murdered Mr. Borden. He wrapped the axe in his own clothing and somehow managed a getaway, thus carrying away with him all trace of the murder weapon.

321

COCOS ISLAND

If you are interested in going treasure hunting, the Costa Rican Government has everything all laid out for you. You make your application in due form and in due time you get a charter. You are then enfranchised to go a-digging on Cocos Island with the provision that if you find any loot, you must pay a rake-off to the Costa Rican Government—a sort of income tax, so to speak, on your activities as combination day laborer and gambler.

For though no one as yet has found as much as a dime on Cocos Island, the Costa Rican Government is justly convinced that the island is just reeking with riches and that somehow, some day, a lucky spade will uncover a handful of diamonds.

For three glittering treasures lie entombed on this fabulous tropical isle—a tiny mite of land barely six miles from coast to coast.

The Costa Rican Government hasn't exactly waited for you to come along and give it a percentage of the millions that lie interred. They themselves preempted the situation some years back by practically digging up the island with convict labor. But, as we said before, of the three glittering treasures that lie entombed on this tropical isle nary a nugget has ever been found.

Records worthy of belief state that a Captain Edward Davis buried a hoard of gold on Cocos Island in 1709. However, except for a record of the amount of the treasure, little that is authentic is known of this enterprise.

The second treasure is reputed to be 150 tons of gold, which the pirate Benito Bonito captured when he plundered a ship off Mexico. He sailed for Cocos Island where he is supposed to have left his loot.

But the big swag was cached on Cocos in 1821 and the facts here are fairly well verified. Here's the story:

When Simon Bolivar rode on Peru with the banners of South American freedom, the aristocracy of Lima trembled for its wealth. Every ship in the city's harbor was loaded with treasure to be sent to Spain. Into these holds there poured the accumulation of three centuries of plunder, stolen by the Conquistadores from the native Incas. In that fateful year of 1821, into the *Mary Dier*, at anchor in the harbor of Lima, went the wealth of Lima's gorgeous cathedral—rubies, emeralds, diamonds, pearls, gold—gold in coins, gold in bullion, gold in every cubic inch of a life-sized statue of the Virgin and Child.

It was too much for Captain Charles Thompson, the skipper of the *Mary Dier*. Instead of delivering his precious cargo to the Spanish authorities, he headed for Cocos Island. Here he buried the treasure and drew a careful map showing its exact location.

It is not clear what happened after this. Apparently the *Mary Dier* was lost, and although Thompson survived, with his map, it was not until 20 years later that the wily captain succeeded in lining up an expedition to drain the wealth of Cocos. But Fate swore that Thompson should put no hand on the treasure he had despoiled. Before his ship sailed, Thompson lay a-dying. As he gave up the ghost, he willed his chart to his partner, Keating, and gave him full directions.

Keating set sail with a Captain Boag. When they reached Cocos Island, the crew learned the object of the trip and mutinied for a share of the treasure. Boag and Keating slipped ashore at night and hid out in the jungle. Once again, it is not clear what happened after this, but ap-

arently Boag died under mysterious circumstances. Keating returned home without the treasure, but with his precious map.

When Keating died some years later, he bequeathed his map to a mariner named Fitzgerald. Fitzgerald died in 1894 and left the chart to Commodore Curzon Howe, R.N.

In 1929, a middle-aged Englishman by the name of Campbell happened to read about the Cocos Island treasures and was bitten by the Cocos idea. He approached the Howe family who generously provided him with Thompson's original chart. He then prevailed upon a yacht-owning friend by the name of Guinness to sail to Cocos Island to hunt for the three lost treasures.

And now comes the mystery! When Campbell reached Cocos, he followed the directions of the chart to the letter. The treasure was alleged to be buried in a cave near the headwaters of a creek that flows into Chatham Bay. The chart cites exact compass directions to the spot. The cave was described as guarded by a flat wall of stone with a door in it.

But though Campbell scrupulously obeyed every instruction, when he reached what should have been a vault stuffed with precious gems, *he found nothing at all!*

Where are those three haunting treasures of Cocos Island hidden? Why hasn't anyone been able to find even a glint of its fabulous wealth? It is well established that a German named Gessler spent a full 16 years raking the tantalizing turf in fruitless quest of Coco's buried millions.

How is it possible that such a tiny bit of land can so deftly conceal the three enormous treasures that pulse beneath its placid palms?

SUGGESTED SOLUTIONS:

(1) The landmarks on Cocos have changed with time. Tropical storms, roaring through Cocos with whirlwind force, have uprooted tree and hillside and have rendered the contours of the earth different from what they were 100 years ago. Perhaps the treasures have been buried beneath a small landslide. Perhaps the cave lies beneath a huge amount of sand and stone which totally destroyed all recorded signs of the treasure site.

(2) Thompson himself changed the map at one time or another to avoid sharing the treasure with his partner, Keating. Thompson was just the type of man to do this. He committed the directions to memory, thinking that after he had lured Keating to the island with his chart, he would kill him and make off with the whole loot. Before his death, he was too selfish to confess what he had done.

(3) One of the many treasure hunters who probed Cocos actually found the treasure and made off with it. The finder had some good reason to conceal his success. Perhaps it was just a fear of being hijacked. In any case, the finder despoiled Cocos and destroyed the identifying signs of the treasure site.

SHOW ME

Show me the first President's dentures—
    and I'll show you the George Washington Bridge.

Show me a mixture of fennel and tabasco—
    and I'll show you a fiasco.

Show me where Stalin is buried—
    and I'll show you a Communist plot.

Show me a young lad's bed—
    and I'll show you a boy-cott.

Show me a wily halfback with a knack for sketching—
    and I'll show you an artful dodger.

Show me a workman who dismantles a roof—
    and I'll show you an eavesdropper.

Show me a squirrel's nest—
    and I'll show you the Nutcracker Suite.

Show me Santa's helpers—
    and I'll show you subordinate clauses.

Show me a famous surgeon—
    and I'll show you a big operator.

Show me a cat that just ate a lemon—
    and I'll show you a sourpuss.

Show me a cross between a fox and a mink—
    and I'll show you a fink.

Show me a one-word commercial—
    and I'll show you an adverb.

Show me a famous composer's liquor cabinet—
    and I'll show you Beethoven's Fifth.

Show me Eve's perfume—
    and I'll show you an Adam balm.

Show me a man convicted of two crimes—
    and I'll show you a compound sentence.

Show me a singing beetle—
    and I'll show you a humbug.

Show me two dozen satified rabbits—
    and I'll show you 24 carats.

Show me a cross between a cannon and a bell—
    and I'll show you a boomerang.

Show me a pharaoh who ate crackers in bed—
    and I'll show you a crummy mummy.

Show me a stolen message—
    and I'll show you a missing link.

Show me a healed shaving scar—
    and I'll show you an old nick.

Show me a frog on a lily pad—
    and I'll show you a toadstool.

Show me a man who's afraid of Christmas—
    and I'll show you a Noel Coward.

Show me a burned-out post office—
    and I'll show you a case of blackmail.

Show me a baker who ran out of custard—
    and I'll show you a humble pie.

Show me a cross between a mule and a fox—
    and I'll show you a fool.

Show me a monarch who takes tea at four—
    and I'll show you the King's English.

Show me a fowl with an artificial leg—
    and I'll show you a lame duck amendment.

Show me a low-cut dress—
    and I'll show you a cold shoulder.

Show me a gang of beggars—
    and I'll show you a ragtime band.

Show me a flagellant witch—
    and I'll show you goulash.

Show me an arrogant insect—
    and I'll show you a cocky roach.

Show me a manhole at a street intersection—
    and I'll show you a connoisseur.

Show me Mohammed Ali's safe-deposit box—
    and I'll show you Cassius' Cash Can.

Show me a football player with keen intuition—
    and I'll show you a hunchback.

Show me a violin maker—
    and I'll show you a man with guts.

Show me a magician's notebook—
    and I'll show you a spellbinder.

Show me a girl who shuns the miniskirt—
    and I'll show you hemlock.

Show me a toddler caught playing in the mud—
    and I'll show you grime and punishment.

Show me a tall beachcomber—
    and I'll show you a longshoreman.

Show me a golden wedding anniversary—
    and I'll show you high fidelity.

Show me a filibustering senator—
    and I'll show you a figure of speech.

Show me a diminutive barber—
    and I'll show you a shortcut.

HOW TO SOLVE WORD SEARCH PUZZLES

You are given a large jumble of letters and a list of words; the object is to find these words in the block of letters. The words may appear left-to-right, right-to-left, down a column, up a column, or even diagonally.

In each case, the first word on the list is located for you.

Happy hunting!

A GIRL'S BEST FRIEND

Waiting to be cut out of the rough below are the 35 terms, all of which would set Lorelei Lee's eyes agleam. Think of each one as a carat on a stick and get to it.

If you can circle all in 15 minutes, you win a gold star; 10 minutes or less means you sparkle like diamonds.

Solution on page 486

AFRICA	FACETS	MELEE
BALLAS	FIRE	NASSAK
BLACK	GEMS	ORLOFF
BORT	HARD SUBSTANCE	PALE BLUE
BRILLIANCE	INDIA	POLISHED
CARAT	INDUSTRIAL USES	PRECIOUS STONE
CLEAVAGE	JEWELRY	PURE CARBON
COLOR	JONKER	REFRACTION
CRYSTALS	KOH-I-NOR	SANCY
CULLINAN	MINERAL	SETTING
CUTTING	MINING	SOUTH AMERICA
EXCELSIOR		YELLOW

```
I S R E K N O J T N A N I L L U C M
N O S A N C Y U R N A S S A K E I P
D U R P E P A I O O S Q B C D N F O U
U T A S A A O L B C D M H R E I L L
S H Q A T L N O B R A C E R U P M I
T A A C B E E I L A I R A G F S T S
R M P I B G N B M T L L U J I A T H
I E U R N D R O L N S L L V R U K E
A R N F I O O F T U W J A A E C D D
L I O A Y R L K M S E O C S N V S G
U C I O S C O Z E W S U L A I C T R
S A T R E L C I E G T U B L U H E O
E A C L T D A L S T A E O I E O C N
S V A O T E R T I L L V E I I Y A I
W V R F I Y R N S Q E J A P C O F H
W V F F N T G S F Y X C E E L E M O
J I E H G N I N I M R G X K L N R K
H A R D S U B S T A N C E E L C M P
```

HOME GROWN

Farming is a large part of our American economy. It is hard, but rewarding, work.

Plow through our list and see what kind of farmer you'd make by finding all the things that a farmer uses and the daily chores he must do.

You can form words vertically, horizontally, or diagonally. The words you are looking for are listed below.

Solution on page 486

BARN	CROPS	FENCE
CHICKENS	CULTIVATE	FERTILIZE
COMBINE	EGGS	FIELD
COWS	FARMER	GRAIN

HARROW	PLANT	SHED
HARVEST	PLOW	SILO
HOED	RAKE	SOWER
LIVESTOCK	RANCH	TILLAGE
MILKED	REAP	THRESHER
ORCHARD	ROOSTER	TRACTOR
PASTURE	SEEDS	TROUGH
PITCHFORK	SHARECROP	WEEDS

```
R E M R A F G A C H A R V E S T
W T H S B P E O I Q C R T K N D
U O F V A N M R R M J A E A L D
K C L F W B X A T Y V B L Z E E
D R F P I O K G M I H P N K I H
C E O N A E L X T K L P L J O S
F J E F D B L L Y P T I U R S Q
H E G I H Z U D A S M G Z V G E
G T K C U C M S H Q N P R E G W
U V N L S S T R A C T O R A E L
O A W P X U R I Y A O Z L O I B
R F O E R S H D P S M L C V I N
T R G E E W Q O T L I O E J N R
C G S E R O R E R T K S B P C E
T H D F U C R E V C T W I D X H
R S A F E I Z D E O H J Y L A S
E P N R E S M T C L U A K R O E
W R A O S N E K C I H C R V D R
O H Q E B P C A G E Y O X D W H
S H C (N R A B) E Z F W E E D S T
```

HOMETOWN

This puzzle will take solvers back to their old hometowns where things were a bit more friendly and familiar. See how many words below you can find. It's impossible to get lost if your memory's good.

You can form words vertically, horizontally, or diagonally. The words you are looking for are in the accompanying box.

Solution on page 487

BANKS	DOGS	GREEN
BOARDS	DUMP	HEALTH
BUSES	ENGINEERS	HISTORIC DISTRICT
CENTER	FIRE	LABORER
CHURCH	FLAG	LAKES
CLERK	FOLKS	LIBRARY
DINER	GARBAGE	MAIN STREET

MASTER PLAN   PROBATE   STORES

MAYOR   RESIDENTS   TAXES

NEIGHBORS   SCHOOLS   TOWN MEETINGS

PARKS   SENIOR CITIZENS   VOTERS

PERMITS   SEWERS   WELFARE

POLICE   ZONING

```
C P S U T S R E E N I G N E S D
O C V V Z P A R K S W E X A K C
J H P V O S T I M R E P Q W L E
S U P L E T A B O R P A F E O N
N R I M E N E I G H B O R S F T
I C E N U E O R M P X K G R Y E
E H U W V D W J S A E Q S Z B R
H Y O M E I F D M R Y D S B G E
T C I R T S I D C I R O T S I H
O R N L C E R Q S A D R R B E E
W E L F A R E I O A O Y G A L F
N R F B E G A B R A G F L S Z S
M O Z U L P T B N N S T H Y C E
E B T K H R E N I D H S A C H R
E A M S A T J N O K G Z I X J O
T L A K E S O Y R A R B I L E T
I F S N E Z I T I C R O I N E S
N I M A S T E R P L A N L K W F
G E X B U S E S C H O O L S D K
S M R Q L G T E E R T S N I A M
```

BREAKING POINT!

We've all heard the expression "brittle as glass." Here are some words for you to find that are related to the words in that statement.

You can form words vertically, horizontally, or diagonally. The words you are looking for in the accompanying box are listed below.

Solution on page 487

BREAK	FLIMSY	GOSSAMER
BRITTLE	FOIBLE	IMPAIR
BUST	FRACTURE	INFIRM
CRACK	FRAGILE	PERISH
CRISP	FRAGMENT	SHATTER
CRUMBLE	FRAIL	SHIVER
CRUMPLE	FRANGIBLE	SNAP
DAINTY	FRIABLE	SPLINTER
DEFECT	GAUZY	SPLIT
DELICATE	GIMCRACK	TENUOUS
EGGSHELL	GLASS	UNSOUND
FEEBLE		WEAK

A G J K D B I H E F R A G I L E
R I A F B N E R D T I L P S G C
R E K S F R U L T B A M U G V N
W C T I Q T I O C S P B S D O W
L A R T C J Z T S I Y H R X E G
F M K A A T M H T N E S F E K D
O R R Q C H G P N L U T X C A V
R F A E S K S A L O E W A I U K
R C F I A L J B U G Z R N Y H F
E E K D L P A N S Z C T E M R I
D L M T E Q E P S M Y W O A F N
E S B A R T U Z I P V E G E X G
L A U E S C A G Y R L M D E H I
P J S B E S I C E B E I L N M F
M E T K Q F O V I N L B N P O Y
U C R M O S I G T L M P A T S P
R T A I U H N R V U E I S M E W
C E B D S A H Z R Y R D I I X R
F L P G R H O C I N U L M J R L
E Q B F R I A B L E F S K R T C

COLORFUL CAPER

Painting is a beautiful art and a fun hobby for people of all ages. You'll win a blue ribbon if you can find all our artistic words.

You can form words vertically, horizontally, or diagonally. The words you are looking for are in the accompanying box.

Solution on page 488

Solution on page 488

ACADEMIC	HIGHLIGHT	PALETTE
BROKEN (color)	IMPASTO	PANEL (picture)
BRUSHES	KNIFE	PIGMENT
CANVAS	LANDSCAPE	PORTRAIT
CARTOON	LIMNER	SCUMBLE
EASEL	MAHLSTICK	SKETCH
ENCAUSTIC	MEDIUM	STILL LIFE
FRESCO	MINIATURE	TEMPERA
GENRE	MURAL	TEXTURE
GLAZE	NIMBUS	VALUE
GOUACHE	OILS	VARNISH
GROUND		WATER (colors)

338

```
I K R A P G B J E A C L A R U M
L M H E G O I F C H E L E M E D
E Q P L T P R A T P C U O D N B
S B A A R A D T A W S A I A V R
A Z N X S E W C R D Y U U Z N U
E G E C M T S H E A M N E O F S
F N L I P D O L I A I J O K G H
I Q C R N O B S N M R T M R L E
L N U A J M T D B U R E O V F S
L C L G U B M U E A F U P I H A
L M U C K S S A C L N O N M P E
I V S T K W T S H D R K O Q E T
T Y V E X N A I B L V C I R C T
S G T A E Z G F C E S A U D J E
C C N M R H Q L H E K T L M R L
H A G E L N I P R O A N I U L A
R I N I K M I F O I L S T C E P
P A G V N O B S N S C X T D K U
K H Y E A X R I H W E H L V E I
T Z R M G S M B J T F E R N E G
```

FISHY

There are many different kinds of fish to be found in our oceans, sounds, and lakes. Many of them make for very good eating. Here's our own ocean of fish for you to reel in.

You can form words vertically, horizontally, or diagonally. The words you are looking for are in the accompanying box.

Solution on page 488

Solution on page 488

ALBACORE	KINGFISH	SHARK
BARRACUDA	MARLIN	SNOOK
BASS	PERCH	STURGEON
BLUE (fish)	PICKEREL	SWORDFISH
BULLHEAD	PIKE	TARPON
CARP	POLLACK	TROUT
CATFISH	RUNNER	TUNA
CHAR	SAIL (fish)	WAHOO
CRAPPIE	SALMON	WALLEYE
DOLPHIN	SAUGER	WEAKFISH
FLOUNDER	SAWFISH	WHITEFISH
GRAYLING		YELLOWTAIL

```
N S G K J C A S E H S I F W A S
H I K B I M R R T V N C X O D B
Y T L F U N O A T U O R T W U E
F L N R Z C G R P G R A Q L B P
I L F I A H E F H P D G L I L C
O J O B H M K S I G I H E R N M
B P L U N P I Q N S E E Y O X S
C A Z V N F L I L A H U P T N Y
A W R A D D L O D I B R O I E C
T M I R G Y E P D F A D L L K E
F J O K A H I R O T P S L Q S E
I W L R X C W N H J F O A U R K
S B G Y K R U S E G W V C H R T
H Z A E U D I D K T E A K A I S
R C R N Y F L R A M A P H Q N A
X E N V E E E I Y E K S N O R L
L E H T W G L O U U F T O S O M
R A I C U B Z L C O I K D P H O
M H N A J N B B A S S Q I R E N
W L S K P R A C F W H C R E P G
```

341

POPPIES

There's a posy of 52 words pertaining to poppies in this one. As you find them, circle them in the maze and cross them off the list.

If you find them all in 20 minutes, you're a first-class poppy-picker; 12 minutes or less means everything's coming up poppies for you!

Solution on page 489

ANNUAL	GARDEN	PETALS
ARGEMONE	GENUS	PERENNIAL
APERTURE	GREECE	PINNATE
BASE	HERB	PONDS
BEAUTY	HUGE	PORES
BUDS	HYGROSCOPIC	SEEDS
COLORS	ICELAND	SEPALS
COMMON	IRELAND	SNOW POPPY
CORN POPPY	JUICE	SOWN
CRIMSON	LEAVES	SPECIES
DISK	LOBED	STAMENS
ENGLAND	MACLEAYA	STIGMAS
EUROPE	MILKY	SUNNY
FALL	MOISTURE	WALES
FIELDS	NAME	WELSH POPPY
FLAT	OPIUM	WHITE
FLOWERS	ORIENTAL	WIND
	PAPEVAR	

343

MYTHICAL MONSTERS

These creatures have, by tradition, been depicted as monsters of one sort or another. The only threat they pose to you, however, is in locating the 32 of them in this puzzle.

If you can find them in 20 minutes, that's monstrous; 12 minutes or less makes you a prodigy of nature yourself!

Solution on page 489

ANTLION		DRAGON
BASILISK	CHIMERA	DRAKE
CENTAUR	COCKATRICE	GRIFFIN
CERBERUS	CYCLOPS	GORGON

HIPPOCAMPUS   MERMAN   SALAMANDER

HIPPOGRIFF   OGRE   SEA HORSE

HIRCOCERVUS   OGRESS   SIMURGH

HYDRA   PHOENIX   SPHINX

KRAKEN   PYTHON   WIVERN

MANTICORA   ROC   XIPHOPAGUS

MERMAID   SAGITARRY   ZOMBI

```
E  C  I  R  T  A  K  C  O  C  Y  L  D  K  N
B  H  Y  D  R  A  G  O  N  S  S  E  R  G  O
H  I  R  C  O  C  E  R  V  U  S  A  A  R  I
C  P  Y  E  L  N  X  W  A  B  K  H  K  I  L
R  P  H  N  S  O  I  F  F  E  G  I  E  F  T
E  O  R  O  S  V  P  Y  N  R  N  P  X  F  N
D  C  C  G  E  B  P  S  U  E  O  P  Y  I  A
N  A  E  R  M  N  H  M  S  A  H  O  R  N  R
A  M  N  O  E  Y  I  R  C  R  T  G  A  M  O
M  P  T  G  R  S  O  X  S  E  Y  R  T  E  C
A  U  A  B  M  H  T  P  N  M  P  I  T  R  I
L  S  U  G  A  P  O  H  P  I  X  F  I  M  T
A  Y  R  E  N  H  X  C  I  H  H  F  G  A  N
S  K  S  I  L  I  S  A  B  C  I  P  A  I  A
I  B  M  O  Z  C  E  R  B  E  R  U  S  D  M
```

345

GET THE ANGLE

There's a special angle to this word search puzzle. Each of the 25 words listed has been fiendishly buried in the square so as to form an angle. The first word, *baseball*, has been circled to get you started off on the right foot. As you see, you will have to go in two directions to circle each word. This means you may be going both vertically and horizontally (as in the example), or vertically and diagonally, or horizontally and diagonally. In addition, of course, you may have to go forwards or backwards. Keep a sharp lookout for the angles.

If you succeed in finding 12 words; that's all right; 15 is pretty acute; and 20 shows you have an eagle eye!

Solution on page 490

BASEBALL	FOUNTAIN	MONTREAL
CHEMICAL	GIGANTIC	OBITUARY
COALESCE	HOLIDAYS	ORGANIZE
COCKTAIL	JUDICIAL	SHOELACE
CURRENCY	JUMP ROPE	STUDIOUS
ELEPHANT	KENTUCKY	SWIMMING
EXPORTED	LUNCHEON	TROMBONE
FANCIFUL	MARGINAL	VIRGINIA
	MONOPOLY	

```
N T I C E X P O R T E X L L A B O M
A B M M I W S I T E E Y A J K E A T
G A I L U Y U O A D E A R L U S C I Y
I S N N A C R A L A E R T A A A E Y
G E G D P E N O M M O N N B U B C K
E T I N E R Z T A O Y O O O O T A C
M P L U C Y N I Y C M S M Z G I L U
E C O C L A I D N A G R O I R B E T
H A H R H U O E D U T S N N A O N G
C O L P P H R O Y L O P O O H E A I
C U E F M L R S L V I R G S K N V G
F V L O U F U L P N A A I K T A I L
I P E U J O C P M O R T C N H A R A
C H E M I U A E B E P O A I N I G I
N C I D C N R T O H C N U L L M P C
A O W U A T A I N M A R G A J U D I
F A S T L N A F E E L E N S H O A L
A L E S C E O M A R G I C O L E E C
```

347

DRAGONS

All of the words listed below have something to do with dragons. Since the pen is mightier than the sword, all you have to do to slay them is to circle the words in the puzzle. The words are hidden backwards, forwards, up and down, and diagonally. Check them off the list as you find them.

If you find them all in 20 minutes, that's fine; 10 minutes is fantastic!

Solution on page 490

APOPHIS	FIRE-BREATHING	SCALY
BARBED TAIL	HERALDRY	SERPENT
BAT WINGED	HUGE	SHARP-SIGHTED
BEOWULF	KING ARTHUR	SIGURD
CHINA	LANCELOT	SMOKE
EVIL	LIZARD	SNAKE
FABLES	MONSTERS	ST. GEORGE
FANTASY	MYTHOLOGY	ST. MICHAEL
FICTION	PENDRAGON	WAR EMBLEMS

```
S H A R P S I G H T E D L Y X S N H
H E Y D C M W O X E K O M S N I V E
O G L K L T O O A O P B A L C G U R
W U B B E I S N O I T C I F C U W A
C H A F A N T A S Y O Z E B E R T L
O E I G G F A M N T A N A I I D Y D
B E K A N S D V L R E T C D S W G R
R A K P M I F C D P W R E G A I O Y
U S R N E E H H I I G G S R L L L I
H H G B L N M T N A R U E C A L O L
T A S A E I D G A O R M T N A T H E
R F H I V D E R E E B I C S N L T A
A B L N I D T G A L R E J E F K Y H
G C S U L K T A E G L B P J Z Q M C
N Q D A W S O M I O O R E K R M R I
I P O N H O S M T L E N U R L O U M
K M E I E N E J O S G S A N I A C T
(A P O P H I S) B Y S A N I H C F M S
```

349

FEATHERED FRIENDS

You are no birdbrain if you can find the 25 birds hidden in this puzzle. In fact, you're probably an experienced bird watcher, used to looking up, down, sideways, across, and even backwards, which is what you have to do to find every last hidden bird. Circle them and check them off the list as you find them.

If you find them all in 10 minutes, you're as sharp as an eagle; if you do it in 7 minutes or less you're really soaring.

Solution on page 491

Solution on page 491

BLUEJAY	EAGLE	ORIOLE
CANARY	FALCON	OWL
CHICKEN	FINCH	PIGEON
COOT	GOOSE	QUAIL
CROW	GULL	ROBIN
CUCKOO	HAWK	TERN
DOVE	HERON	TURKEY
DUCK	LARK	WREN
	LOON	

```
N  I  C  A  N  A  R  Y  L  C
I  E  O  W  L  H  E  T  O  R
B  B  R  O  A  K  N  O  O  O
O  H  L  W  R  O  T  N  N  W
R  C  K  U  C  I  E  G  P  K
G  N  T  L  E  K  O  U  I  C
O  I  A  A  C  J  E  L  G  U
O  F  G  I  K  R  A  L  E  D
S  L  H  E  R  O  N  Y  O  T
E  C  U  C  K  O  O  V  N  I
Q  U  A  I  L  T  E  R  N  S
```

NO BED OF ROSES

The flowers in this garden are scattered like none you've ever seen before. All 19 blossoms listed below are to be found among the letters if you can dig them out. Words read horizontally, vertically, forwards, backwards, and diagonally.

When you are finished, the uncircled letters which remain will spell a secret message. To get you started, the first word has been circled in the puzzle.

If you find them all in 10 minutes, pin a flower on your lapel; if you do it in 7 minutes or less you get a bouquet.

Solution on page 491

BUTTERCUP	DOGWOOD	PETUNIA
CAMELLIA	HIBISCUS	POPPY
CARNATION	IRIS	ROSE
CROCUS	LILAC	SUNFLOWER
DAFFODIL	LILY	TULIPS
DAISY	MUM	VIOLET
	PANSY	

```
C A R N A T I O N M A B
G A D O G W O O D U R U
H I B I S C U S D M C T
L R E N P E T U N I A T
V I O L E T O F P F M E
D S L S U N F L O W E R
A L P A N S Y I P O L C
I C R O C U S L P W L U
S T U L I P S Y Y E I P
Y D A F F O D I L R A S
```

VEGETABLE STEW

Hidden in this puzzle are the names of 27 different vegetables. To dig them out you will have to search vertically, horizontally, diagonally, and backwards. Circle and list them on a separate piece of paper as you find them. You're all on your own, with no list from us to guide you.

Don't get into a stew if you don't discover them all: 18 is peachy; 22 makes you a vegetarian supreme; and 25 earns you a chef's chapeau.

Solution on page 492

```
B R U S S E L S S P R O U T S
E R H C A N I P S A A T R U A
E N O N I O N S N R G A T R U
T E A C H E T R A S A M A N E
S E H H C O S S E L B O S I R
T K L S R O S U B E A T R P K
K O I R A Q L M G Y T F E E R
A H M A N U E I O A U S P A A
Y C A M N G Q U C O R N P S U
R I C E A S T S E A R A E E T
E T A B O Y Y N I M O H P L L
L R B P O T A T O E S P S S E
E A R K O T N A L P G G E U A
C A U L I F L O W E R  R O S M
```

352

TRIVIA

Norbert Wiener, the M.I.T. mathematician, was a child prodigy. He read when he was three and a half. He was a college freshman at age 12. He got his B.A. degree at 14, and his Ph.D. when he was 18.

Many doctors are of the opinion that the most common cause of constipation is the use of laxatives. Thousands of Americans use one nostrum after another, so that today, there are over 25,000 preparations sold in drugstores throughout the United States to cure constipation. Physicians estimate that only 50% of these preparations are safe, and that no less than 20% are unsafe, while 30% require further study.

George Washington wore dentures. The reason he always looked so stern in his portraits was because of the danger that if he relaxed, his teeth would fall out.

Joe Bilskosky was out of a job and out of luck. A dedicated fisherman, he couldn't find enough worms for bait. So Joe went into the business of farming worms. Today, he does a fine business on his three-acre worm farm at Alhambra, California. Now his income is okay, and his fishing is okay.

There are 773,692 words in the King James Bible (excluding the Apocrypha), and 3,566,480 letters. For proof, any Doubting Thomas may simply count the letters for himself.

Speaking of Doubting Thomas, he was not the noted 13th century theologian philosopher, Saint Thomas Aquinas, but a much earlier Saint Thomas. He was, in fact, one of the original Twelve Disciples. He earned his epithet because he at first doubted the Resurrection of Jesus.

The Emperor of Japan, Hirohito, traces his lifeline back 2,653 years. Custom dictates that he cannot be touched by any other man. So when the Emperor falls ill and calls in a doctor, the physician must use silk gloves to take the Emperor's pulse.

■

Mononucleosis is now called "The Kissing Disease." The disease became known in 1920, but it took about 30 years more to find out how it was transmitted. In 1950, the chief physician at West Point Military Academy discovered that after the weekends, the incidence of the disease greatly increased among cadets. He concluded that the disease was primarily spread through prolonged kissing.

Damage to the ear can occur upon being subjected to a noise of 85 decibels. Planes roaring off aircraft carriers produce 105 decibels. Sound of 140 decibels can be lethal and can actually kill.

■

Two-thirds of the human race does not get enough to eat. Starvation is rampant throughout India. In the city of Calcutta, over 600,000 people live in the streets. The sidewalks are their homes, and most have just about enough food to keep body and soul together. There are also large sections of Africa where the population is badly undernourished.

■

Lizards are not deaf. In fact, they hear very well. They just don't pay much attention to sounds.

■

Pravda, the Russian newspaper which has the world's largest circulation, is read daily by over 9,000,000 persons.

■

The tern summers in the Arctic, and winters in the Antarctic. This amazing bird flies over 22,000 miles on each round trip.

■

There are about three trillion cigarettes produced each year, roughly about 1,500 for each person on the face of the earth.

Headache, suffered by one out of every 12 Americans, is a symptom—not a disease. Doctors estimate that 90% of all headaches are psychogenic.

■

The most common disease in the United States today is high blood pressure. One out of every ten adults suffers from this ailment, which is the cause of 60,000 deaths every year.

■

Recent studies show that a moderate use of wine may reduce the incidence of arteriosclerosis by as much as 50%.

■

Acute alcoholism kills more people every year than the use of any other drug.

The largest shark in the world, the whale shark, is not dangerous to man. It lives only on minute plankton, a type of seaweed.

■

The average person in the United States eats a ton of food a year. This figure includes liquids.

■

Half the people in the United States wear eyeglasses.

■

Everyone is born farsighted. Most individuals develop 20-20 vision at about the age of five. However, this keenness of vision soon fades and becomes the exception.

■

The body contains some 600 muscles, as compared to only 200 or so bones.

The only beneficial effects of sun-bathing are psychological. Dermatologists insist that exposure to the sun is harmful to the skin.

■

In the United States, the land of the free and home of the brave, somebody commits suicide every 20 minutes. Every day, at least 1,000 people throughout the world take their own lives.

■

The Union Army lost more men through disease during the Civil War than it did through battle.

■

It is estimated that over half of all Americans over 65 have false teeth.

■

How many drops are there in a pint? Well, there are two cups in a pint, and eight ounces in a cup. An ounce contains two tablespoons, and a tablespoon is equal to three teaspoons. Finally, a teaspoon contains 120 drops. So one pint contains 11,520 drops.

■

As one grows older, one should bathe less. Doctors estimate that more skin disease is caused from excessive cleanliness than lack of cleanliness.

Although leprosy is an ancient disease and the general opinion is that the United States is more or less free of it, there were 200 residents in New York City last year who suffered from leprosy.

In the 19th century, students at Cambridge University, England, were not permitted to keep a dog in their rooms. Lord Byron, the famed poet, complied with the rule—he kept a bear instead.

■

One of the greatest killers in the world is schistosomiasis, a disease which afflicts some 250,000,000 people throughout Asia. This scourge is spread by a parasite harbored by snails in infested waters.

■

For those who cannot swim the English Channnewl, there are more ingenious modes of crossing that body of water that will attract even greater publicity. For example, one man rowed across the Channel in a coffin, while another man walked across it shod in wooden boots in the shape of flatboats. Still another enterprising individual traversed the Channel in an inflated rubber suit sporting a sail the size of a bath towel.

The symbol "&," known as the ampersand, and used for the word *and* in hundreds of different languages, was invented by Marius Tiro of Roman in 63 B.C. Actually, the ampersand was one of 5,000 such signs invented by Tiro in the world's first shorthand system, but only the ampersand has survived.

■

Try this for your next birthday party: who can consume the most ice cream in the least amount of time? For the record, you'll be competing with the champ, one Bennett D'Angelo, who, on August 7, 1977, won the contest at Dean Dairy, Waltham, Massachusetts by eating three pounds, six ounces of ice cream in 90 seconds!

A Harvard medical professor has declared that the greatest single curse in medicine is the curse of unnecessary operations.

QUADRUPLE WHAMMY

In Dogpatch, a whammy is a hex or a bad-luck sign. Here are four whammies in one. From top to bottom in 20 minutes is good enough; 17 minutes is above par; and 14 minutes or less is first-class.

Solution on page 492

RATTAN RACEWAY

You won't race through this misnamed puzzler. A journey of 20 minutes is no big deal; 16 minutes, rather good; and 13 minutes or less, simply astounding.

Solution on page 493

DEAD ENDS

This traditionally-styled labyrinth may look easy at first, but watch out! You'll find most of your paths will go nowhere fast before you can discover the through route. A solution in 12 minutes is fair; 10 minutes is good; and 7 minutes or less is the living end.

Solution on page 493

RIPPLES

Ripples upon ripples make a wave, and waves can be very upsetting. But don't get upset, you'll find the way to the bottom—sooner or later. Twelve minutes is fair for this one; 10 minutes is good; and a solution in 7 minutes or less makes quite a splash.

Solution on page 494

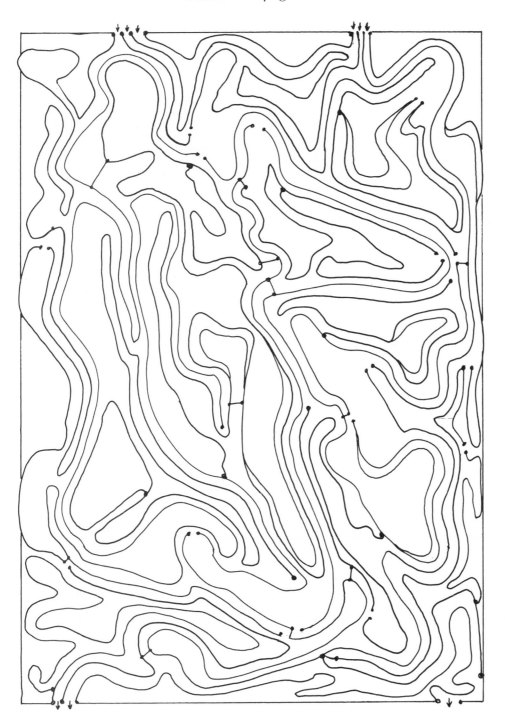

CURVES AND BARS

Start anywhere at the top and find a way to the asterisk. If you can discover the route in 20 minutes, that's nothing to write home about; 15 minutes is fine; and a solution in 10 minutes or less is worthy of note.

Solution on page 494

TULIP TREE

This tulip tree can boast only one lonely tulip, but plenty of mind-bending twists and turns. From top to bottom in 15 minutes is fair; 10 minutes is good; and 7 minutes or less is topnotch.

Solution on page 495

GOTHAM

A crowded town, Gotham! And no expressway that will take you right through. Going from house to house—just like a traveling salesman—is the only way to make your fortune. Don't let the closed doors get you down!

Start from any of the "In" spots and get to either of the two "Out" locations. Do not cross any lines on the way.

Solution on page 495

SNUG AS A BUG IN A RUG

This old flying carpet holds many a disappointment for that bug looking for a snug way through.

Start at the top in between any of the fringes, and if you persevere, you'll come out through any of the exits at the bottom of the rug.

Solution on page 496

HOUSING DEVELOPMENT

Pity the census taker who must wend his way through the streets of this community.

Start at either of the ingresses marked "In" at the top of the puzzle. Work your way through the maze without crossing any lines, and come out at where it says "Out." If you get this job done in 10 minutes, you're doing real fine.

Solution on page 496

KING TUT'S TOMB

Old King Tut's treasure is certainly guarded by an elaborate maze. Make your way in through any of the three entrances and try to find your way out through the one opening to the Treasure Room.

In your peregrinations and travels, you must not cross any of the black lines.

Solution on page 497

ENTRANCES

TREASURE ROOM

RUTHLESS RHYMES

The ditties below might well have been penned by the Marquis de Sade. Whoever is responsible for these shameless sentiments should find coal in his stocking next Christmas.

Little Willie, mean as hell,
Pushed his sister in the well,
Mother said, while drawing water,
"My it's hard to raise a daughter!"

Baby Bobby in the tub;
Ma forgot to place the plug;
Oh what sorrow! Oh what pain!
There goes Bobby down the drain!

Father, I regret to state,
Cut his daughters up for bait,
We miss them when it's time to dine,
But father's fish taste simply fine.

Willie saw some dynamite,
Couldn't understand it quite;
Curiosity never pays;
It rained Willie seven days.

Willie poisoned father's tea;
Father died in agony.
Mother came, and looked quite vexed:
"Really, Will," she said, "what next?"

Pity now poor Mary Ames,
Blinded by her brother James;
Hot nails in her eyes he poked—
I ne'er saw Mary more provoked.

Little Will, with father's gun,
Punctured grandma, just for fun.
Mother frowned, upon the lad:
'Twas the last shell father had.

Little Willie lit a rocket
Which his Pa had in his pocket.
Next day he told Uncle Dan,
"Papa is a traveling man."

Willie, hitting at a ball,
Lined one down the schoolhouse hall
As through the door came Dr. Hill —
Several teeth are missing still.

Willie as the fire burned low,
Gave it a terrific blow.
Grandpa's beard got in the draft;
Dear me, how the firemen laughed!

I had written to Aunt Maud,
Who was on a trip abroad,
Then I heard she'd died of cramp—
Just too late to save the stamp.

Little Willie hung his sister;
She was dead before we missed her.
Willie's always up to tricks!
Ain't he cute? He's only six!

Father heard his children scream,
So he threw them in the stream;
Saying, as he drowned the third,
"Children should be seen, *not* heard!"

When Grandmamma fell off the boat
And couldn't swim, and wouldn't
   float,
Willie just stood by and smiled.
I very nearly slapped the child.

Sam had spirits naught could check,
   And today, at breakfast, he
Broke his baby sister's neck,
   So he shan't have jam for tea!

Willie in the cauldron fell;
See the grief on mother's brow!
Mother loved her darling well;
   Darling's quite hard-boiled by now.

O'er the rugged mountain's brow
   Clara threw the twins she nursed,
And remarked, "I wonder now
   Which will reach the bottom first?"

Auntie, did you feel no pain
   Falling from that apple tree?
Would you do it, please, again?
   'Cos my friend here didn't see.

HOW'S BUSINESS

Here are some likely responses to the above question by various trades-
men.

SAID THE SAILOR:	*Knot bad.*
SAID THE COFFEE SALESMAN:	*It's a grind.*
SAID THE DRUMMER:	*It's hard to beat.*
SAID THE ASTRONOMER:	*Things are looking up.*
SAID THE DRESSMAKER:	*Just sew-sew.*
SAID THE DEMOLITION WORKER:	*Smashing!*
SAID THE STREETCLEANER:	*Things are picking up.*
SAID THE PIANIST:	*Right on key.*
SAID THE BULLFIGHTER:	*In the red.*
SAID THE GUNSMITH:	*Booming!*
SAID THE BOTANIST:	*Everything's coming up roses.*
SAID THE BARTENDER:	*It's been pretty tight lately.*
SAID THE LOCKSMITH:	*Everything's opening up.*
SAID THE SEWER WORKER:	*I've been getting to the bottom of things.*
SAID THE MUSICIAN:	*Nothing of note has been happening.*
SAID THE COUNTERMAN:	*Pretty crummy.*
SAID THE COUNTERFEITER:	*We're forging on.*
SAID THE ICEMAN:	*Not so hot.*
SAID THE GRAVEDIGGER:	*Monumental!*
SAID THE TEACHER:	*My work is classy.*
SAID THE ZOO KEEPER:	*It's beastly!*
SAID THE FLOOR WAXER:	*Going smoothly.*
SAID THE DAIRY FARMER:	*Cheesy, in a whey.*
SAID THE TOBACCONIST:	*It's a drag.*
SAID THE BAKER:	*I've been making a lot of dough lately.*
SAID THE PILOT:	*Pretty much up in the air.*
SAID THE PHOTOGRAPHER:	*Everything is clicking—and developing well.*
SAID THE DEEP-SEA DIVER:	*I'm about to go under.*

ACES AND KINGS

This is a simple and pleasant card trick to amuse an audience with. You can challenge your friends to figure out how it is done—it is not too hard to figure this out—and give a prize to the one who gets the solution fastest.

All you need are eight cards from a regular deck—all four Aces and all four Kings. Remove these cards from the deck and show them to your audience.

Announce that each Ace wants its mate beside it, and that you can arrange it easily. Turn your back and arrange the cards in the following order:

Holding the eight cards in a deck (with the King of Spades on top and the King of Diamonds on the bottom), proceed in this manner:

Put the top card on the bottom of the deck. Turn the next card face up on the table and at the same time announce, "Ace of Clubs."

Put the next card on the bottom of the deck. Turn the next card face up on the table next to the Ace and at the same time announce, "King of Clubs."

Put the top card on the bottom of the deck. Turn the next card face up on the table and at the same time announce, "Ace of Diamonds."

Put the top card on the bottom of the deck. Turn the next card face up on the table and announce, "King of Diamonds."

Put the top card on the bottom. Turn the next card up and announce, "Ace of Hearts." Put the top card on the bottom. Turn the next card face up and announce, "King of Hearts."

You now have two cards left. Put the top card under the other. Turn the other card face up and announce, "Ace of Spades." The last card is the King of Spades.

See how long it takes your friends to figure out the correct arrangement for the cards.

373

THE THREE-PILE CARD TRICK

Here's a card trick that's puzzling, fascinating, and automatic. It works every time.

You need 21 cards—any 21 cards from a regular deck will do. You lay them face up in three columns, seven cards in each column, as shown in Diagram 1.

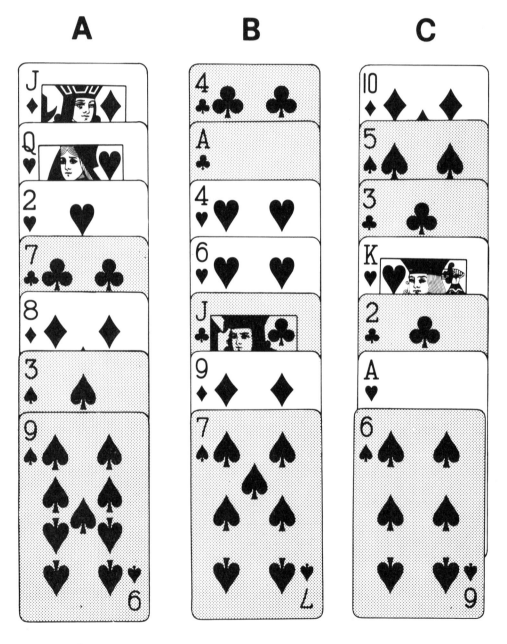

DIAGRAM 1

Announce to your audience that they are to choose one of these cards and you will guess which one it is. Ask someone to step forward. Tell him you will turn your back and he is to choose a card and show it to the audience and then replace it. When you turn around again, ask him which row the chosen card is in.

Now, pick up the cards very carefully. Be sure to pick up the row that contains the chosen card second, so that those seven cards are in the middle when you put your deck together again.

Now lay the cards out on the table again, but this time instead of going down to form your three rows, go across, as in Diagram 2.

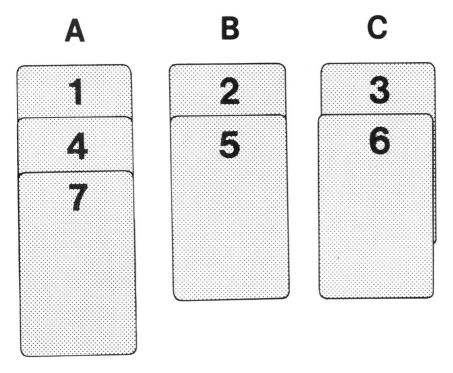

DIAGRAM 2

Ask the selector to tell you which row the chosen card is in now. Once again, pick up the cards, being careful to put the row that contains the chosen card in the middle.

Repeat the same procedure once more. It doesn't matter whether you go across or down to form your three rows of seven cards each.

Then, when you lay the cards out for the fourth and last time, count to yourself as you place each card on the table, because the 11th card will be the chosen card. Make a mental note of it.

When the cards are arranged in the three rows, pretend to be doing some heavy thinking. Then, when inspiration comes, point to the chosen card. Your audience will be dumbfounded.

SPELLBINDING CARDS

This is a delightful card trick that never fails to entertain and impress an audience. You can show it over and over again and your audience will beg you for the secret. You can be generous and reveal it, or you can challenge them to figure it out themselves. It may take some time, but it can be done.

You need 13 cards for this game, all the cards in one suit, from the Ace through the King. You may show them to your audience. Now announce that the magic of these cards is that they can spell. They will arrange themselves in the proper order when their names are spelled.

Turn your back and arrange your 13 cards in the following order:

You are ready to do your spellbinding act now. Hold the 13 cards in a deck in your hand (with the three on top and the five on the bottom). Put the top card on the bottom of the deck as you recite, "A." Put the next card on the bottom of the deck as you recite, "C." Put the next card on the bottom of the deck as you recite, "E." Turn the fourth card face up and put it on the table as you announce, "Ace!"

Put the next card on the bottom of the deck as you recite, "T." Put the next card on the bottom of the deck as you recite, "W." Put the next card on the bottom of the deck as you recite, "O." Turn the next card face up on the table next to the Ace and announce, "Two!"

Put the next card on the bottom of the deck as you recite, "T." Put the next card on the bottom of the deck as you recite, "H." Put the next card on the bottom of the deck as you recite, "R". Put the next card on the bottom of the deck as you recite, "E." Put the next card on the bottom of the deck as you announce, "E." Turn the next card face up on the table next to the Two and announce, "Three!"

Continue in this fashion, spelling out the names of the cards in sequence until you reach King. You will surely be applauded at the end.

See if anyone in the group can figure out in what sequence the cards must be arranged to do this trick successfully. If they are too frustrated or impatient to take the time, perhaps you will be willing to share your secret.

SIXES

Here is a trick that should really be performed only once, or at most, twice.

You tell your friend that you can, by thought transference or concentration, influence his choice. You are going to put two stacks of cards on the table, and you're going to tell him in advance which one he will choose.

So you write on a piece of paper: "You will pick the six pile." Then you request that he pick up either one of the two piles. No matter which one he picks up, you say, "See, I told you, you would pick up the six pile."

In one pile, you have put four cards, each one of which is a six. If he picks up that pile, you face up all the cards in that stack and you say, "See, I told you, you would pick up the six pile. See, they are all sixes."

In the other pile, you place six cards; it doesn't matter what they are. If he picks up this pile, you count the cards, one by one, and you triumphantly declare, "See, I knew you would pick up the six pile. Here are six cards: one, two, three, four, five, six."

You then hastily put the two piles together, shuffle them, and reintroduce the cards into the deck. In this way, your trick will not become known.

If you do the trick again, do not do it with six cards; do it with seven. But in this instance, you have one pile of four cards which contains four sevens, and another pile which contains exactly seven cards.

THE EIGHT-CARD TRICK

This is a great parlor trick that is bound to astound and confuse everyone. To perform it, you need a confederate who has a good memory and strong concentration.

You take eight cards out of a deck, as follows: *Ace, two, three, four, five, six, seven, eight.* You tell the company that your confederate is gifted with clairvoyance. The confederate is sent out of the room.

While he is gone, the audience picks one of the eight cards, shows it to you and to everybody, and places the chosen card inside an envelope. The envelope is sealed.

Your confederate is called back into the room, and handed the envelope. He feels the envelope, stares at it, performs all kinds of hocus pocus, and then calmly announces that the envelope contains a six.

The envelope is opened, and sure enough, it does contain a six.

Presumably, this was a lucky guess. But when your man repeats this performance again and again, it's no longer a lucky guess. *It's an astounding trick!* How does he do it?

Well, here's where his memory and concentration come into play.

You pick out eight people whom you know, and your confederate knows. You write down their names on a piece of paper, and make a copy of this piece of paper. You give each of these eight people a number. For example:

John is No. 1

Bill is No. 2

Grace is No. 3

Mack is No. 4

Susan is No. 5

Pete is No. 6

Georgina is No. 7

Steve is No. 8

Your confederate has this list, and you have it. It's up to you both to memorize the names and the numbers before you begin your trick.

Then what happens is this: If your company happens to pick a three out of the eight cards, you put the three in an envelope and give it to Grace, who is No. 3. When Grace gives your confederate the envelope, he immediately knows it contains a three.

If the card happens to be a six, you would give the envelope to Pete who is No. 6. So when Pete turns over the envelope to your confederate, he immediately knows it is a six.

IDENTIFYING A COIN

Take eight coins that are given to you by your audience—it doesn't matter what coins they are—and put these eight coins into a hat. You declare that after the audience picks one coin out of the eight, and after they toss the chosen coin into the hat with the seven other coins, you will unfailingly select the one coin that has been picked.

This seems miraculous. How do you do it?

Well, you say that to make sure there's no mistake about the *identity* of the coin, you want the coin passed around to everybody present so that everybody has a chance to look at the coin, and examine the date, and can certify what particular coin was chosen. Take your time about this. Insist everybody look carefully at both sides of the coin.

Then tell the last person to toss the coin back into the hat. You put your fingers into the hat, and without looking at any of the coins, you miraculously draw out the chosen coin. Everybody is astounded. How is this done?

When you feel around in the hat, you pick out the *warmest* coin. The warmest coin will be the coin that has passed through many hands. The heat of many fingers will have been transmitted to the metal so that you will be able to detect the right coin without faltering and without error.

You can do this trick two or three times without fear of having your magical power discovered.

GRAVITY MAGIC

Here is an excellent trick to show at a dinner table. It is bound to create conversation and excitement, and you'll be the life of the party. Amaze your friends with this gravity-defying stunt.

Take a look at this setup. A fork and spoon are interlocked. See Picture 1.

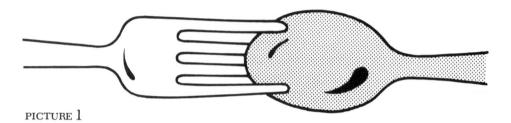

PICTURE 1

A toothpick has been inserted in one of the spaces between the tines of the fork, and this toothpick has been placed on the rim of a glass in such a way that the fork and spoon are suspended in air. See Picture 2. This balance is not too difficult to achieve.

PICTURE 2

But here comes the funny part. You light both ends of the toothpick with a match, and both ends start to burn. See Picture 3.

Ask your fascinated audience what they think will happen.

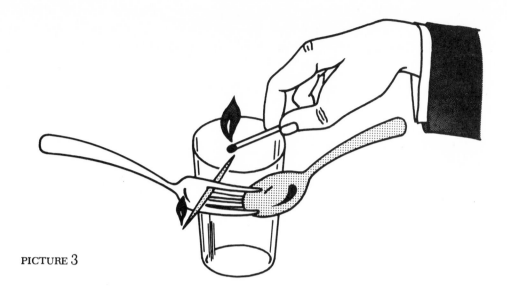

PICTURE 3

Some of your audience will believe that the fork and spoon will fall *towards* the glass, and others will say that the fork and spoon will fall *away* from the glass.

But the fact is that the fork and spoon do not fall at all! They stay suspended on the side of the glass. A dramatic conclusion, indeed! How does this work?

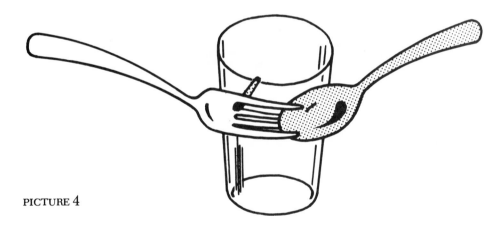

PICTURE 4

The answer is that when you hung the fork and the spoon on the glass, you achieved a perfect balance. In this balanced setup, the center of gravity did not lie beyond the rim of the glass. It is an optical illusion that fools everybody. The fact is that the weight of the spoon and the fork is so distributed that these pieces are really supported *by that part of the toothpick that goes up to the rim of the glass*. The part of the toothpick beyond the rim of the glass supports nothing.

381

BLOWING
THROUGH A WALL

To perform this trick, you need a bottle and a candle. You light the candle, and then you place a large bottle—a large soda bottle will do—directly in front of the candle.

The strange fact is you can blow out the candle by blowing against the bottle. How does this strange phenomenon come about?

The answer is, when you blow against the bottle, the air currents rejoin each other on the other side of the bottle and form an air stream strong enough to extinguish the flame.

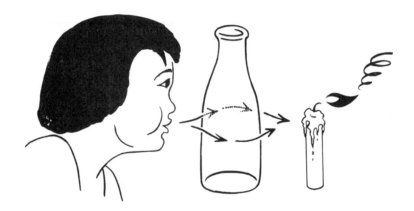

THE MYSTERY EYE

You ask a friend to put a coin on the table face up. Then you tell him to cover the coin with a piece of plain white paper.

You now announce you can tell the date on the coin without lifting the paper. How do you do it?

Well, it's easy. You simply run a pencil back and forth over the surface of the paper, and then lo and behold, the date of the coin will be revealed.

UP-seed-DAISY

To demonstrate your powers over the birds in the air, over the fish in the sea, and over grape seeds—drop a grape seed into a glass of ginger ale . . . It will sink to the bottom of the glass.

Command the seed to rise to the top! . . . Watch mouths gape as it does.

Command it to sink once more! *It will!*

As awe and wonderment encompass you, you may explain that the action of the seed is caused by the carbon dioxide bubbles in the ginger ale. The seed dropped in the liquid will sink of its own weight to the bottom of the glass. There it will be surrounded by gas bubbles. As soon as sufficient bubbles cluster around the seed, they will lift it to the top of the glass as they rise.

As the gas escapes at the top of the liquid, the seed will again respond to gravity and descend to the bottom.

You must be careful to time your commands with the formation of the bubbles, contriving not to let on that you are carefully watching the glass.

TRICKY TRIANGLES

Next time you're sitting around waiting to be served the next course, instead of getting bored and irritable and ruining your mood, or consuming all the bread and rolls in sight and ruining your appetite (not to speak of your waistline), try whiling away the time pleasurably and profitably with this challenging puzzle. All you need are eight matches or toothpicks.

Now, what we're asking you to do is to place these eight sticks down on the table so that they form four triangles and two squares. That should keep you busy until the Yankee Pot Roast comes along—it might even keep you busy until the cows come home.

OK—we wouldn't want to add to your frustration. The diagram below shows how it's done. Now you can challenge your next dinner partner to do this, and you can sit by smugly as your friend struggles with furrowed brow.

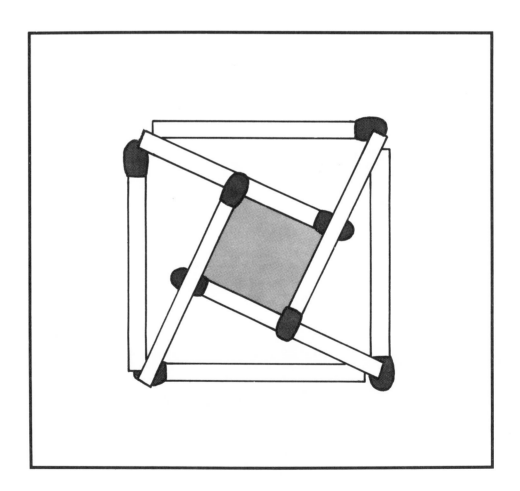

ODDS OR EVENS

Announce that you will challenge anyone to pick a number from one to 30 and you will be able to tell whether the number is odd or even; and, what's more, you will be able to tell exactly what the chosen number is!

It's really quite simple, and infallible! Here's how you do it:

After the number has been chosen, you show the chart below, which, of course, you have copied out of this book onto a piece of paper or cardboard. Ask someone to tell you which columns the chosen number appears in. Then, in your head, you add up the numbers that appear at the very top of the columns designated. First announce whether the number is odd or even. Of course you will be right. Then pretend to concentrate very hard and announce exactly what the number is. Of course, you will be right again.

For example, suppose the number chosen is 15. Your audience will tell you that their number appears in columns A, B, D, and E. You add up the numbers at the top of these columns—2, 1, 8, 4, and you get 15. First you announce the number is odd. Then after thinking for a few seconds you announce the number is 15.

A	B	C	D	E
2	1	16	8	4
27	5	24	9	23
14	17	28	30	20
15	11	17	10	7
18	9	30	27	12
10	21	21	14	15
22	3	18	26	6
7	29	22	28	30
19	19	23	13	5
26	7	19	11	21
23	15	26	29	14
6	5	27	24	22
3	23	25	12	13
11	13	20	15	29
30	27	29	25	28

HOW SELF-ASSERTIVE ARE YOU?

Are you an introvert, extrovert, or ambivert? The introvert is concerned with inner emotions, reflection, and subjective thinking. The introvert tends to shy away from people and find self-assertion uncomfortable. The extrovert is a doer, interested in action, other people, the outside world. The extrovert tends to have a clear idea of goals and enjoys manipulating people and events to achieve goals. The ambivert shares about equally the traits of the other two. All of us possess both introvert and extrovert qualities, but most of us lean a bit more in one direction than the other.

To find out where you fall, choose the one of the three solutions given for each question or situation which comes nearest to the way you believe you would react.

Answers on page 497

1. A traffic cop stops you and says, "This is the main street of Moose-town, not a race track." He starts writing you a ticket. Would you:
   a. Swallow hard and keep still.
   b. Say you were only going thirty.
   c. Smile and say, "Now, Buddy, let's talk this over."

2. If you were asked to give a talk at a meeting, would you:
   a. Feign illness and not go.
   b. Prepare a speech, but read it.
   c. Be glad for the chance to say what you think.

3. A friend invites you to a picnic, saying she will meet you there and introduce you to the gang. Upon arriving, you find that she has not yet shown up. Would you:
   a. Stand apart from the group waiting until she arrives.
   b. Introduce yourself to the group and tell them you are waiting for your friend.
   c. Join the group in what they are doing and then lead them in a game you enjoy.

4. You are walking down a street in which a truck loaded with barbed wire is parked. You see a woman dash across the street, catching her skirt on trailing strands of wire, which tear away a large strip of material. Would you:
   a. Blush and walk by pretending not to have noticed.
   b. Yell at the truck driver.
   c. Go to the woman and offer to help her.

5. You are planning a new venture, but have not yet completed the arrangements. A good friend asks you what is new. Would you:
    a. Say nothing and keep your plans to yourself.
    b. Tell him you are contemplating a change, but have not completed your plans.
    c. Tell him you're glad he asked and tell him the whole story.

6. Your boss has just given you an order which you happen to know will be disadvantageous to him. Would you:
    a. Take the order obediently and say nothing.
    b. Acknowledge his authority, but tell him if you follow this order, it will have bad results.
    c. Explain to him in detail why it is not a good thing to do.

7. Someone else has just been given the promotion you had hoped would fall to you. Would you:
    a. Feel personally slighted, and wonder what they don't like about you.
    b. Admit you're disappointed, and analyze why the other person deserved it more than you did.
    c. Have a talk with the boss about it.

8. You are entertaining a visitor who tends to monopolize the conversation. Would you:
    a. Let him talk on and enjoy himself.
    b. Try to draw others into the conversation.
    c. Interrupt him and direct the conversation yourself.

WOULD YOU MAKE A GOOD COUNTERSPY?

Every boy and girl has sent a secret message at some time or other. Some amateur cryptographers have grown up to become important members of their country's secret service. It takes a special kind of skill to figure out secret codes. You have to be able to see relationships and manipulate abstract symbols.

This quiz will tell you whether you should apply for a job with the CIA.

Answers on page 497

1. Can you decipher this famous statement made by Benjamin Franklin?

   ETSAWSEKAMETSAH

2. Decode this quotation from the Book of Jeremiah (I:19.)
   GSVB HSZOO MLG KIVEZRO ZTZRMHG GSVV

3. Decode this simple numerical cipher and you will have a well-known American slogan.
   9-14 7-15-4 23-5 20-18-21-19-20

4. The following pattern is a variation of a coding system developed by the ancient Greeks.

	1	2	3	4	5
1	A	F	L	Q	V
2	B	G	M	R	W
3	C	H	N	S	X
4	D	IJ	O	T	Y
5	E	K	P	U	Z

   Use the above code to decipher this famous quotation attributed to General Patton.

   53-54-44 43-33-13-45 11-23-51-24-42-31-11-33-34 43-33
   22-54-11-24-41 44-43-33-42-22-32-44

5. If the hymn *ROCK OF AGES* is written:

TQEM QH CIGU

What is the title of this famous song?

COGTKEC VJG DGCWVKHWN

6. This code and its variations has been called by different names, such as the pigpen cipher because of its shape, or the Rosicrucian or Masonic cipher because of its use by those organizations. It also played a role in the Civil War.

A	D	G
B ·	E ·	H ·
C ··	F ··	I ··
J	M	P
K ·	N ·	Q ·
L ··	O ··	R ··
S	V	Y
T ·	W ·	Z ·
U ··	X ··	

Using the above code, decipher this statement:

OBSERVATION TEST

There may not be anything wrong with your vision, but how observant are you? Here are 15 questions to test how carefully and accurately you perceive things. Write your answers in the blanks or circle the correct answer. Allow yourself 10 minutes to complete the test.

Give yourself 10 points for each correct answer. A score of 70 is passing fair; 100 shows you have a keen eye; and 120 or better makes you a veritable Sherlock Holmes.

Answers on page 498

1. How many surfaces does this

    object have? _____

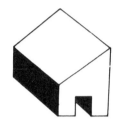

2. Which two figures are identical?

   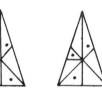

    (a)   *(b)*   *(c)*   *(d)*   *(e)*   *(f)*

3. Which two figures are identical?

    (a)   *(b)*   *(c)*   *(d)*   *(e)*   *(f)*

4. Which two figures are identical?

    (a)   *(b)*   *(c)*   *(d)*   *(e)*   *(f)*

5. Which two figures are identical?

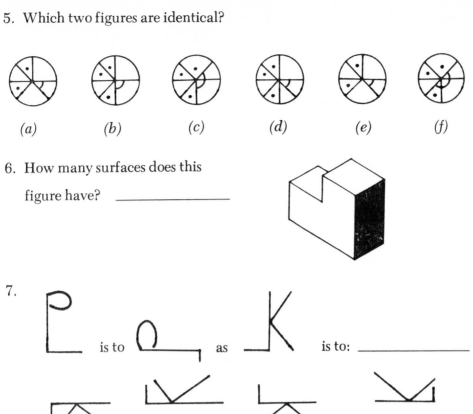

(a)   (b)   (c)   (d)   (e)   (f)

6. How many surfaces does this
   figure have? _____

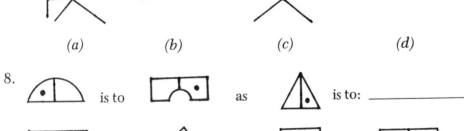

7.

   is to ___ as ___ is to: _____

(a)   (b)   (c)   (d)

8.

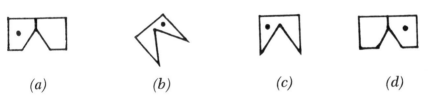

   is to ___ as ___ is to: _____

(a)   (b)   (c)   (d)

9.

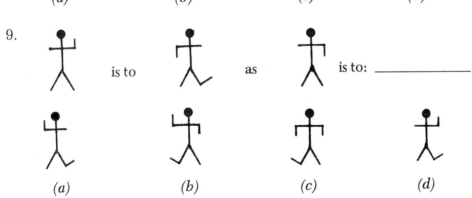

   is to ___ as ___ is to: _____

(a)   (b)   (c)   (d)

10.

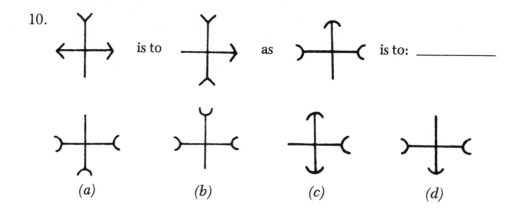

(a)   (b)   (c)   (d)

Questions 11-15 are based on the following figures:

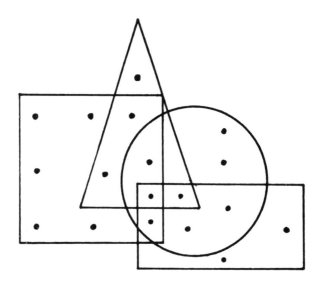

11. How many dots are in the triangle, but not in the circle?

    _____

12. How many dots are common to the rectangle, triangle, and circle?

    _____

13. How many dots are common to the circle, square, and triangle?

    _____

14. How many dots are common to the rectangle and square?

    _____

15. How many dots are common to all four figures: the square, the rec-
    tangle, the circle, and the triangle? _____

ARE YOU VAIN?

There is a considerable difference between having self-confidence or self-respect and being conceited or boastful. Actually, the person who knows his own abilities and is proud of his accomplishments finds it unnecessary to brag. It is the person who is unsure of himself who finds it necessary to make himself feel better by boasting. "To be a man's own fool is bad enough, but the vain man is everybody's." (William Penn).

This test will help you assess whether you truly value yourself, or hide your uncertainty behind your vanity.

Answers on page 498

1. What is your reaction to the picture at right?
    a.   It is a symbol of vanity.
    b.   It depicts friendship.
    c.   It has no special meaning to me.

                                                    YES   NO

2. Do you spend more money on your clothing and your appearance in general than you can afford? ____ ____

3. When eating out with friends, do you tend to overtip the waiter? ____ ____

4. Do you often surreptitiously try to glance at yourself in mirrors and at your reflection in the store windows you pass? ____ ____

5. Do you dress appropriately for your age? ____ ____

6. Are you personally hurt when someone criticizes your work? ____ ____

7. Are you willing to admit when you are wrong? ____ ____

8. Do you go out of your way to mention important people you know? Are you a name-dropper? ____ ____

9. Do you feel that if you want anything done right you have to do it yourself? ____ ____

10. Do you sometimes exaggerate or tell "little white lies" in order to impress others? ____ ____

393

HOW SOCIABLE ARE YOU?

When they are in a social group, some people chatter on and on like an endless tape recording. They seem to feel free to sermonize or interrupt. Relating to others involves listening as much as talking. According to research studies, and contrary to popular belief, women do not talk more than men. It is a matter of personal makeup, not a sex characteristic.

This test will help you determine how popular with, or sensitive to, others you are.

Answers on page 498

1. Write your initials on one of the blocks in this diagram.

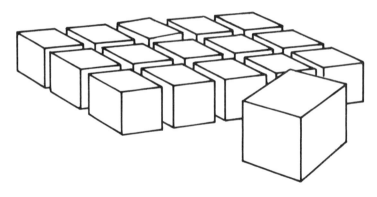

2. Which of these punctuation marks do you find most pleasing: A, B, C, or D?

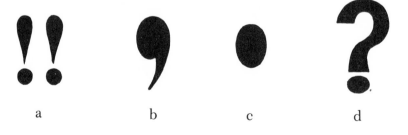

a   b   c   d

3. If you were to select a painting for your living room, which would you prefer?
   a. A Parisian café scene.
   b. A seascape.

4. How would you prefer to spend an evening?
   a. Reading a book.
   b. At a party.
   c. At the theater or a movie.

	YES	NO
5. Do you spend much time thinking about your possessions?	——	——
6. Are your memories more concerned with happy moments than with unpleasantness?	——	——
7. Do you find looking at the sea, desert, mountains, and fields soothing?	——	——
8. Are you economically comfortable with no money worries for the future?	——	——
9. Do you wish you had more relatives and more opportunity to visit with them?	——	——
10. Would you like to attend more parties?	——	——
11. Do you have a secret goal you are working to achieve?	——	——
12. Do you watch your health carefully?	——	——
13. Do you know something about the care of a garden or potted plants?	——	——
14. Do you have good aim (shooting, bowling, hammering, etc.)?	——	——

HOW DETERMINED
ARE YOU?

There is an old, old saying, "Where there's a will, there's a way." Educators, psychologists, and employers often note that those who fail are not necessarily less intelligent or less gifted than those who succeed, but are easily discouraged, possess little perseverance, and tend to view life with the anticipation of failure rather than success. This test evaluates your own attitudes.

Answers on page 499

1. You are planning to wallpaper your den. Which of the patterns shown below would you most likely select?

A   B   C

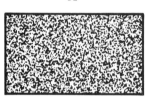 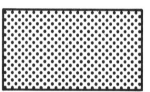 

Put yourself in the following situations and check the reaction nearest your own.

2. You have an important appointment. Your car has a flat a mile from the place of the meeting. You would:
   a. Wait for help.
   b. Walk to the meeting.
   c. Change the tire.

3. You will be starting a new job shortly. You would:
   a. Take courses and/or read materials which may help you.
   b. Try to learn on the job.
   c. Keep your eyes and ears open for another position in case your new one doesn't work out.

4. Your romance is on the rocks. You would:
   a. Look for someone else who appreciates you.
   b. Hope that time will heal the wound.
   c. Seek help from a counselor, psychologist, or psychiatrist.

5. Do you every say or think, "I'm going to get that done if it kills me?"
   a. Never.
   b. Occasionally.
   c. Quite often.

396

6. You have just started a new hobby, such as learning to play golf, make ceramics, build a boat, or hook a rug. You are moving slowly in this endeavor and encountering many problems. You would:
   a. Abandon the whole idea.
   b. Finish off what you started any old way.
   c. Try to learn from your errors and improve your skill.

7. When you are trying to solve a problem, does the solution come to you in your sleep?
   a. Occasionally.
   b. Never.
   c. Quite often.

8. When you undertake something, either on the job or as a hobby, do you have a distinct reason for what you are doing?
   a. Never.
   b. Sometimes.
   c. Almost always.

9. You have a heavy cold. You would:
   a. Continue with your normal activity, doing the best you can.
   b. Go home to get a rest.
   c. Follow your doctor's orders to the letter.

10. You want something that costs a considerable amount of money, such as a trip to Europe, new furniture, or a car. You would:
    a. Put the desire out of your mind as an impossible dream.
    b. Figure out a budget and save consistently for your objective.
    c. Pray for an unexpected windfall.

HOW WELL-LIKED ARE YOU?

With a very few neurotic exceptions, everyone wants to be accepted and liked. Indeed, some pay a high price to appear popular—from trying to buy friendships with money to the misuse of sex to gain attention. The real test of how well-liked you are is the everyday behavior of those around you, and whether you have friends you can depend on during an emergency.

The following test will help you assess whether or not people really like you.

Answers on page 499

1. Which of the three drawings marked A, B, & C comes closest to describing how you feel with people around?

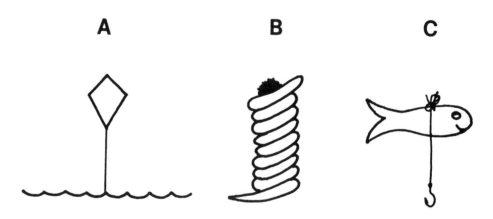

A   **B**   **C**

2. When you are confined to your home or the hospital because of illness:
   a. Many people call or send cards.
   b. You sit it out pretty much alone.
   c. Several of your best friends check in.

3. When you run into a group of friends:
   a. All of them say hello.
   b. Most keep on with their conversations.
   c. Some greet you more enthusiastically than others.

4. People you know:
   a. Seem to go out of their way to be nice to you.
   b. Are preoccupied with their own lives.
   c. See you when it is convenient.

5. If you are short of money:
   a. Many people are there to help you.
   b. Everyone else is broke, too.
   c. There is always someone you can depend on.

6. When you have a birthday:
   a. Many people remember the date.
   b. You have to hint for cards and presents.
   c. Some old standbys never forget.

7. People come to you for advice or help:
   a. Often.
   b. Seldom or never.
   c. On certain kinds of problems.

8. Which statement best describes your feelings?
   a. I like most people.
   b. I feel estranged from many people.
   c. I am highly selective in choosing my friends.

9. If you were asked to help in a community drive, you would:
   a. Make the time to participate actively.
   b. Beg off for some reason.
   c. Work a little to show your support.

10. When you return from a vacation:
    a. People call and come to welcome you home.
    b. No one seems to notice that you were away.
    c. You call friends to tell them you are back.

11. You are chosen to be the leader or decision maker:
    a. Many times.
    b. Never.
    c. Sometimes.

12. You are:
    a. Occasionally the brunt of a joke.
    b. Often teased.
    c. A self-effacing humorist.

13. When with people much older or younger than you, you:
    a. Find their conversation genuinely interesting.
    b. Are bored.
    c. Try to look interested even if you are not.

14. Generally speaking you:
    a. Confide in those close to you.
    b. Go to many people with your tales of woe.
    c. Try to solve your own problems.

CAN YOU KEEP A SECRET?

The ability to keep a secret requires self-control which is an important feature in the mature personality. The blabbermouth is disliked socially, and is a hazard in business. At the international level, the security of nations sometimes depends on silence. Walter Winchell, the noted columnist, said, "I usually get my stuff from people who promised somebody else that they would keep a secret." This test will tell how well you rate as a "secret risk."

Answers on page 499

1. Don't think! In the drawing room below there are two loose blocks. There are also three empty spaces in the mass of blocks. Draw lines from block A and block B to the hole or holes of your choice.

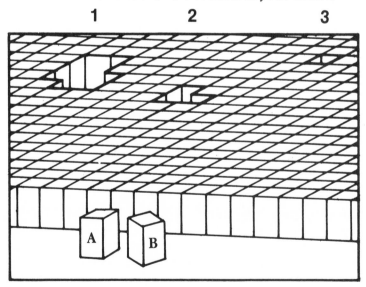

2. Think! In the situations given below, check the answer that best describes what you would do:

   A. A friend who is going to be given a surprise party in an hour comes to your house in dirty clothes covered with paint. You would:

a. Alert him about the party so he can change.
  b. Say nothing.
  c. Hint about his clothing.

B. A child tells you what Santa Claus is bringing him. You would:
  a. Alert his parents to what he wants.
  b. Listen with pleasure.
  c. Respond with what Santa is bringing to you.

C. You can select only one magazine. Your choice would be a:
  a. News or family publication.
  b. Confession or gossip magazine.
  c. Hobby, sports, or trade periodical.

D. A friend tells you of a secret romance. You would:
  a. Bind your other friends to secrecy and tell them the news.
  b. Record the news in your diary.
  c. Say nothing.

E. An employer confides that he is going to fire a staff member. You would:
  a. Warn the employee to look for a new job.
  b. Let information come through channels.
  c. Confidentally tell others on the staff.

F. When people confide secrets to you, you:
  a. Feel flattered and enjoy it.
  b. Wish people would not involve you.
  c. Enjoy passing the secret along.

3. Don't think! Put your initials on one of the two boxes below.

A   **B**

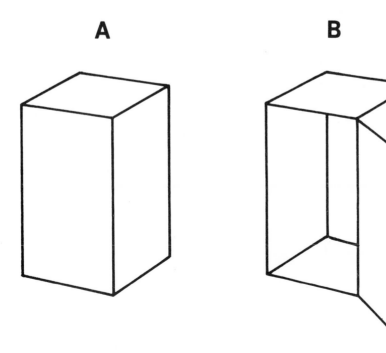

HOW WELL
DO YOU CONCENTRATE?

In our world of noise and constant interruptions and demands, it is easy to become so distracted that you can't concentrate on the task at hand. The art of working under pressure is one which can be developed. Use this test as a starting point to evaluate how well you are able to concentrate. There is no time limit. Work at your normal speed.

Answers on page 500

1. Study the group of numbers on the left to find the relationship that will tell you what number is represented by X in the other group on the right.

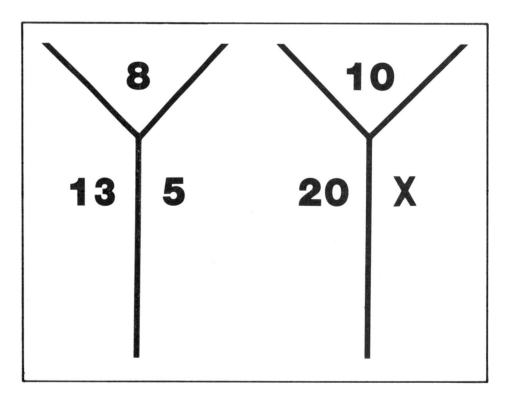

2. If FRANCE is spelled numerically as 61811435, what countries do these two groups of numbers spell?

   a. 19161914 _____

   b. 92011225 _____

3. What is the second vowel in the name of the month that follows October? _____

4. What is the second letter in the name of the day which is the day that comes after the day after Friday? _____

5. Which letter in the word DEMAND is nearest the end of the alphabet? _____

6. Study the following pairs of words. One pair does not follow the pattern of the others. Which one do you think it is?

    goat:tug   boat:tab   sad:does   blind:did   dug:good

7. Follow the instructions given below, step by step to fill in the missing letters.

    __ __ S __ __ __ U __ Z __ __ __ __

S is between N and W. Z comes between X and K. T should be placed before U. R comes after W. A comes before N. M comes after X. F should be placed to the right of M. L is the next to the last letter as you read to the right.

8. In the diagram below, the 12 blocks form a square with 4 blocks on each side. Can you rearrange the 12 blocks so there will be 5 blocks on each side of the block pattern?

DO YOU FEEL INFERIOR?

Many of us harbor feelings of inadequacy. Some seek attention and sympathy by explaining in detail what sorry messes they are. Psychiatrists say that often the blustery and boastful person is, in reality, trying to hide feelings of inferiority; and the quiet little guy or gal may be warm and snug with inner security.

Answer the questions below to help determine whether or not you nurture a sense of inferiority.

Answers on page 500

1. Which illustration in the drawing below would best describe your usual mood when you awake to face a new day?

2. When you are asked to do an important job you didn't expect, how do you react? Check the drawing which best describes your immediate reaction.

3. You are trying to solve a problem when someone comes and silently looks over your shoulder. You would:
   a. Feel jittery.
   b. Be flattered.
   c. Put his presence in the back of your mind.

4. When an acquaintance fails on a project, you often:
   a. Are secretly pleased.
   b. Try to fill the breach.
   c. Worry almost as much as if it were your own error.

5. If someone makes you the brunt of a joke, you:
   a. Wait for the moment when you can tell an embarrassing story about him.
   b. Add to the story and make it more ludicrous.
   c. Explain the serious side of the situation.

6. With an unlimited amount of money, you would:
   a. Buy the luxuries you most want.
   b. Go all out with new possessions.
   c. Save it.

7. If you were invited to meet an important celebrity, you would:
   a. Be pleased to have the opportunity.
   b. Find an excuse for not going.
   c. Buy new clothing and nervously plan your behavior.

8. You think that:
   a. Most people are better than you.
   b. Everyone has strengths and weaknesses.
   c. Few have your assets and abilities.

9. If you won a trophy, you would:
   a. Place it in a conspicuous spot in your home.
   b. Let your family or friends suggest where you should put it.
   c. Tuck it away.

10. You sincerely believe:
    a. There is nothing you do really well.
    b. You do many things fairly well.
    c. You excel in one or two worthwhile skills.

ARE YOU A PLEASURE TO BE WITH?

At one time or another, each of us has said about some person, "I like him, but he annoys me." Then there are those who give a soothing quality to life.

Most of us are not aware of some of our social habits and behave automatically and unconsciously. Before criticizing others, it is wise to study yourself to find out if you have any characteristics which, according to psychological studies, are bothersome to others.

In order to try to see yourself as others see you, be as honest as you can in answering these questions.

Answers on page 500

	YES	NO
1. Do you have several stock phrases you use constantly?	____	____
2. Are you careless about your table manners and/or smoking habits?	____	____
3. Do you tend to keep touching the person with whom you are carrying on a conversation?	____	____
4. Do you try to shock or entertain people by telling off-color stories?	____	____
5. Does time mean so little to you that you are often late or wear out your welcome by staying too long?	____	____

406

6. Do you rattle coins in your pocket or play with car keys? ___ ___

7. When sitting or standing, is it difficult for you to keep your feet still? ___ ___

8. Do you find it hard to know what to do with your hands? Are you constantly moving them—twiddling your thumbs, touching your hair, etc.? ___ ___

9. When attending a group event (movie, lecture, church, etc.) are you prone to whisper to your neighbor? ___ ___

10. Do you squirm in your clothing constantly adjusting your belt, fingering your tie, straightening your skirt, stockings, or trousers? ___ ___

11. Do you bite your fingernails? ___ ___

12. Do you leave your clothing and personal property strewn about your home or office? ___ ___

13. Do you enjoy arguing or contradicting others? ___ ___

14. Is your voice much louder (or much softer) than the average person's? ___ ___

15. Are your feelings easily hurt? ___ ___

16. Is your conversation centered around yourself and your activities? ___ ___

17. Are you a "conversation hog," monopolizing the talk for prolonged periods of time? ___ ___

18. Do you avoid looking into the eyes of the person you are having a conversation with? ___ ___

ANECDOTES YOU'LL ENJOY

The stories which follow are supposed to be true.
In any case, they are quite amusing.

■

"Instead of denying gossip, I shall silently wrap myself in my dignity and virtue," declared Marie Antoinette when rumor linked her name with that of General Lafayette.

"Hmmm," replied her husband, Louis XVI, "take care not to catch cold in such light garments."

■

Empress Marie Louise felt nothing but contempt for Napoleon. "Why," she asked him on the eve of the Russian invasion, "must you keep fighting for more territory and power? We Hapsburgs fight only for honor."

"I suppose," Napoleon replied, "that all of us fight for whatever we lack most."

■

"By Jove," cried the proud warrior Mark Antony, when he found out he had fathered twins by Cleopatra, "I feel as if I had won two great victories with one easy battle."

■

The author d'Alembert had Mme. de Staël, the most brilliant woman of her time, for his dinner partner; on his left sat glamorous Mme. Recamier. "How fortunate," he exclaimed rapturously, "to sit between Wit and Beauty!"

"Yes," said Mme. de Staël, "and without possessing either!"

■

Aspasia was celebrated for her supreme beauty and intellect— but not for her virtue. When Pericles shocked ancient Athens by leaving his wife for her, Aspasia declared, "I have told Pericles *everything* in my past!"

Her illustrious friends were impressed. "What honesty!" said Sophocles, "What courage!" echoed Phidias, "What a memory!!!" exclaimed Socrates.

Emperor Franz Josef I, a notorious old flirt, once admired a bosomy opera singer who wore a strapless evening gown. "What keeps your dress up, my dear?" he smirked.

The young beauty replied: "Only your age, your Majesty!"

■

"Must you go?" pleaded an infatuated baroness who had thrown a splendid party for Johannes Brahms.

"Not at all," replied the composer, putting on his hat and heading for the door. "It's entirely a matter of choice."

When Oscar Wilde lectured in New York, a literary patroness became infatuated with him. The eccentric British author enjoyed being lionized, but could not stand the lady's constant fawning. Receiving another of her invitations: "Mrs. X will be at home Tuesday, from 5 to 7," he replied: "Mr. Oscar Wilde likewise."

■

Alexander the Great was so infatuated with luscious Phyllis that he took her along even on his military campaigns. Once, when he was ill, Aristotle visited him and felt his pulse. "My fever is gone," said Alexander.

"I know," smiled the philosopher, "I met her in the doorway."

MATHECROSTICS

Here you have all the answers—you make up the problems. Fill each blank with a number from 1 to 9 so that the answers come out right for all the problems in the rows across and down. You may use a number more than once.

Solutions on page 501

1.

	×		÷		=8
×		×		+	
	×		−		=3
÷		−		−	
	+		−		=9
=2		=8		=7	

3.

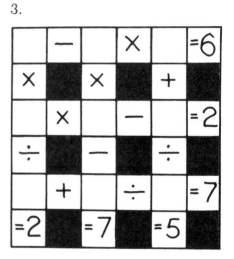

2.

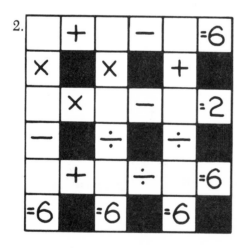

4.

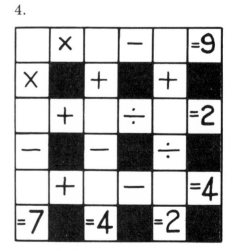

5.

	+		÷		=8
+		−		×	
	×		−		=6
−		×		÷	
	−		−		=1
=5		=9		=4	

6.

	÷		×		=8
×		+		×	
	×		−		=6
÷		−		÷	
	×		−		=8
=9		=1		=6	

7.

	×		−		=4
+		×		+	
	÷		+		=7
−		−		−	
	×		÷		=3
=6		=5		=6	

8.

	−		+		=7
÷		×		+	
	+		−		=4
×		÷		+	
	+		÷		=5
=3		=2		=8	

WAGERS YOU CAN'T LOSE

The bets which follow are fun bets. You don't really bet money on them. You just bet one of your friends, and you have fun.

1. I bet I can put myself through a keyhole.

   You write "Myself" on a piece of paper, and then push it through a keyhole.

2. I bet I can jump across the street.

   Just go across the street and jump a few times.

3. I bet I can stand two inches away from you without your being able to touch me.

   You stand on the other side of a closed door.

4. I bet I have a piece of paper with some handwriting on it that you would surely pay 95¢ for.

   Show a dollar bill and point to the signature of the Secretary of the Treasury.

5. I bet I can write a longer word than you can, no matter how long a word you write.

   Write "A Longer Word than You Can."

6. I bet I can put my fingers into a cup of tea without getting them wet.

   Just fill a cup with dry tea leaves, and put your fingers into it.

7. I bet I can stay under water for a whole minute.

   Fill a glass with water and hold it over your head.

8. I bet you cannot answer four questions wrong, no matter how hard you try.

   Ask him three questions which he will probably answer incorrectly. Then say, "Let me see . . . that's three questions so far, isn't it?" He will answer your fourth question correctly.

9. I bet you can't take off your coat alone.

   As soon as he starts taking off his coat, you just take off your coat, too.

10. I bet I can place eight dimes on a table in the shape of a letter L (as shown in the diagram, and by moving only one dime, end up with five dimes in each column.

Pick up the dime at the top of the vertical column, and place it on top of the bottom dime in the vertical column. There will now be five dimes in each column.

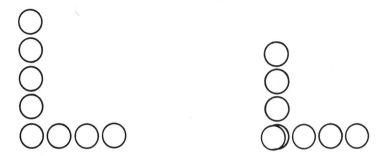

11. I bet I can put a dollar bill across the top of two water glasses and put a quarter on top of the dollar bill without having the dollar bill fall.

    The dollar bill will not cave in, if you fold it twice lengthwise into an accordion fold. Now it's strong enough to support a quarter.

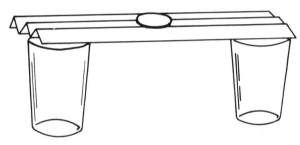

12. I bet that I can pick up three matches with a fourth match.

    You need four matches—large kitchen matches. Arrange three matches in a tripod, keeping their heads together. Now set the three matches afire with the fourth match, which you have left. Blow the flames out. The three matches will be fused together so you can now lift them by placing the fourth match underneath the tripod.

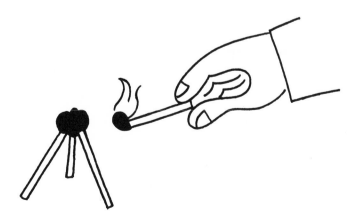

MATH ODDITIES

Here's a trick with the number 8:

$$9 \times 9 + 7 = 88$$
$$9 \times 98 + 6 = 888$$
$$9 \times 987 + 5 = 8888$$
$$9 \times 9876 + 4 = 88888$$
$$9 \times 98765 + 3 = 888888$$
$$9 \times 987654 + 2 = 8888888$$
$$9 \times 9876543 + 1 = 88888888$$
$$9 \times 98765432 + 0 = 888888888$$

Here's a simple arrangement of numbers that shows a tricky result:

1	2	3	4	5	6	7	8	9
9	8	7	6	5	4	3	2	1
1	2	3	4	5	6	7	8	9
9	8	7	6	5	4	3	2	1
								2
2	2	2	2	2	2	2	2	2

The numbers in each column of this square add up to 34, whether you add them vertically, horizontally, or diagonally.

1	14	15	4
8	11	10	5
12	7	6	9
13	2	3	16

SHORT ROAD TO WEALTH

I'll tell you a plan for gaining wealth,
    Better than banking, trade, or leases;
Take a bank note and fold it across,
    And then you will find your money IN-CREASES!

This wonderful plan, without danger or loss,
    Keeps your cash in your hands, and with nothing to trouble it;
And every time that you fold your money across,
    'Tis plain as the light of day that you DOUBLE IT!

THE SEAL OF THE UNITED STATES

Here, directly below on this page, you see the great seal of the United States—the luckiest country in the world.

Strangely enough, the entire design of this seal is based on the number 13. In this famous seal there are:

13 LETTERS IN "E PLURIBUS UNUM"

13 STARS IN THE HALO

13 CLOUDS TO FORM THE HALO

13 STRIPES ON THE SHIELD

13 ARROWS IN ONE CLAW

13 LEAVES ON THE BRANCH

13 BERRIES ON THE BRANCH

13 FEATHERS ON THE EAGLE'S NECK

CROSSWORD PUZZLE NO. 1

Solution on page 502

ACROSS

1. Smarted
6. Bulk
10. Bridge
14. Pith helmet
15. Encourage
16. Story
17. Major wire service (abbr.)
18. Cereals
20. Gained
22. China, e.g.
23. Came upon
25. Fixed routine
27. Vex
29. Support
31. Be inclined
33. Foot part
34. Dog type
36. "Money is the ____ of all evil"
38. Witch's concoction
41. Minister
44. Shortly
46. No in Dundee
47. Article
48. Close eyes (falconry)
50. Disorder
52. Yes in Yucatan
53. Eye infection
55. Notices
57. Linger
59. Rip
61. Light source
63. Society column word
64. Deteriorate
66. Anger
68. Balance
71. Contemporary
74. Turns to the right
76. Extinct bird
77. ____ snail's pace (2 words)
78. Cry of pain
80. Genuine
82. Two (prefix)
83. Streetwear for Caesar
85. Raise
87. Ideal
89. Opposite of 33 across
90. Allot
91. Serves at a tea

DOWN

1. Post office purchase
2. Imbiber
3. Northern Michigan (abbr.)
4. Recent (prefix)
5. Mechanism
6. Overcome
7. College degree
8. Stitch
9. Cease
10. Thoroughfare (abbr.)
11. Part of a horse's leg
12. Toward shelter
13. Approach
19. Nipper
21. Mesh
24. Outdoes
26. Long-lived Biblical character
28. Weep
30. Sets
32. Entrance
35. Leaves
37. Labor
39. Comfort
40. Fence in water
41. "What is ____ is prologue"
42. Prefix for bellum or diluvian
43. Angler's implement
45. *High* ____ (1952 Gary Cooper film)
49. Tragic king
51. Layer
54. Ground gained in football
56. Pollution
58. Abound
60. Poor man's caviar
62. Capital of South Dakota
65. Endeavor
67. Confederate hero
69. Solemn
70. Animal appendages
71. Arithmetic (colloquial)
72. Indian tribe
73. Average
75. Coarse hominy
79. Tiny
81. John (British slang)
84. Gangster Capone
86. Toward
88. German pronoun

CROSSWORD PUZZLE NO. 2

Solution on page 502

ACROSS

1. Light beams
5. I hear (Latin)
10. In favor of
13. Bicycle part
14. High-stakes car race (2 words)
16. Andean mammal
17. Some
18. Chosen few
19. Paddle
20. Many (slang)
22. Orant's "over and out"
23. Baseball great Cobb, the "Georgia Peach"
24. Finished
25. Community
28. "There is Nothing Like a ____" (*South Pacific*)
29. Ancient Greek battleground; long footrace
33. Centuries-old board game
35. Douglas and Nichols
36. Alter ____
37. Curse
38. Cavities
39. Underdone
40. Suffix meaning "full of"
41. Doorways
42. Tortoises' nemeses
43. Type of athlete
45. Gland
46. Powder
47. Take on
48. Monogram of famous rabbit
50. Volcano product
53. Body of water
54. Hawaiian food staple
55. Greeting to eaters of 54 across
57. Cigarette by-product
58. River in British Columbia
60. Cycle race
62. Master of ceremonies
63. Busy insect
64. Uptight
65. Raced

DOWN

1. Pass on
2. Jewish month
3. Sweet potato
4. Single skis
5. Term in printing or marbles
6. Vessels
7. 24-hour period
8. With it
9. Poem
10. Proper
11. Sacrament
12. Beasts ot burden
13. Scheme
15. Factory
21. "____ if by land..."
24. Hyphen
25. Appropriates
26. Metalliferous rocks
27. Used to be
28. Inhibit
29. Distance runner
30. Valentine symbol
31. Monster
32. Negative responses
33. Sounds like a dove
34. Lock part
35. Musical work
38. "____ off"
39. Ethnic group
41. Risible antelope
42. Barriers
44. Western state
45. Clamor
47. Steed
48. Afflicted by ennui
49. Wait
50. Greek meat staple
51. Lily plant
52. Cast a ballot
53. Go by
54. College in NYC
56. Play part
57. Weight
59. Mischievous child
61. Prefix: again

CROSSWORD PUZZLE NO. 3

Solution on page 502

ACROSS

1. Shape at an angle
6. Effervescent drink
10. October birthstone
14. Breathing
15. Neat
16. Chemical weapon
17. Old Scratch
18. Shakespearean villain
19. Ireland
20. Greek letter
21. Slight depression
23. Hair curler
25. Peddle
27. American Indian
28. Be in debt
29. Paddle
31. Buzzard
35. Ride a bike
38. Mineral springs
40. Mythical land
41. Dodge
42. Owns
43. Cow's stomach
45. Tennis term
46. Darling
47. About 70% of you
48. Perfidy
51. Obtained
52. Total
53. Doctors' org.

55. I used to be (Latin)
59. Symbol
62. Move fast
64. Inventor Whitney
65. Strong wind
66. British school
68. Mete
70. Adhesive
71. Persecutor of Christians
72. Paris's river
73. Level
74. Forest animal
75. Gait-setting horse

DOWN

1. Foundations
2. Fill with joy
3. Essential
4. Woman's name
5. Give temporarily
6. Backbone
7. Make a speech
8. Archaeological site
9. Romantic
10. Fluffy breakfast fare
11. Bucket
12. Land measure
13. Lupine look
22. Slip
24. Nocturnal bird

26. Burden
30. British beverage favorite
31. Flower container
32. Single
33. Cord
34. German river
35. Hide
36. At any time
37. Appointment
38. Repel
39. Butter serving
43. "... ____ if by sea"
44. Appraise
46. Laud
49. Dormant
50. "A Boy Named ____" (song by Johnny Cash)
51. Fuel
53. Idolize
54. Estate house
56. Souvenir
57. By oneself
58. Bishop's hat
59. Ingredients in 10 down
60. Grain for brewing
61. Color of melancholy
63. Fastener
67. Golfer's pedestal
69. Grassland

CROSSWORD PUZZLE NO. 4

Solution on page 502

ACROSS

1. Walk
5. In between
9. Athena's birds
13. Absent
14. Ice cream receptacle
15. Trick or ____
16. Back of the neck
17. Joining of two streams
19. Be mistaken
20. Distress signal
21. Catch some rays
22. Morning moisture
23. Ease
25. Taste
27. Small lake
28. Repeals
33. Part of a platform
35. Recede
36. Bull (Spanish)
37. Charged particle
38. Ladder parts
39. Stain
40. Walkway
42. Press
43. Rise in ground
45. Together (French)
47. Indefinite word
48. *Charlotte's* ____
49. Cork
52. Novel by H. Rider Haggard

55. British beverage
57. Dine
58. Permissive
59. Popular candy
62. Television (slang)
63. Regions
64. Gaelic
65. Cupid
66. Requirement
67. Envisions
68. Cute

DOWN

1. Wooden plank
2. Sentient
3. Ladies' trouser style (2 words)
4. Face part
5. Harmony
6. Bullwinkle, e.g.
7. Tavern
8. Handy
9. Mineral source
10. Travel
11. Irish product
12. Goulash
15. Garment
18. Gaelic girls
20. Done for
24. "...His only begotten ____"

26. Word from a Poe title
28. "Home on the ____"
29. Border
30. Pseudonym (French, 3 words)
31. Word with race or strip
32. Angered
33. Conduit
34. Roman ears, to Marc Antony
35. Roll up
38. Bridge term
41. Chop
43. Source
44. Prankster
46. Allots
47. Part of the good ol' U.S. of A.
49. One of five
50. Prelude to parturition
51. Put forth
52. Bridge
53. "____ lies..."
54. Fencer's instrument
56. Surname of actors Leon and Ed
60. Former slang word for home
61. Wrath
62. Word used with 43 down

419

CROSSWORD PUZZLE NO. 5

Solution on page 503

ACROSS

1. Set of tools
4. Parrot
9. Rascal
14. Mountain in Sicily
15. "Joyful, Joyful, We ____ Thee" (hymn)
16. Work
17. Inferred
19. At a distance
21. Italian pronoun
22. Coop
23. Seafaring group
24. Varnish ingredient
25. River in Texas
28. Crate
29. Price of transportation
30. Comedian King
31. Ship's record
32. Streetcar
34. Tease
35. Navy women
37. Compile
40. "____ Ain't Necessarily So" (*Porgy and Bess*)
41. Sleeveless cloak
42. Scruff
44. Singular of 21 across
45. Drainage ditch
47. Rare
49. Wrong
50. Brainstorm
52. Rear, to members of 23 across
53. Singer Perry ____
54. Wan
56. South American nation
58. Abyss
59. Playwright Burrows
60. Camp unit
61. Old card game
62. Soldier
63. Verdi opera
64. Jet routes
68. Proverb
70. Nervous
72. Estuary (Spanish)
73. More recent
74. Egresses
75. Likely

DOWN

1. Child
2. Chemical suffix
3. Small portion
4. Medieval weapons
5. Arabian seaport
6. Food fish
7. Southern state (abbr.)
8. Rubs against
9. Cabbage salad
10. Train part
11. From (Latin)
12. Tooth
13. Surname of actor Vincent
18. "Once ____ a time"
20. Measurements of length
23. Canary's home
24. Tibetan monk
25. The City of Light
26. Chosen few
27. Mr. Calloway
28. Small harbors
29. Renown
31. "____ of luxury"
33. Absorbed
35. Suffix for silver or hard
36. Army acronym now in general use
38. Bangs
39. Biblical city of sin
41. Give over
43. Social insect
46. Trick
48. Supermarket aid
49. Large snake
51. Copied
53. Dog breed
54. Heathen
55. Tolerate
57. Growing out of
58. Hearts
60. Level
61. Enumerate
63. ____ of reason
64. Black cuckoo
65. Coach Parseghian
66. Lyricist Harburg
67. Stayed put
69. ____, shucks!
71. Prefix meaning former

CROSSWORD PUZZLE NO. 6

Solution on page 503

ACROSS

1. Guard
5. Smooth
9. Lion's trademark
13. Broadway hit of the late 60s
14. Layer
15. Young eel
17. Key
18. Direction indicator
20. Computer food
21. Reliable
23. Mr. Sharif or General Bradley
25. Ablaze
26. Señorita
28. Hole in a needle
29. Swedish coin
30. Gulf
33. Swindled
35. Las Vegas hotel
37. ____ *Town*
38. Is broadcast
41. Fido and Tabby
43. Venerate
44. Heroic poem
48. Satires
51. Mouths (Latin)
52. Be buoyant
55. Tiny
56. Playful aquatic mammal
58. Cut off

59. Partner of royal scepter
61. Farm sight
63. Diamonds (slang)
64. Subjunctive or conditional
66. Boon
70. Vat
72. Banish
74. Director Kazan
75. Brew tea
77. Tied
78. Hotel commodity
79. Novelist Ferber
80. Wise
81. Tennis terms

DOWN

1. "____ is my Son, in whom..."
2. ____ *of Eden*
3. Moses' river
4. Fantasizes
5. Corsets
6. Ventilation
7. Famous fiddler
8. One-humped camels
9. Musical note
10. Stale
11. Arthurian utopia
12. Withdraw
16. Prices

19. Appian ____
22. Coin to stop on
24. Advice (archaic)
27. Fights an imaginary opponent (compound)
30. Krupke or Muldoon
31. Tint
32. Game-show host Fleming
34. Battery terminal
36. Manipulate
39. Discolor
40. Golfer's tool
42. Health resort
45. Marijuana (slang)
46. Anger
47. *My Mother the* ____
49. Comic-book hero
50. Food fish
52. Flutters
53. Find
54. Revealed
57. "...the topless ____ of Ilium"
60. Fish product
62. Miss Dunne
65. Prima donna
67. Lily plant
68. Disturbance
69. Hoover and Aswan
71. Barbie's boyfriend
73. Support
76. Mr. Kettle

CROSSWORD PUZZLE NO. 7

Solution on page 503

ACROSS

1. Small wheeled vehicle
5. Coffee cup
8. Stage
12. Proportion
13. Bull (Spanish)
14. Center
15. Tiny quantity
16. Van Cliburn's instrument
17. Gain
18. Japanese Buddhism
19. Advise
20. Lairs
22. Recluse
24. Speaker part
27. Tree
28. Matches
29. Behold
30. "Too many cooks spoil the ___"
33. Count
34. Launching platform
35. Mature
36. Kind of nut
37. Deceased
38. Insect
39. Jutlanders
40. Small bird
41. "Parting ___ such sweet sorrow"
42. Cuts into cubes
43. "Ich ___ ein Berliner" (John F. Kennedy)
44. Take away
46. Big cat
50. Hawaiian dance
51. Irritate
52. Bustle
53. Parched
55. Itinerary
57. Decorate
58. Piece of jewelry
59. Singer Williams
60. Minos' island
61. Dessert item
62. Letter
63. Intentions

DOWN

1. Provide food
2. Do penance
3. Border
4. *A Farewell ___ Arms* (Hemingway)
5. Whimper
6. Vase
7. Benevolence
8. Play parts
9. Breakfast fare
10. Slip up
11. Quill
12. Demolish
13. Car part
16. Walkway
19. Want
21. Mysterious (variant)
23. Ship's officer
24. ___ *of Hoffman*
25. Gladden
26. Western show
28. Scalps
30. Hair feature
31. Wash
32. Choose
33. Doctrine
34. Golfer's term
36. Card game
37. Tiny bits of cloth
39. Use a telephone
40. Grape, e.g.
42. Tedious routine
43. Bundle
45. Concentrate
46. Sympathy
47. Sultan's playground
48. Prepares for publication
49. Caesar's city
51. Discourteous
53. Circle part
54. Estuary
56. Indefinite pronoun
57. Three (prefix)
60. The Golden State (abbr.)

CROSSWORD PUZZLE NO. 8

Solution on page 503

ACROSS

1. Stuff
5. Cry of grief
9. Ancient Greek community
14. Self (prefix)
15. African nation
16. Escape
17. Skier's milieu
19. Pale
20. Bravery
21. Place of worship
23. Black in Bologna
25. Work unit
26. Nervous
28. Presence of mind
30. French pronoun
31. Ambled
35. Acquires
37. Malt beverage
38. Brings up
40. Lucifer
43. Thing
45. Student's study aids (slang)
47. Tedious person
48. Long-running morning news program
50. Reaches across
52. Fresh
53. Hastened
55. Most silent
57. The Keystone State (abbr.)
59. Speaks
61. Fencer's weapon
62. Wave (Spanish)
64. Peruse
66. Cuts
70. Stylish shop
72. Small fruit
74. Danger
75. Novelist Zola
76. "Be it _____ so humble..."
78. Miss Moreno
79. Adored
80. "_____ to you!"
81. Appear

DOWN

1. Throw
2. Pass judgment
3. Particle
4. Swabbed
5. Morning
6. Statute
7. Astronaut Shepherd
8. Muscle
9. Dedicates
10. Actress Le Gallienne
11. Masculine
12. Aromas
13. Twilled fabric
18. Senior
22. Wading bird
24. Falsify
27. Periods of time
29. Knife
31. Attend
32. Singing voice
33. Requirements
34. Falls
36. Blarney, e.g.
39. Declare
41. Greek war god
42. Salamander
44. Atlas contents
46. Small pieces
49. Longed for
51. Nap
54. Color
56. Simple tools
57. Impersonated
58. Texas tourist attraction
60. Vaults
63. Came to earth
65. Prima donna
67. Pennsylvania city
68. Ceremony
69. Close noisily
71. Arena cheer
73. Prized possession
77. Again (prefix)

423

CROSSWORD PUZZLE NO. 9

Solution on page 504

ACROSS

1. Reverberate
5. Arrangement
10. Flagellate
14. Regretted
15. Homily
16. Was borne
17. Signal for motion (2 words)
19. Man or Wight
20. Aged
21. Baseball terms
22. Part of Ireland
24. Paroxysms
25. Small insect
26. "When in the ____ . . ."
29. Obverse (slang, 2 words)
33. Be in harmony
34. Urgent request
35. King (Latin)
36. Taunt, reproach
37. Blessings
38. Actress Storm
39. One of the Gabors
40. Aaron and family
41. Provide food
42. Miss (Sp.)

44. Most docile
45. Buddies
46. College in New York City
47. Rise
50. Players
51. Make lace
54. At what time?
55. Flexibility
58. Ore deposit
59. Wash
60. Cupid
61. Beginning
62. Amphetamines (slang)
63. Note

DOWN

1. Therefore
2. Ringlet
3. Obey
4. Lyric poem
5. Pay homage
6. Corrects
7. Labels
8. Expression of distaste
9. Certain flowers
10. Arm parts
11. Welcomer
12. Inactive
13. British lord

18. Din
23. Circuits
24. Gratis
25. Valleys
26. Cells
27. Pointed arch
28. Name of eight popes
29. ____ the Red Menace
30. Angry
31. Removes (editor's term)
32. Put forth
34. Harbors
37. Makers
38. Contest
40. Cereal ingredient
41. Desert plants
43. Began
44. Savored
46. Behind the times
47. Cobbler's tools
48. Footwear
49. Yield
50. Sugar source
51. Hour
52. Fissionable particle
53. Novice
56. Sass
57. Rotary part

CROSSWORD PUZZLE NO. 10

Solution on page 504

ACROSS

1. Courage
6. Hair
10. Display
14. Tolerate
15. "...what ____ lurks in the..."
16. Hatteras, e.g.
17. Snooze
18. *Quid pro quo* (3 words)
20. Half a score
21. Element #82, symbol Pb
23. Touches
24. Satiety
25. Secure
27. Beset
30. Kind of song
34. Play
35. Audacious one
36. Pale
37. Model
38. Certain jails
39. Poverty
40. Diamonds (slang)
41. Sole
42. Feydeau play
43. Slum building
45. Vocation
46. Apply oil (slang)
47. Hourglass filler
48. Reference book
51. Power
52. Mr. Reiner
55. Feature of some airplanes
58. Breathing
60. Gentlemen
61. Connecticut college
62. Kind of car
63. Fencer's instrument
64. Well-known garden
65. Produce

DOWN

1. Huge
2. Competent
3. Legal claim on property
4. Poem
5. Image
6. Tin, e.g.
7. Eager
8. Insect egg
9. Gnome
10. Conceal
11. Loathing
12. Iridescent stone
13. Dampens
19. Proposal
22. Antlered animal
24. Celebrity
25. Fabric
26. Metric units
27. Confess
28. Vestige
29. Swindled
30. Peter or Paul
31. Conscious
32. Terpsichore's art
33. Join
35. Robot airplane
38. Small blister
39. Protectorate
41. Divert
42. Dream
44. Pass
45. Container
47. Tocsin
48. Church part
49. Fall
50. Folk tales
51. Remove (printing)
52. Go by car
53. Washington office
54. Curb
56. Soap ingredient
57. Young man
59. Hawaiian necklace

CROSSWORD PUZZLE NO. 11

Solution on page 504

ACROSS

1. Weapon's handle
5. Grind
9. Fat
14. Culture medium
15. Object of admiration
16. Hindu queen
17. Talk wildly
18. Star stage
19. Tidiness
20. Said
22. Flightless bird
24. Actor Randall
25. Pronoun
26. Tyke
28. Poker stake
30. Electricity
32. Kind of window
36. Extraterrestrial
39. Report
41. Anger
42. Golf stroke
43. Cut
44. Leave out
45. Summer in St. Moritz
46. Piece of 39 across
47. Lock
48. Mexican shawl
50. Prominent person
52. Bath powder
54. Constellation
55. Compass point

58. Shoo!
61. Spanish article
63. Commotion
65. Alarm
67. Skater's milieu
69. Wait
70. Socrates' forum
71. Margarine
72. Verve
73. Article of faith
74. Noted satellite
75. Minus

DOWN

1. Spartan
2. Christian love
3. Be partial
4. Star ____
5. Small fish
6. Altar promise (2 words)
7. Part of promise of 6 down
8. South American mammal
9. Gold (Italian)
10. Haggle
11. Within (prefix)
12. Witnessed
13. Strange (variant)
21. Short jacket

23. Beneath
27. Tent
29. Craggy hill
30. Caress
31. Bird
33. Speechless action
34. Greek goddess of discord
35. Soaks flax
36. King Kong and kin
37. Stringed instrument
38. Journey to Juvenal
40. Flower part
43. Facade
44. Globe
46. Mineral spring
47. Implement
49. Garb
51. Call over
53. Billiards shot
55. Expression of enjoyment
56. Ice-cream concoctions
57. Small birds
58. Expectorated
59. Prison
60. Soon (archaic)
62. Farm building
64. Son of Adam
66. Feline
68. New (comb. form)

426

CROSSWORD PUZZLE NO. 12

Solution on page 504

ACROSS

1. Sapphire, e.g.
4. Paper case
9. Seizes
14. Reverence
15. Surprise
16. Livy's language
17. Dominate
19. It is (16 across)
20. Straw
21. Thus
22. Skin ailment
24. Deity
25. *It Had to Be* ___
26. 1978 musical film starring John Travolta
29. Statute
30. Dispatched
31. Gambles
32. State
33. Nothing
34. Curved molding
35. Embrace
36. Common metal
39. Italy's largest river
40. Goal
41. Nut
42. Midwestern state (abbr.)
43. Mission
46. As of now
47. Lamented
49. Strange
50. Small quantity
51. Dull finish
52. Aria
54. Limb

55. Puts off
56. "___ for one..."
57. Greek letter
58. Allot
59. Cicero's six
60. Penguin's relative
61. Goal (French)
62. Spice
66. Manifest
68. Mitigated
70. Steal from
71. Musical notations
72. Word of comfort
73. Cockpit

DOWN

1. A gift
2. Female sheep
3. Checkers
4. Scale note
5. Overweight
6. Whip
7. 19 across in German
8. All-purpose interjection
9. Happy
10. Actor Walston
11. Directional preposition
12. Native American mammal
13. Nose
18. Elizabethan-age explorer
20. Geronimo's greeting
23. Lummox

24. Giddy
25. Bark
26. Feel blindly
27. Demanding nature
28. Adjectival suffix
29. Dawdle
30. Slight taste
32. I am (16 across)
33. Egg drink
35. Secreted
36. Chopped
37. Devoid
38. ___ *of Spring*
40. Plus
41. Conducted
44. Pastry
45. Confusion
46. Starchy vegetable
47. Home of Richard Burton
48. Schedule abbreviation
50. Three (prefix)
51. NY museum
52. Enjoy
53. Martini adjunct
54. Inquire
55. Hinder
57. Sets
58. Calliope, e.g.
60. Mr. Carney
61. Nonsense!
63. Bow
64. Indian region
65. Diminish
67. Spanish for 19 across
68. And (16 across)
69. Concerning (16 across)

CROSSWORD PUZZLE NO. 13

Solution on page 505

ACROSS

1. Jason's ship
5. Wild hog
9. Apiece
13. Farm structure
14. Plead
15. Missile
17. Over
18. Swamp grass
19. Condition
20. Corrects
22. Unproductive
24. Letter
25. Dine
26. Mediterranean, e.g.
27. Contained
28. Verbose
31. Unwed
33. Conceit
34. Auto
35. European capital
39. Historical period
40. Spigot
41. Tattle
42. *All about* ____ (1950 film)
43. Human
45. Pastry
46. Mr. Majors
47. Accord
49. Mix
51. Kodak product
54. Innovative
55. As well
56. Tennis term
57. Vegetable
58. Precipitated
62. Coronet
64. Price
67. Current
68. Legate
69. Scorch
70. Level
71. Obtains
72. Tortoise's rival
73. Torn

DOWN

1. Top
2. Chamber
3. Blood
4. Laid bare
5. Explode
6. Metalliferous rock
7. Epoch
8. Blush
9. Simple
10. Skill
11. Desire
12. *Grand* ____ (1932 film classic)
16. Marijuana (slang)
21. 24 hours
23. Loose overcoat
26. Knight's title
27. Solicitous person
28. Cry
29. Monster
30. Bellow
31. Patsy
32. Biblical character
34. Dog
36. Remove from type
37. Kiln
38. Lack
40. 2,000 pounds
41. Operate
44. Amount
45. Receive applause
48. Look for
49. Large snake
50. Loaf
51. Clotho, e.g.
52. Cake cover
53. Permission
55. That place
57. Country (French)
59. Abide
60. Sir Anthony ____
61. Depression
63. Decay
65. Word of discovery
66. Sailor (slang)

CROSSWORD PUZZLE NO. 14

Solution on page 505

ACROSS

1. Smooth
5. Monsters
10. Dice
14. Without (Latin)
15. Lean
16. Hanged patriot
17. Nose around
19. Gaelic
20. Toward shelter
21. Elongated fish
22. Winglike structures
24. Minister
26. Make a web
27. Eye infections
28. Hurry
31. Western heelwear
32. Pharmacist's abbreviation
34. Fall flower
35. Celestial bodies
36. *Mal de* ____
37. Spit out
38. Discoloration
39. Red or white
40. Get-up-and-go
41. Severe
42. Networks (anat.)
43. Tin (chem. symbol)
44. Indian woman's garment (var.)
45. Lost weight

46. Cut off
47. Wraith
48. Football team
50. Great ____
51. Lawyers' organization
54. Carry on
55. Tasty
57. Composer of *Bolero*
59. State with certainty
60. Suit fabric
62. Woman's name
63. Mentally healthy
64. German author
65. Actress Barbara ____

DOWN

1. To be (Latin)
2. Climbing plant
3. Organic compound
4. New (comb. form)
5. Bone (Latin)
6. Gather piece by piece
7. Infrequent
8. Naval rank (abbr.)
9. Skier's maneuver
10. Pursues
11. Stops
12. Margarine
13. Equal
18. Treatise

23. Type of equation (abbr.)
25. Makes public
26. Mulligatawny, e.g.
27. Iberian nation
28. Door fasteners
29. Colorado resort
30. Pace
31. Gaze intently
32. Lamp resident
33. Footstep
35. Pilot
36. Catcher's glove
38. Power
39. Cry
41. Rescue
42. Stairway part
44. Harsh
45. Hubbub
46. Gables or hills
47. Walks in water
48. Historical periods
49. Volcanic flow
50. Bucks' mates
51. Eager
52. Venerable English historian
53. Astronaut Sheperd or actor Hale
56. Be obliged to
58. Malt beverage
61. Of (Sp.)

CROSSWORD PUZZLE NO. 15

Solution on page 505

ACROSS

1. Frolic
6. Lath
10. Slave
14. Arrange
15. Record
16. Smell
17. Flooring
18. H_2O
19. Dossier
20. Brink
21. Bread in Bari
22. Baby's toy
24. Reply
26. Furies
27. Appropriate
28. Mr. Hood
30. New England state (abbr.)
32. Barrel part
35. Globe
36. Animal's foot
37. Nervous condition
38. Embankment
39. Owner of a Colorado mountain
40. Singleton
41. Sharpens
42. Vessel
43. You and I
44. Groups
45. Canadian province (abbr.)
46. Whittle down
47. Strategy
51. Jewels
53. Fail to stimulate
54. Buck's belle
55. 21 across, but now in Bordeaux
56. Begins
58. Foot ailment
59. Otherwise
60. Shag
61. Golfer's targets
62. Stag
63. Aims
64. Outlaw-chasers

DOWN

1. Indulge
2. Animated
3. Heaps
4. Compass point
5. Precedes mi
6. Tolerate
7. Overdue
8. Mimic
9. Foul
10. Mollify
11. Proofreads
12. Rock's partner
13. Gratis
18. Desire
21. English poet (1688–1744)
23. Dry
25. Surface
28. Travels
29. Metal-bearing rocks
30. Model
31. Pitcher
32. Exhibit
33. Prong
34. Blvd.
35. Roam
36. Bowler's target
38. Solitary
39. Liquid measure
41. Rabbit
42. Decorative trim
44. Flag
45. Roman war god
46. Bearing
47. Pitches
48. Graven images
49. Kernels
50. Sight, e.g.
51. Hied
52. Yarn
53. Turn
57. Kitchen utensil
58. Dove call
61. Energy unit (abbr.)

430

CROSSWORD PUZZLE NO. 16

Solution on page 505

ACROSS

1. Desert plants
6. Stance
10. Overcoat
14. Great Lake
15. European mountain chain
16. Air (prefix)
17. Things
18. Comedy genre
20. "___ is the time..."
21. Greek letter
23. Nervous
24. Whirlpool
25. Love to Lucretius
27. Demonstrated
30. Imitator
34. Anxious
35. Sale places
37. Excitement
38. State
39. Raw material
40. Study (slang)
41. Letter
42. Nature's building blocks
44. Policeman's ID
45. Navy officers
47. Orders around
48. Companion
49. Revolutionary War hero
50. Waft
53. London neighborhood
54. Taxi
57. Living to old age
60. Feel about
62. Capable
63. Spoken
64. Nightingale, e.g.
65. Plays
66. Existed
67. Spine of South America

DOWN

1. Face part
2. Car
3. Staff
4. Pitcher Seaver
5. Confidant
6. Starchy
7. Widemouthed jar
8. Health resort
9. Psychic powers (abbr.)
10. Too thin
11. Check
12. Curves
13. Jab
19. Organ parts
22. Peculiar
24. Always
25. Land units
26. Word (French)
27. Serenity
28. Black bird
29. Curved moldings
31. Jack, queen, etc.
32. Saying
33. Volumes
35. Lodge member
36. Extension
40. Container
42. Game marble
43. Explosive
44. Italian city
46. Replicas
47. Predecessor of humbug
49. Arbiter of card-game rules
50. Insipid
51. Wolf (Spanish)
52. Kind of child
53. Lead
54. String
55. Church projection
56. Insects
58. Oath
59. Wrath
61. Hurry

CROSSWORD PUZZLE NO. 17

Solution on page 506

ACROSS

1. Lightweight wood
6. Demolish (variant)
10. Glaswegian
14. Over
15. Wading bird
16. Round pyramid
17. Tellurium (chemical symbol)
18. Finish
20. Early South American
21. Football player
23. Droop
24. Gushes
26. Cease
28. Fido and Fluffy
30. One to a 10 across
31. Impel
33. Leprechaun
35. 20th-century malady
38. Electrum
40. Farewell to Francisco
42. Paid athlete
43. Throb
45. Looked for oil
47. Compass point
48. Blend
50. Transactions
51. Liability
53. Succumb
54. Landlord's income
55. Rower's tool
57. Within (prefix)
59. Be inclined
62. Fence crossings
65. Greek Amor
67. Title of respect
68. Cavity
69. Takes on
72. Cockney possessive
73. Portent
74. Secular
75. Repairs, in a way
77. Cute
78. Otherwise
79. Fishy

DOWN

1. Moderates
2. Catalyst
3. Southern state (abbr.)
4. Taste
5. Over
6. Weapon
7. Assisted
8. Thus (Latin)
9. Princely Italian family
10. Descendant
11. Ponders
12. Half of twice
13. Pekoe and oolong
19. Mature
22. Kitchen utensil
25. ____ Bell
27. Chief executive (abbr.)
29. Playground structure
32. Small weight
34. Instead of
36. Russian city
37. Jove and kin
38. Imitated
39. Think
40. Eagle's nest
41. Faction
44. Sen. Kennedy
46. Pre-Easter season
49. Old Testament book
52. Capability
54. Hotel space
56. Again (prefix)
58. Pact
60. French city
61. Attire
62. Boutique
63. Book
64. Word with fire or white
66. Bristlelike part
70. Salt for Sallust
71. Golfer Snead
76. 3.14159

432

CROSSWORD PUZZLE NO. 18

Solution on page 506

ACROSS

1. Mythical bird
4. Show mercy
9. Kills flies
14. Expression of disgust
15. Actress who portrays Sabrina Duncan (TV series) (2 words)
17. Type of party
18. Female sheep
19. Periods of time
20. Ubiquitous preposition
21. Sequence
23. Sulfuric, e.g.
24. A gift
25. Biblical widower
26. Levantine bread
27. Chums
28. Facial feature
30. Bridge plays
31. Tiny
32. Tint
33. Cabbagelike vegetable
34. David Doyle's character (see 15 across)
37. Exists
38. Strong wind
39. End of 44 across
40. Musical note
41. First name of 43 across (see 15 across)
43. Actress who plays Chris Monroe (see 15 across)
44. Limb
45. ____ Grande
46. Competition
47. Food fish
48. Unite
50. Defeat
51. Act selfish
52. Beverage
53. Lacunae
54. Charred
57. Midwestern state (abbr.)
58. Glow
59. Sizable
60. Reverence
61. Actress who portrays Kelly Garrett (see 15 across) (2 words)
64. Direction to a horse
65. Widemouthed jars
66. Prongs
67. Slip up

DOWN

1. Wheel marks
2. S-shaped moulding
3. Character with the voice of John Forsythe (see 15 across)
4. Clay pigeon
5. Dog's feet
6. Consumed
7. Prefix meaning "again"
8. Throws out
9. Quantity (slang)
10. Seven-day periods (abbr.)
11. Arsenic (chemical symbol)
12. Entire
13. Highbrows
16. Melody
22. Charged particle
23. Assistant
24. Highlander
26. Accumulation
27. Bother
28. Stylish
29. Awed silence
30. Orb
31. Lumber
33. Boxing term
34. Foretell (archaic)
35. Paradise
36. Hindu philosophy
38. System, pattern
39. Truth
42. Seabird
43. Young girl
44. Valises
46. Meal
47. Weight unit
48. Stringed instrument
49. Perfectly suited
50. Word with yard or dance
51. Euphoric states
53. Men (slang)
54. Location
55. Pitcher
56. Ruminant
58. Winglike part
59. Storage compartment
62. Ovid's 150
63. Companion to 40 across

CROSSWORD PUZZLE NO. 19

Solution on page 506

ACROSS

1. Italian capital (Italian)
5. Bounder
8. Tennis returns
12. Harbor
13. Quantity
14. Largest continent
15. Oast
16. Type of boat
17. 1 across, e.g.
18. Through (Latin)
19. Whirl
20. Erie or Michigan
22. Persuaded
24. Eisenhower or Washington
27. Gesture of agreement
28. Hamburger
29. Bay State (abbr.)
30. Main force
33. Auctions
34. Urban dwelling (abbr.)
35. Debit
36. Begat
37. Flooring
38. Dined
39. Combats
40. Race official
41. ____ be it
42. Miss Rand
43. Put on
44. Hazes
46. Pale colors
50. Diving bird
51. Crashes into
52. Fish eggs
53. Student pilot's acid test
55. Stop
57. Yield
58. Stage item
59. Radiate
60. Strode
61. Evergreens
62. Failure
63. Cry of woe

DOWN

1. Bird of poetry
2. Clear
3. Guys
4. Article
5. North American mammal (slang)
6. I love in 1 across
7. Used up
8. Henchman
9. Willow
10. Small piece
11. State
12. Famous comedian
13. Skidded
16. Hurried
19. Robert Burns, e.g.
21. Uninvited picnic guests
23. Hotels
24. High winds
25. Abundant
26. In the future
28. Soiree
30. Good time (colloquial)
31. Helicopter part
32. Take advantage of
33. Famous American soprano
34. Intent
36. Stilled
37. Hue
39. Mexican dish
40. Make salad
42. Busybodies
43. Female knight
45. Permit
46. Beyond
47. Author Jong
48. Cherishes
49. Embryo
51. Police action
53. Mata Hari, e.g.
54. Prospector's goal
56. Flightless bird
57. Young woman (slang)
60. Atlantic state (abbr.)

CROSSWORD PUZZLE NO. 20

Solution on page 506

ACROSS
1. Put on
6. Still
10. Crows
14. Indian lodge
15. Personal (prefix)
16. Lake or city
17. Take on
18. Move
19. Poker ploy
20. Wiseacre
21. Muslim leader
23. Madison Square ____
24. Adverbial suffix
25. Budge
26. Batter's ploy
27. Ship's storehouse
28. Scare
32. Seasoning
34. Commerce
35. Cuckoo
36. Blow a horn
37. Want badly
38. Detroit athlete
39. River in Romania
40. Bell sound
41. Moon valley
42. Elaborate
44. Shield part
45. Swiss-cheese feature
46. Break

47. Verses (abbr.)
49. Insist
52. Theatre part
53. Draw
54. Nimble
55. With (Latin)
56. "____ Were the Days"
58. Lady reporter in *Superman* comics
59. Initial form of some plants
60. Instruct
61. Revise
62. Adept
63. Georgia university

DOWN
1. Anile garment
2. Now
3. Excited
4. Lacuna
5. Make eligible
6. Tobacco product
7. Father of Abel
8. Movable cover
9. Truman's home state (abbr.)
10. Insufficiency
11. Dry
12. Knowledgeable
13. Perceived

19. Kitchen feature
22. Prefix for eastern or western
23. Show the way
25. Footwear
26. Indian warrior
27. Intimates
28. Rack
29. Pursues
30. Organic compound
31. Number of Muses
32. Did a cobbler's job
33. Native of Cracow
34. Choctaw, e.g.
37. Young one
38. Roster
40. Hag
41. Floral design
43. Mountain house
44. Annoy (slang)
46. French dessert
47. Eyeshade
48. Type of thrush
49. Miss Evans
50. Mild oath
51. Small (prefix)
52. Brief halt
53. Dorothy's dog
55. Chicago athlete
57. Prefix for 44 down
59. College degree

CROSSWORD PUZZLE NO. 21

Solution on page 507

ACROSS

1. Stiff-necked
5. Moist
9. Ceiling
14. Miss Hayworth
15. Pertaining to the mouth
16. Wash away
17. Certain sports matches
19. Link
20. Taste
21. Evil spirits
23. Arrests (slang)
25. Urban railroads
26. Slope
28. Level
30. Compass point
31. Soft voices
35. Small insect
37. Free
38. Ship features
40. Commotion
43. Greek god of war
45. Harvests
47. "____ thyself"
48. Rings out
50. Puts into storage
52. Summer on the Seine
53. Stays put
55. Recluses
57. Letter abbreviation
59. Put on spottily
61. Partnership
62. Perform
64. "____ it and weep"
66. Tourism
70. Unit in troy system
72. Small drink
74. Nation
75. Slip away
76. Persia
78. Sufficient (archaic)
79. Trite
80. Detective Wolfe
81. Nurse

DOWN

1. Poke
2. Mature
3. Piece of news
4. Country homes
5. I give (Latin)
6. Mr. Carney
7. Principal
8. Fold
9. Abates
10. Belfast paramilitary group
11. Action
12. Objects of adoration
13. To the point
18. Certain fasteners
22. Word with campaign or tactics
24. Sizable
27. Snoops
29. Holding frame
31. Prepare a gift
32. Rent
33. Notions
34. Roofing stone
36. Article of faith
39. Genetic mutation
41. Smallest unit in music
42. Sheepish ladies
44. Used a playground structure
46. Dulcet
49. Initiated
51. Bright
54. Take to court
56. Turkish inn
57. Timed
58. Florida city
60. Tidal ____, site of Wilbur Mills's embarrassment
63. Equine gait
65. Dreadful
67. Watermelon plant
68. Black (poetic)
69. Scandalous
71. Simian
73. Equal
77. Surname of an Ian Fleming villain

CROSSWORD PUZZLE NO. 22

Solution on page 507

ACROSS

1. Close noisily
5. Surrounded by
9. Feels concern
14. Carry
15. Have the audacity
16. Breathing
17. Religious depictions
19. Tombstone abbreviation
20. Depression
21. Much separated
23. Carbonated water
25. Overhead trains
26. Hand part
28. Mythical Georgia plantation
30. If (Italian)
31. Weigh
35. Dissolve
37. I love (Latin)
38. Kingly
40. Heads' opposite
43. Conserve
45. Competitor
47. Make small cuts
48. Movement
50. Pavarotti, e.g.
52. Chemical ending
53. Turkish monetary unit
55. In the wrong order
57. Gangleader Barker
59. Secluded hollow
61. Half (prefix)
62. Spanish cheer
64. Joint
66. Big ____
70. Appraises
72. Particle
74. Tantalize
75. Love in Livorno
76. Margarine
78. Baseball team
79. Solitary person
80. Lion's call
81. Snow vehicle

DOWN

1. Mix
2. Mine feature
3. Comic-book hero
4. Honeydews, e.g.
5. To, to Tibullus
6. Blemish
7. Roman rainbow goddess
8. Train station
9. 1972 film starring Liza Minnelli
10. ____ mode (2 words)
11. Small hill
12. Drawbacks
13. One of five
18. Step
22. Kind of duck
24. Sire's mate
27. On the level
29. Cry of woe
31. Throw
32. Gen. Bradley
33. Work of fiction
34. Lunatic
36. Prongs
39. Country roads
41. Row
42. Raced
44. Oklahoma city
46. *The ____ One* (Waugh satire made into 1965 film)
49. Bureau
51. Pay
54. Beverage
56. Becomes mature
57. Point
58. San Antonio landmark
60. Cabinet department
63. British school
65. Venus de ____
67. Bucket
68. Serf
69. Source of clarinet's sound
71. Before
73. Marijuana (slang)
77. Hospital part (abbr.)

CROSSWORD PUZZLE NO. 23

Solution on page 507

ACROSS

1. Speed
5. Big ____
8. 1954 science-fiction classic about giant ants
12. Was mistaken
13. Hour (Latin)
14. Part
15. Taunt
16. WWII development
17. Ireland
18. *Much ____ about Nothing*
19. Fireman's implement
20. Thoroughfare
22. Member of a Moslem order
24. Lamp
27. Before
28. Ancient stringed instruments
29. Three-toed sloth
30. Type of tent
33. Worries
34. Sea eagle
35. Poet Khayyam
36. Used diligently
37. S-shaped moulding
38. Man in *Stalag 17*
39. Facial hair
40. Saracens
41. That thing
42. Appears
43. City in Morocco
44. Cores
46. "____ is golden"
50. President Carter's middle name
51. Special type of printing plant
52. Rower's implement
53. Cherished
55. Fill with cheer
57. Money drawer
58. Concerning (2 words)
59. Rational
60. Theatre part
61. Army food
62. Rudolf Abel or James Bond
63. Golfing tools

DOWN

1. Group of lions
2. Tree (Latin)
3. Letter of the alphabet
4. Emcee Sullivan
5. Presage
6. Epoch
7. Told
8. Pleasant experiences
9. Throng
10. Inventor Whitney
11. *Twelve Angry ____* (1957 film)
12. Mild oath
13. Corned beef product
16. Ascended
19. Take on
21. Dollar bills
23. Swerve
24. Enticed
25. Less common
26. Baseball teams
28. Dens
30. Subject
31. Overact
32. Manhandle
33. Dollars (slang)
34. Self-esteem
36. Unsurpassed
37. Seep
39. Milwaukee product
40. Thaw
42. Watches carefully
43. Penalty
45. Draws nigh
46. Location
47. Din
48. Telephones
49. ____ Stanley Gardner
51. "...a ____-splendored thing"
53. Not too bright
54. Compass point
56. Ambit
57. Neckwear
60. To

CROSSWORD PUZZLE NO. 24

Solution on page 507

ACROSS

1. Roman war god
5. Famous British porcelain
10. Cease
14. Wings (Latin)
15. Harbor
16. Evergreen tree
17. Inlet
18. Rub out
19. Peruvian Indian
20. Concerning (archaic)
22. Urban railroads
23. Penetrate
24. After Tues.
25. Triumph
27. Rim
29. Earth
30. Carpet
31. Word with change or serpent
34. Primitives
37. Teachers, sometimes
39. Mine entrance
40. Spinning like ____ ____ (2 words)
41. Gets by
45. Navigator's device
48. Before
49. Jungle beast
50. Impresses
51. Moslem ruler
52. Thing (Latin)
53. International distress call
56. Suffix for micro- or peri-
59. Vegetable
61. Steeple
63. Temporary habitation
64. Skin layer
66. Shah's dominion
67. Spoken
68. Gabriel, e.g.
69. Fisherman's tools
70. Used to be
71. Ripped off
72. Cypress offshoot

DOWN

1. Type of parrot
2. "____ at last"
3. Spoke incoherently
4. Perceived
5. ____ Stoops to Conquer
6. Progenitors
7. Egg-shaped
8. Grand finale of a meal
9. Compass direction
10. Backbone
11. Slight coloration
12. "____ upon a time."
13. Fruit
21. Small branch
23. Standard breakfast fare
26. Anger
28. Owed
29. Information
31. Bristle
32. Greek Cupid
33. Venomous snakes
34. Identical
35. Jewish month
36. Grape plant
38. Bugle call
42. Football, e.g.
43. Prefix for log or graph
44. Python
45. *Crème de* ____
46. Be obliged
47. Jumble
51. First temptation
53. Temptress
54. Speechify
55. Word with horse or common
56. Barge
57. International relief organization
58. Mr. Sharif
60. Therefore
62. Color of flamingos
64. German article
65. Malt beverage

439

CROSSWORD PUZZLE NO. 25

Solution on page 508

ACROSS

1. Rainbow
4. Truncated
9. Handed out cards
14. Young woman (slang)
15. Down source
16. Church officer
17. ____ Isle
19. Blow up
21. Men's garments
22. Comedian Paulsen
23. Former Portuguese colony in India
24. Storage building
26. Foxy
27. Canvas shelter
28. Buddy
29. Earthwork
32. Chemical symbol for beryllium
33. Miss Gardner
34. Norse Jupiter
35. Laud
39. Indicates
41. Four musicians
42. Football play (2 words)
43. "History is ____" (Henry Ford)
44. Miss Lupino
45. ____ I Lay Dying (Faulkner)
46. Large edible bird
47. Rug surface
48. Useful part of cotton plant
51. Droop
52. Valley (British)
53. Egg (comb. form)
54. ____ canto
55. Word with case or well
58. Aristocratic
60. Liken
63. Impulses
64. Harangue
66. Mythical land
67. Ermine
68. Widow parts
69. ____ for the Seesaw

DOWN

1. Number of years
2. Ewe's partner
3. Risible Ohio city
4. Seven ____
5. Sword handle
6. Ends' partners
7. Scale tone
8. Three-base hit
9. Nimble
10. Building wing
11. Proverb
12. Reveal
13. Take out to dinner
18. Cincinnati athlete
20. Negative vote
24. Card suit
25. Place of safety
26. Japanese coin
27. Bodily excretion
29. Flower of forgetfulness
30. British statesman (1897–1977)
31. Force (Latin)
32. Stop a car
35. Word plays
36. Wanderer
37. Type of car or chair
38. Day's march
40. Out loud
41. Whither (Latin)
43. Marsh
46. Equine gait
48. Phony
49. Unconcealed
50. Argot
51. "Oh, say can you ____ . . ."
52. Cocktail party fare
54. ____ of both worlds
55. Read metrically
56. Carry
57. City in Iowa
59. Word with bag or break
61. Melee
62. Former name for Tokyo
65. Egyptian god

CROSSWORD PUZZLE NO. 26

Solution on page 508

ACROSS

1. Passion
5. Study of coats-of-arms (abbr.)
8. "Arrivederci, ____"
12. Group of witches
13. Conserve
14. The Emerald Isle
15. Pinnacle
16. Beach item
17. Urban area
18. Through (Latin)
19. Kitchen part
20. Fragrant wood
22. Country homes
24. Went bad
27. Blemish
28. Fiber
29. Perform
30. Bird of poetry
33. Grew weary
34. Past
35. Comedian King
36. Exposed
37. Originate
38. Speck
39. Cords
40. Spassky's game
41. Indefinite article
42. Bird of spring
43. To's partner
44. Paraphraser
46. Hue and cry
50. Noble (Ger.)
51. Foremost part of a ship
52. High card
53. Country road
55. Colloquialism
57. Matures
58. *Omnia vincit* ____ (Vergil)
59. Pecans
60. Happening
61. Grows blurred
62. West or Largo
63. Small projectile

DOWN

1. Ambles
2. Without stealth
3. Tease
4. ____ *masse*
5. Raptor
6. Night before
7. Retrogressed
8. Draw back
9. Bay window
10. Cambridge campus
11. ____ *Wednesday*
12. Horn or Good Hope
13. Male offspring
16. Level
19. Musial or Laurel
21. Burden
23. So be it
24. Fathers
25. Sides
26. Condemns
28. Temptress
30. Electronic device
31. Unaccompanied
32. Large tub
33. Tropical mammal
34. Dined
36. Songbird
37. Like a ____
39. Popular flower
40. Boast
42. Rough ____
43. Out of
45. Poison
46. Experts
47. Enthusiastic
48. Aroma
49. Examination
51. Compassion
53. Youngster
54. Friend (Fr.)
56. Owed
57. Miss Gardner
60. *Mr.* ____ (TV series)

CROSSWORD PUZZLE NO. 27

Solution on page 508

ACROSS

1. Tittles' partners
5. Sorrow
10. Street sign
14. Lake or canal
15. Lyric poem
16. Native of Warsaw
17. Deserve
18. South African grassland
19. Up to the task
20. Surfeit
22. Walk
23. Greek letter
24. Volume
26. Alter
29. Arena
33. Roman tutelary deities
34. Path
35. Cuckoo
36. Son of Adam and Eve
37. Muse of love poetry
38. Sponsorship (variant)
39. Transgression
40. Collect
41. Mother of Nausicaa (Greek myth)
42. Sea creature
44. More expensive
45. Pledge
46. Group of animals
47. Special status
50. Drew back
54. Dismounted
55. Expensive piece of beef
57. Slave of Amneris
58. Cyrano's most prominent feature
59. Cold flash
60. Make neat
61. Machinery
62. Thick
63. Consumes

DOWN

1. Army vehicle
2. Spoken
3. Part of 1 down
4. Guardian
5. Consecrate
6. 57 across, e.g.
7. "Whatever ____ Wants" (*Damn Yankees*)
8. Unusual
9. Soak, as flax
10. Products of friction
11. Ear part
12. Widemouthed jar
13. Unwanted greenery
21. Swine
22. Labor
24. Ships
25. Oil (Italian)
26. Division
27. Nun's attire
28. Amphitheatre
29. Loud noise
30. Avid
31. Join
32. Pennypincher
34. Garbage
37. Give off
38. Shoot out
40. ____ cry (2 words)
41. British prefix for plane
43. Cheering follower
44. Wooden frame
46. Cures
47. Phyllis Diller's husband
48. Medicinal plant
49. Passport adjunct
50. Bridle part
51. Italian monetary unit
52. Emend
53. Water barriers
55. University degree
56. "When in ____ course..."

CROSSWORD PUZZLE NO. 28

Solution on page 508

ACROSS

1. Slumps
5. Couples
10. Pre-Easter period
14. Diagram
15. Sibling, sometimes
16. Winglike
17. Verdi heroine
18. Gladden
19. Roman statesman, bitter enemy of Julius Caesar
20. Beginnings
22. Insufficiency
24. Doze
25. French cap
27. Grow into a long stalk
29. Gorcey or Durocher
31. "___ pig's eye" (2 words)
32. Bishopric
33. Australian bird
34. Aquatic mammal
37. Recordings
41. Insect eggs
43. Time of history
44. Town map
45. Serious crime
47. Take excessive delight
50. Metric measurement

51. Cheer
53. Miss Gabor
54. Political ideology
55. Abrades
59. Irish product
61. Exclamation of discovery
62. Sups
64. Fruit juice
67. Strong emotion
69. Anachronism
71. Venetian version of dollars
72. Greek Mars
73. Fleeting moment
74. Eager
75. Valley (British)
76. Passover feast
77. Kennedy, Baxter and Bessell

DOWN

1. Mineral springs
2. Dismounted
3. Social butterflies
4. Trap
5. In attendance
6. Garlic (French)
7. Terrible tsar
8. Makes the grade
9. Lies dormant

10. Milk for little Marcus
11. African antelope
12. Concerning birth
13. Figure of speech
21. The Supremes, e.g.
23. Regimen
26. Spud
28. Lowest tide
29. Miss Horne
30. Moslem ruler
35. Sooner than
36. Composer of *Bolero*
38. Querulous
39. Pieces of corn
40. Plant trunk
42. Rail
46. Back of the neck
48. Revealer
49. Bowling alley
52. Vital organs
55. Lettuce dish
56. Task
57. Poe bird
58. Cubic meter
60. Success
63. Slipped
65. Parched
66. Cincinnati team
68. Compass point
70. Rocks

CROSSWORD PUZZLE NO. 29

Solution on page 509

ACROSS

1. Walkway
5. Perched
9. House (Spanish)
13. Greek nymph
14. Bring out
15. Asian ruler
16. Actor Connery
17. Ballots
18. Borrow for a price
19. Bone (comb. form)
20. Before
21. Possessions
23. Story
25. Distress signal
26. A proof of innocence
29. ____ *Loves Me* (Broadway musical)
32. Bicycle power source
36. Precursor
38. Overripe
40. Compass point
41. American author
42. Corner
44. Marine plant
45. Recent (comb. form)
46. Extinct bird
47. Squanders
49. Upright
52. African mammal
54. Peer
55. Mr. Parseghian
57. Victory (Greek)
59. Gain
62. Performed
63. Precipitation
67. Kiln
68. Hackneyed
70. Prefix for Chinese or European
71. Italian city
72. Assistants
73. Convinced
74. Style
75. Large crucifix
76. Leg part

DOWN

1. Mexican money
2. Playing cards
3. ____ *Touch of Mink* (1962 film with Cary Grant and Doris Day)
4. Insect (compound)
5. Decorates
6. Stringed instrument
7. One form of H_2O
8. Finals, e.g.
9. Cherry red
10. So be it
11. Harmonize
12. Painting, poetry, etc.
14. Always
22. Jump
24. One (Scottish)
26. Rapidly
27. Kind of beer
28. Greek goddess of peace
30. Character played by Bob Crane
31. Building extension
33. Greek letter
34. Wrath
35. Kind of contract
37. Scottish cap
39. Part of NORAD
43. Holiday drink
44. Footnote indicator
48. Make inquiries
50. Arab garment
51. Three (prefix)
53. Made whole
56. Fragrance
58. Famous date in March
59. Pontiff
60. Wading bird
61. Mountain in Greece
62. Tragic queen of Carthage
64. Soon (archaic)
65. Unused
66. Bump
69. One destination in Hope-Crosby film series

CROSSWORD PUZZLE NO. 30

Solution on page 509

ACROSS

1. One's home ground
5. Styles
10. *Much ____ about Nothing*
13. Under 21
14. Enforced absence
15. Cover
16. Character portrayed by Linda Lavin or Ellen Burstyn
17. Leftist
18. Tony's killer in *West Side Story*
20. Tennis term
21. Deserve
23. Missing judge
24. Exists
25. Maelstrom
26. Stare
27. Slog
28. Buttering up
32. Ointment
33. Intimate
34. Appia or Sacra
35. O'Hara plantation
36. Scrape
37. Catch the breath
38. Mr. Baba
39. Cries
40. Legal system
41. Flying objects
43. Window part
44. Indigo plant

45. Diversion
46. Ancient Roman penny
48. Mention
51. Monetary penalty
52. Bankers' org.
53. Nimble
54. Altar (Latin)
55. Edsel
57. Is able
58. Manmade fiber
60. Greek staple
61. Dutch town
62. Winter annoyance
63. Crimson or ebb

DOWN

1. Roofing or flooring
2. Connected whole
3. Mythical bird
4. Independence
5. Jolly
6. Beasts of burden
7. Acted
8. Subway's alter ego
9. Exude
10. Perched
11. Eat
12. Fragrance
13. African nation, capital Bamako
19. The folks who brought you this book

22. Put two and two together
23. Desist
25. Miss Fitzgerald
26. Cemetery units
27. Villainous Trojan prince
28. Hubbub
29. Dodge
30. Soprano Stevens
31. South Pacific island
32. "____ Hai"
33. Fisherman's basket
35. Scottish hat
36. Icy
37. Left
39. Best returns in tennis
40. Kennedy administration
42. Move easily
43. Peter or satyr
45. Tremendous
46. Superior to
47. Mentally sound
48. Rat or human
49. Mild oath
50. "____ eyes have seen..."
51. Cleaving tool
52. Caught up in
54. Sailor's "yes"
56. Yalie
59. ____ *dente*

CROSSWORD PUZZLE NO. 31

Solution on page 509

ACROSS

1. Superior
5. Impresses
9. Sharpen
13. Wings (Latin)
14. Mischievous child
15. ____ *Gauche*, Paris quarter
16. Torn
17. Bearing
18. Concept
19. Falls asleep
20. Skill
21. Goes in
23. Small mountain lake
25. Surname of actresses Sandra and Ruby
26. Mister (Spanish)
29. Cutting tool
32. Sketches
36. Tocsins
38. Soldiers
40. Sass
41. Meerschaum, e.g.
42. What you do to Cain
44. Cocktail mixer
45. Poem
46. Petroleum
47. Piano type
49. Takes a break
52. Thing (law)
54. Outstanding people (British slang)
55. Sandpiper
57. Small branch
59. Give away
62. Tiny
63. Soaks
67. Shah's kingdom
68. Anesthetic
70. Jewel
71. Discover
72. French pancake
73. Surname of pianist Peter
74. Golfer's items
75. Attaches
76. Chew

DOWN

1. Type of dance
2. Butter substitute
3. Smooth
4. Consider worthwhile
5. Oak seeds
6. *Heaven Can* ____ (1978 film with Warren Beatty)
7. Printer's measures
8. Amphetamines (slang)
9. Essayist, e.g.
10. Conceal
11. Always
12. Afternoon socials
14. Box
22. Actor Beatty
24. Limb
26. Flavor
27. Drop syllables in poetry
28. Spine tops
30. Deft
31. Midwestern state (abbr.)
33. Solitary
34. With greater expanse
35. Quarrels
37. Theatre-owner's favorite abbreviation
39. French possessive adjective
43. Tune
44. Monotonous rhythm
48. Hawaiian food staple
50. Developments
51. Body of water
53. Makes tea
56. Choose
58. *The Way We* ____ (1973 film)
59. Fissure
60. New York waterway
61. Weathercock
62. Cry of delight
64. Unobstructed
65. Substitute (prefix)
66. Gradual
69. Three (prefix)

CROSSWORD PUZZLE NO. 32

Solution on page 509

ACROSS

1. Slat
5. Headgear
8. Sailors (slang)
12. Mythical being
13. Created
14. Cradle of civilization
15. Take on cargo
16. Small orchestras
17. Peel
18. ____ *Maria*
19. Bowling alley
20. Pitch
22. Fate
24. Quite a few
27. Pen contents
28. Scout's badges
29. Thanks (British slang)
30. Inception
33. Paddled
34. Portable bed
35. Was clothed in
36. Challenged
37. Sharpen
38. Dined
39. Plunged
40. Fruit drink
41. Mrs. Kettle
42. Rescues
43. Like father like ____
44. Conspired

46. Meanders
50. British nobleman
51. Rational
52. Baby word
53. Staff
55. Lukewarm
57. Forehead
58. English river
59. Send out
60. Products of Poe or Petrarch
61. Thoroughfare
62. Send a bill
63. Horse fodder

DOWN

1. Exit
2. Mountain chain
3. Bind
4. Chemical symbol for helium
5. Sugar source
6. Appose
7. Irked
8. January birthstone
9. Willow
10. Place for storage
11. Unhappy
12. Opposite of 11 down
13. Synonym of 24 across
16. Financial institution
19. Dryer by-product

21. Roman poet (43 B.C.–18 A.D.)
23. Grow weary
24. Stitched
25. Make amends
26. In the future
28. *O tempora! O ____!*
30. Francis Marion's milieu
31. Entire
32. 100 square meters
33. Babbled madly
34. Cape or fish
36. Amused
37. Prefix for quarters or sight
39. Social engagement
40. Geometric solid
42. Boiled slowly
43. Type of soil
45. Puccini work
46. Cool one's heels
47. Plumed bird
48. Chambers
49. "…out of a ____ ear"
51. Make thread
53. Train unit
54. River (Spanish)
56. Flightless bird
57. Large snake
60. North Italian river

CROSSWORD PUZZLE NO. 33

Solution on page 510

ACROSS

1. Skin blemish
5. Actor Steiger
8. Social engagement
12. Klaxon
13. Word with salt or gold
14. Composer Stravinsky
15. Odds' partner
16. Bowling alleys
17. Swerve
18. Tennis term
19. Astronaut Rogers
20. Black (poet.)
22. Raised paved surface
24. Idle talk
27. Lodge member
28. Opera superstars
29. NYC landmark
30. Was concerned
33. Inspire loathing
34. "Rocks"
35. Spoken
36. Destined
37. Slender
38. Contretemps
39. *Private* ___
40. On hand
41. Before noon (abbr.)
42. Eatery
43. Pelt
44. From the side
46. Little fishes
50. Arkin or Alda
51. Tops
52. By way of
53. Speed
55. Perry Mason's milieu
57. Telephone
58. Dismounted
59. Absence of difficulty
60. Choral composition
61. Ceremony
62. Sere
63. Periods of history

DOWN

1. Type of meat
2. Command
3. Bandleader Brown
4. Printer's measure
5. Skater's surface
6. Uno
7. Earned
8. Turf pieces
9. Operative
10. ___ the line
11. Go wrong
12. Show to a chair
13. Archaic weapon
16. Serendipity
19. *The* ___ *Soprano*
21. Phoenician deity
23. Angler's equipment
24. Organ parts
25. Coherent
26. Foe
28. Inhibit
30. Sea growth
31. Scent
32. Uncooked
33. Composer of *Bolero*
34. Lyricist Gershwin
36. Provided funding for
37. Seabird
39. Italian monetary unit
40. Smallest in the litter
42. Remove
43. Closed hand
45. Opposite of 35 across
46. Mother in Montmartre
47. Egg-shaped
48. Tricks
49. Ubiquitous spice
51. Active
53. Golfer's goal
54. The former Mr. Clay
56. Paddle
57. Machine part
60. But in Bologna

448

CROSSWORD PUZZLE NO. 34

Solution on page 510

ACROSS

1. Caesar or slaw
6. Mild expletive
10. Attire
14. Conscious
15. Upon
16. Smell
17. Truths
18. Ice cream holder
19. Bird of peace
20. "...in the ____ of the beholder"
21. Basic unit of chemistry
24. Legal matter
25. Parched
26. Redirect
28. Deprived of food
31. Bullring
33. Instant
34. Winglike
35. Walked
39. Snaky fish
40. Chic
43. Miss Arden
44. Table (Spanish)
46. Folk dance
47. Ancient (archaic)
49. Donald Duck's girlfriend
51. Looks of distaste
52. "...preserve, protect and ____"

55. Athletic competition
56. Miss Gabor or Fraulein Braun
57. Vanquishes
60. Edge
63. Commanded
65. Silently says yes
66. Exchange
68. City and gulf in Arabia
69. Musical group
70. Covers the interior
71. Comedian Foxx
72. Witnessed
73. Symbols of oppression

DOWN

1. Strongbox
2. Absent
3. Product of tatting
4. Skill
5. Has earned
6. Sped
7. Minuscule particle
8. Musical sound
9. Buyers
10. Apollo or Thor
11. Worship
12. *Irish* ____
13. French seaport
22. Prevaricate

23. Container
25. Circle segment
27. Large tub
28. Curb
29. Depiction of genealogy
30. Afflicts
31. Tin Pan ____
32. Fence part
34. Affirmative votes
36. Counsel (British)
37. Finished
38. Tooth (Latin)
41. Symbols of Neptune
42. In good faith
45. Fruit drink
48. Permit
50. Plus
51. Tennis term
52. Preclude
53. Get away from
54. Timeworn
55. Creation of Erle Stanley Gardner
58. Direction of ship's prow
59. Songstress Adams
60. Military distinction
61. Thought in Thiers
62. Navy food
64. Goal
67. ____ de Janeiro

449

CROSSWORD PUZZLE NO. 35

Solution on page 510

ACROSS

1. Mountain in France or Italy
4. Stone monument
9. Afflict
14. German pronoun
15. *Mater lingua*
16. Church feature
17. Songfest (compound)
19. Roofing stone
20. Tiny bite
21. Athletic match
23. Month (Spanish)
24. Croat or Serb
26. Assault
28. Is successful at 26 across
29. "Oh, give me a ____ . . ."
30. Shredded
31. Moral failing
32. Kitchen necessity
33. Response (abbr.)
34. Military crew
37. Concerning
38. Aunt (Spanish)
39. Atmosphere (comb. form)
40. Egyptian sun god
41. Merchant
44. Troll
45. "Let us ____"
47. Move swiftly
48. Kind of gin
49. Net
50. Peel
52. Kind of bovine
53. Road in Rome
54. Altar to Apuleius
55. Long machine arm
56. Feather scarf
57. Salary in St. Moritz
59. Giving back
64. Metal brick
65. ____ *Laughing* (1961 Carl Reiner film)
66. Teachers' org.
67. *The 39* ____ (1935 Hitchcock film)
68. Severe
69. Eye affliction

DOWN

1. Onager
2. Fabius' 52
3. *Nom de plume* (2 words)
4. Strike
5. Such (Spanish)
6. WWII abbreviation
7. Dawdles
8. Hire
9. Inglorious
10. Building wing
11. Endurance
12. Corroded
13. Lock of hair
18. Granted
22. Egocentric pronoun
24. Word with cake or stop
25. Paramour
26. Relative of 67 across
27. College in New Rochelle, New York
28. Humor
31. To be (Spanish)
34. Put off
35. Incensed
34. Tier
38. ____ *Little Indians* (1966 film based on Agatha Christie)
39. Medicinal plant
42. Set up
43. Payable
44. Milieu
45. Vice-abbot
46. Holds on to
48. Macy's, Rich's, etc.
50. City liberated August 25, 1944
51. Common contraction
52. "Is that ____?"
55. Wagers
56. ____ and bred
58. Child's toy
60. Genevieve or Jeanne d'Arc (abbr.)
61. Thrice (Latin)
62. After taxes
63. Festive

CROSSWORD PUZZLE NO. 36

Solution on page 510

ACROSS

1. Insects favored by Napoleon and Vergil
5. Die down
10. Arrived
14. Widemouthed jar
15. Relating to the cheek
16. Greek god of war
17. Pace
18. Babble on
19. Tidy
20. Unmitigated
22. Food morsel
23. Silly, pointless
24. Holy ____
25. Charged particle
27. Whirlpool
29. Emerald ____
30. Poor man's caviar
31. Monk's title
34. Bauble
37. Position
39. Half of a dilemma
40. Perched
41. One of the Twelve
45. Packages
48. Number of amendments in the Bill of Rights
49. Thing (Latin)
50. Urban disturbance
51. Castle adjunct
52. Globe
53. Make lace
56. Avarice
59. Cleopatra's end
61. Steeple
63. British nobleman
64. Bend over
66. Wading bird
67. Bones (Latin)
68. Nervous
69. Home of 66 across
70. Strip
71. To eat (German)
72. Three (Spanish)

DOWN

1. Fraudulent
2. Make cheerful
3. In crowd
4. Fill
5. Electrical unit
6. Minor nobleman
7. Winglike
8. Rags
9. Before
10. Shrewd
11. District
12. Ogrish
13. Italian noble family
21. Gamble
23. Brainstorm
26. Bullring bravo
28. Finish an *i*
29. Motels
31. Rasp
32. Irritate
33. Social insects
34. Demonstrative pronoun
35. Lasso
36. Press clothing
38. Diplomacy
42. Walked on
43. Meadow
44. Country homes
45. Suggest
46. Tune
47. Reiner and Roy
51. Purple Heart, e.g.
53. Famous *flumen*
54. Wake
55. Examines
56. Mess, melange (slang)
57. Mother of JFK and RFK
58. Gaelic
60. *My Three* ____
62. Half a quart
64. Sault ____ Marie
65. Writing tool

CROSSWORD PUZZLE NO. 37

Solution on page 511

ACROSS

1. Addled
5. Put in position
10. Church feature
14. Away from the wind
15. Regretted purchase
16. Close
17. Numerical suffix
18. Controversial power source
19. Dog in *Peter Pan*
20. Classify
22. Hides
25. Chasm
27. Great Lakes canal system
28. Secondary academy (abbr.)
30. Tempest
32. Plum, cherry, or beefsteak
37. Greek letter
39. Sign of the zodiac
41. Clocked
42. Uncommon
44. Men
46. Provide temporarily
47. Vision
49. Slowly (music)
51. Compass point
52. Declared
54. Emends
56. Expression of indecision
57. Sponge
59. Native of Aberdeen
60. Brow
65. Nut
69. On top of
70. Close
72. Strange (variant)
73. Raise
74. Indian tribe
75. Pennsylvania port
76. Finishes
77. Jewish school
78. Large amounts (slang)

DOWN

1. Computer input
2. Beverages
3. Prices
4. Corelli and Caruso
5. Candidate's stands
6. Allow
7. Andy's friend
8. "If winter ____ ..."
9. French preposition
10. Name of two of Henry VIII's wives
11. Word with bog or moss
12. Of sound mind
13. Periods in history
21. Miss Coolidge or Miss Moreno
23. Small bed
24. Source
26. Battle of barristers
28. Corrals
29. Commence
31. Free-for-all
33. Cypriot currency
34. Iowa college town
35. Verb feature
36. More unusual
38. Region
40. Dispatches
43. Sup
45. Demanding person
48. Network
50. Indian tribe
53. Buck's mate
55. Surname of Perry Mason's secretary
58. Outdated
60. Golfer's warning
61. Oast
62. Study
63. Is wrong
64. Late
66. Last of the Julio-Claudian emperors of Rome
67. Ireland
68. Caustic substances
71. Grow
74. Midwestern state (abbr.)

452

CROSSWORD PUZZLE NO. 38

Solution on page 511

ACROSS

1. Sufficient
6. House (Spanish)
10. Radar screen image
14. Type of bear
15. Yale alumni
16. Let up
17. Kind of cop
20. Milk (prefix)
21. Bravo! (Spanish)
22. The House of Lords
23. Before
24. Paid athlete
25. Shoe
27. Land measure
28. "...the ____ of the free..."
29. TV screen
32. Exalted
35. Row
36. Fabius' 52
37. Sloping walkway
38. Packrat
39. "In the ____ of the Mountain King" (*Peer Gynt*)
40. Here in Haiti
41. Modify
42. Turn aside
43. Favorite
44. Deceased
45. "A Hymn to ____" (*My Fair Lady*)
46. Petite (suffix)

47. Something that disappears when you stand
48. Man's name
51. Stadium
54. To be (Spanish)
55. Petticoat
56. County in merry old England
60. Type of bag
61. Require
62. Hang in the air
63. At a distance
64. Finales
65. Paradises

DOWN

1. Fruit found in 65 across
2. Grinding tooth
3. Locale
4. Milk in Marseilles
5. Sea eagle
6. Stringed instrument
7. Lily plant
8. Stay put
9. Shade tree
10. Aggrieve
11. Brocaded fabric
12. Bavarian river
13. Cages
18. Rope
19. Poem by Horace

24. "A chicken in every ____"
25. Farm implement
26. Outstanding person (British slang)
27. Talk (slang)
28. Embankment
29. Applaud
30. Anger
31. Prepare soil for planting
32. Valise
33. Competition
34. Send forth
35. Nonglossy finish
38. Strip of wood
39. Skirt bottom
41. Russian territory
42. Mr. van Winkle
45. Damage
46. Become part of
47. Starring roles
48. ____ and well
49. Warning device
50. Imitators
51. Architectural pier
52. Top of a building
53. Miss Place in *Butch Cassidy and the Sundance Kid*
54. Remove
55. Did a blacksmith's job
57. Compass point
58. Top-ranking (abbr.)
59. Novel by Haggard

CROSSWORD PUZZLE NO. 39

Solution on page 511

ACROSS

1. Small drum
6. Word of regret
10. Cover with
14. Macy's, e.g.
15. Hindu queen
16. Aura
17. Distant
18. Large racing sail
20. Brink
21. Son of Aphrodite
23. German industrial city
24. Moslem nation
25. Yawn
27. Unexpected
30. Opera singer
31. ____ mode (French, 2 words)
34. In the manner of an old woman
35. New
36. "It ____ the best of times..."
37. *A Chorus* ____
38. Misleading criterion
39. Where people are often taken
40. Summer in St. Moritz
41. Borge and Andersen
42. To the point
43. *Mal de* ____
44. Romulus' route
45. Phantom
46. Indochinese nation
47. Provide with a roof
48. Discolor
51. Trolley
52. Final figure
55. Ice cream flavor
58. Make sound of a trumpet
60. Female French friend
61. Eponymous Verdi heroine
62. Rabbit fur
63. Last
64. Stink
65. Upright

DOWN

1. Ivan or Peter
2. Mythical Norse king
3. Loud noise
4. Gold (Italian)
5. Umpire
6. Incendiary crime
7. Circuits
8. Cuckoo
9. Without (Spanish)
10. Big name in banking
11. Twelve ____
12. Toward shelter
13. Shredded
19. Location of Mt. Everest
22. Was a candidate
24. Member of *Monty Python's Flying Circus*
25. "What ____?"
26. Declare
27. Historic Massachusetts town
28. Anagrammatic antonym of "untie"
29. Beanery
30. Capital of Delaware
31. Oscar or Tony
32. Lariat
33. Bent out of shape
35. Part of a Roman month
38. Roman statesman, baiter of Carthage
39. Type of duck
41. Artemis
42. Sewing tool
45. "...against a ____ of troubles..."
46. Liquid measure
47. Frog's voice
48. Mast
49. Famous flyer
50. Location of 24 and 46 across and 19 down
51. No man's waiter
52. Top of the spine
53. First name of 24 down
54. Circus structure
56. Auto
57. Hasten
59. Roman household god

CROSSWORD PUZZLE NO. 40

Solution on page 511

ACROSS

1. Fasten together
6. Leak
10. Beatles film
14. Passenger
15. Concerning the mouth
16. Margarine
17. Egg-shaped
18. Turkish currency unit
19. Peaceful bird
20. Part of mph
21. Customers
24. Domesticated animal
25. Peruse
26. Bath requirements
28. Abrade
31. Play part
33. Inseminate
34. Yokel
35. Subdue
39. Part of USAF
40. Most agile
43. Zero
44. Hurried
46. John
47. Carries on
49. Ties
51. Evolve
52. Attach
55. Bread in Brindisi
56. Malt beverage
57. Piloted
60. Lawyers' org.
63. Tiny insect
65. Chorus member
66. *Citron*, but rarely Citroen
68. Oklahoma city
69. Stone surface
70. Happening
71. Sandhill (British)
72. Masculine
73. Transmits

DOWN

1. Trim
2. Not taped
3. Jewish month
4. NY opera house
5. Tenets
6. Word with rock or gold
7. Lake, city, or canal
8. Merit
9. Records (slang)
10. Mortar container
11. Marry in secret
12. Smooth
13. Homer and Ginsberg
22. New Guinea town
23. Male child
25. Also-____
27. Type of blanket or hen
28. Resorts
29. Brad
30. Scarce
31. Oil-bearing plants
32. Female student
34. Make tea
36. Heroine of *The King and I*
37. Catcher's glove
38. Otherwise
41. Figment of the imagination
42. Rolls
45. Infamous insecticide
48. Dined
50. Abode (abbr.)
51. Miss West
52. Celebrated
53. Straighten (variant)
54. Take place, take hold (2 words)
55. Investigate
58. Scarlett's middle child
59. Common Latin abbreviation
60. So be it
61. 007
62. Social insects
64. Dutch town
67. *All About* ____

455

THE ANSWERS

CORNUCOPIA . . . . **page 12**

1. The British Museum
2. Australia
3. New Jersey
4. Churchill Downs
5. 1960s
6. Quetzal
7. Seminoles
8. Birmingham, U.K.
9. Tunisia
10. 21 months
11. Liver
12. Australia
13. Potatoes
14. The Rose Bowl
15. Juniper berries
16. Copper and tin
17. Stinging jellyfish
18. Alben Barkley
19. The Poodle
20. *The Coconuts*
21. A conjurer
22. Chess

EMPORIA OF IMPORT . . . . **page 14**

1. Dallas
2. New York
3. London
4. Hartford
5. Boston
6. Moscow
7. Paris
8. Copenhagen
9. Paris
10. Oslo
11. New York
12. New York
13. Boston
14. Paris
15. London
16. London
17. Madrid
18. New York
19. London
20. San Francisco
21. Chicago
22. Mexico City
23. New York
24. New York
25. Rome

DO YOU KNOW KIDS? . . . . **page 15**

1. *False*   A child's brain and intelligence develop more during the years between birth and age six than during any other period in life.
2. *False*   Babbling is the first experimentation with speech. The infant uses every speech sound in babbling. Ultimately, the baby will retain the sounds of her own language and discard the other sounds.
3. *True*   In addition, the child has reinvented complex grammatical rules and can use most parts of speech almost correctly.
4. *False*   They should be given as much opportunity and space to explore as then can within the rules of safety.
5. *True*   They should not be ignored. What may sound silly to you, is serious to a child. Complex questions should be answered as simply as possible. Your laughter or disinterest may stifle curiousity and cut off an important channel of learning.
6. *False*   If a child shows interest, it is not wrong to try to teach him to read; but do not force a child who has not shown such a desire.
7. *False*   Children learn through all five senses, but some children seem to emphasize one sense more than the others. When a baby puts objects into her mouth, worrisome as it is to parents, she is trying to learn something.
8. *False*   Getting into things is not naughtiness. It is the manifestation of a natural and insatiable drive to learn.
9. *False*   Toys should be creative, capable of being used in many ways. A box can be a house, a boat, a car, or any other wonderful thing the child decides to make it.
10. *False*   The world outside the home provides many learning experiences. Children should go to the market, shoemaker, barbershop with parents. They should meet people outside the family. However, plan your trips so they will be short and still leave time for you to give your child enough attention.

FIT FOR A DOG . . . . **page 16**

1. Dog-eared
2. Gone to the dogs
3. In the doghouse
4. Doggerel
5. Dog's life
6. Dogwood
7. Dogfight
8. Dogtrot
9. Dog it
10. Dogma
11. Dogsled
12. Dogged
13. Raining cats and dogs
14. Dog paddle
15. Dog flower
16. Dogtooth
17. Dog-eat-dog
18. Shaggy-dog story
19. Dog-tired
20. Dogfish
21. Doggone
22. Dog's death
23. Dogcart
24. Dog tag
25. Dog in the manger
26. Dog-cheap
27. Dog days
28. Dogface
29. Let sleeping dogs lie
30. Hot dog
31. Dogwatch
32. Dog nap
33. Dogcatcher
34. Mad dogs and Englishmen
35. Put on the dog
36. Hangdog

1. *False*. Pandemonium was the name given to the principal city of Hell by Milton in *Paradise Lost*, and has since come to mean "a wild unrestrained uproar or tumult." Pneumonia is a disease of the lungs.
2. *False*. An octoroon is a person with one-eighth Negro blood. A macaroon is an almond cookie.
3. *False*. An accolade is a salutation or expression of approval or praise. An aspirin is a headache pill.
4. *False*. The Sugar Bowl is in Louisiana. The Super Bowl is in Texas.
5. *True*. Finocchio looks like celery but tastes like licorice.
6. *False*. Gorgonzola is a strong blue cheese.
7. *True*. Pablo Picasso was born in Malaga, Spain, and studied art in Barcelona and Madrid. He left Spain for artistic reasons, and stayed in exile in Paris for political reasons.
8. *False*. Shakespeare wrote 11 tragedies and 12 comedies.
9. *True*. This motto describes the union of states in The United States.
10. *False*. David slew Goliath with a slingshot.
11. *True*.
12. *False*. Insects possess three pairs of legs.
13. *True*. Latex is a substance found in the rubber tree.
14. *False*. The first emperor of the Holy Roman Empire was Charlemagne. Frederick the Great was King of Prussia from 1712 to 1786.
15. *False*. An estuary is a wide river mouth in a submerged valley.
16. *False*. The Pleiades is a group of stars, and in Greek mythology represents the seven daughters of Atlas.
17. *True*.
18. *False*. Emma Woodhouse is the heroine of *Emma*, a novel by Jane Austen.
19. *True*. Maria Mitchell was an astronomer who lived from 1818 to 1889.
20. *True*. They were: Ulysses Grant, Rutherford Hayes, James Garfield, Benjamin Harrison, William McKinley, William Howard Taft, and Warren Harding.
21. *False*. The 1932 Summer Olympics were held in Los Angeles.
22. *True*.
23. *True*.
24. *False*. Socrates' wife was named Xantippe. Penelope was the wife of Ulysses in Homer's *Odyssey*.
25. *False*. Joan Fontaine, whose real name is Joan de Havilland, is the sister of Olivia de Havilland.
26. *False*. Daylight saving time goes into effect on the last Sunday in April.
27. *True*. An escutcheon is literally an ornamental shield, figuratively a symbol of honor.
28. *False*. Elias Howe is credited for making the first successful machine in 1846.
29. *False*. Florida is the Sunshine State; California is the Golden State.
30. *True*.
31. *False*. They were brothers.
32. *False*. Addison and Steele were English essayists who published *The Spectator* in the early 18th century.
33. *False*. A marimba is a musical instrument resembling a xylophone.
34. *False*. The language of Brazil is Portuguese.
35. *True*.
36. *True*.
37. *False*. More people die of heart disease than of any other disease.
38. *False*. It was written by Booth Tarkington. Mark Twain wrote *Tom Sawyer*.
39. *True*.
40. *True*.

1. *False*. The largest country in the world is the U.S.S.R., at 8,650,000 miles. China is the second largest country, at 3,691,500 miles.
2. *True*.
3. *True*.
4. *False*. A tatterdemalian is a person wearing ragged or tattered clothing.
5. *False*. The most populous country in the world is China. India is the second most populous country.
6. *True*.
7. *False*. Johnny Appleseed's real name was John Chapman. Paul Bunyan was the folk hero of lumber-camp tall tales.
8. *False*. An oxymoron is a figure of speech that combines opposite or contradictory ideas, such as: terribly good, or sweet sorrow.
9. *False*. Vivien Leigh played Scarlett O'Hara.
10. *True*.
11. *False*. Tagliatelle is a type of noodle or pasta. Maria Taglioni was the ballerina.
12. *False*. Aaron Burr killed Alexander Hamilton in a duel.
13. *False*. Mali is a country in West Africa.
14. *True*.
15. *False*. A numismatist is a person who collects or studies money and medals. An entomologist studies insects.
16. *True*.

457

17. *False.* The author of *Volpone* was Shakespeare's contemporary, Ben Jonson.
18. *True.*
19. *True.*
20. *False.* The *New York Gazette,* brought out by William Bradford in 1725, was the first New York newspaper.
21. *False.* Something that is nugatory is worthless.
22. *True,* in 1910.
23. *True.*
24. *True.*
25. *False.* James S. Thurman invented the vacuum cleaner, in 1899. James Thurber (1894-1961) was a popular cartoonist and writer.
26. *False.* A griffin doesn't exist anywhere. It is a mythical animal with the body of a lion and the head of an eagle.
27. *True.*
28. *True.*
29. *False.* Escudos are Portuguese coins. The monetary unit of Peru is the sol.
30. *False.* It is 7:00 P.M. in Cairo, or seven hours later than New York.

BEATLEMANIA. . . . . page 22

1. George Harrison
2. Peter Best
3. The Ed Sullivan Show
4. *Eleanor Rigby*
5. *A Hard Day's Night* (1964)
6. 1967
7. Richard Starkey
8. Liverpool
9. Brian Epstein
10. 1943
11. *Love Me Do*
12. Yoko Ono
13. 1964
14. Buddy Holly
15. George Harrison
16. Paul McCartney
17. *Satisfaction,* sung by the Beatles' chief rivals, *The Rolling Stones*
18. 1974
19. Wings
20. Paul McCartney
21. $1,000,000
22. Don and Phil
23. *Magical Mystery Tour*
24. LSD
25. *Abbey Road*

IN YOUR CUPS. . . . . page 24

1. Potatoes
2. Apples
3. An aperitif
4. Caraway seed
5. Coffee, whipped cream, and whiskey
6. Plain tomato juice
7. Crème de menthe, crème de cacao, and cream
8. Anisette
9. Very dry
10. Kahlua and vodka
11. Corn
12. Campari
13. Sugar cane or molasses
14. 43 percent
15. Whiskey, sugar, bitters, and club soda
16. Justerini and Brooks
17. Tequila, salt, lime juice, and Triple Sec
18. Gin, a dash of vermouth, and a green olive (or a lemon twist)
19. The sap of the Mexican agave plant
20. 8 to 12 percent
21. Cin cin
22. 1/3 of the population
23. Cointreau, lemon juice, and brandy
24. Dark beer made from malt
25. Pony

NAME THE PRODUCT . . . . page 26

1. Pepsi
2. Winston
3. Maxwell House Coffee
4. Marlboro
5. Dutch Cleanser
6. Schlitz. But Miller's is right, too—it used to be their slogan.
7. Cott
8. Excedrin
9. Tetley Tea
10. Charmin
11. Tareyton
12. Miller's
13. Coke
14. Hanes
15. Pillsbury
16. Merit
17. Volkswagen Rabbit
18. Chock Full O'Nuts
19. Jell-O
20. Wheaties
21. Philip Morris
22. Clairol Herbal Essence
23. Heinz Ketchup
24. Seven-Up
25. Palmolive Gold
26. Toyota
27. Purina Dog Food
28. Prell shampoo
29. Cover Girl
30. Dentyne

A LA MODE . . . . page 28

1. 1960s
2. Coco Chanel
3. Empire
4. 1920s
5. A hoop skirt
6. Mary Quant
7. Silk
8. Culottes
9. Hooded cloak
10. Hat
11. Nineteenth
12. Domino
13. Ermine
14. A farthingale
15. Shawl
16. Garter Belts
17. Pillbox
18. Madras
19. Charles Dana Gibson
20. Young girls' pinafores
21. Collar
22. Kimono
23. Cardigan
24. Waist
25. 1970s
26. American
27. 15%

HOUSE BEAUTIFUL . . . . page 30

1. Hepplewhite
2. Piano
3. Canopy for a bed
4. Enamelware
5. Desk
6. Four movable legs, arranged in pairs
7. Staircase
8. Eighteenth
9. An étagère
10. Legs; cabrioles are curved legs common in Queen Anne and Chippendale furniture
11. Three
12. Oak
13. A bed on casters that can be rolled beneath a larger bed when not in use
14. Boston Rocker
15. New York
16. Scandinavia
17. Victorian
18. Windsor chair
19. Clothing
20. Wood-paneling
21. The dining room
22. A pendulum clock enclosed in a tall, narrow cabinet
23. Display bric-a-brac
24. A long wooden bench with arms
25. 92.5%

WHO WAS THAT LADY? . . . . page 32

1. Barbara Stanwyck
2. Joan Crawford
3. Katharine Hepburn
4. Bette Davis
5. Natalie Wood
6. Greta Garbo
7. Irene Dunne
8. Gloria Swanson
9. Greta Garbo
10. Ruth Chatterton
11. Vanessa Redgrave
12. Greta Garbo
13. Ruth Chatterton
14. Norma Shearer
15. Joan Fontaine
16. Ginger Rogers
17. Diane Keaton
18. Greer Garson
19. Leslie Caron
20. Greer Garson
21. Ingrid Bergman
22. Rosalind Russell
23. Isabelle Huppert
24. Anne Baxter
25. Shirley MacLaine
26. Giulietta Masina
27. Julie Andrews
28. Debbie Reynolds
29. Lynn Redgrave
30. Faye Dunaway
31. Joanne Woodward
32. Vanessa Redgrave
33. Genvieve Bujold
34. Maggie Smith
35. Ellen Burstyn
36. Raquel Welch
37. Mia Farrow
38. Julie Andrews
39. Ruth Gordon
40. Barbra Streisand
41. Leslie Caron
42. Elizabeth Taylor
43. Cybill Shepherd
44. Pearl White
45. Julie Christie
46. Sissy Spacek
47. Miriam Hopkins
48. Rosalind Russell
49. Bette Davis
50. Sue Lyon

GEM-DANDY! . . . . page 35

1. Emerald
2. 40th
3. Yellow
4. 200 mg.
5. Cut
6. Corundum
7. Diamond
8. January
9. Russia
10. Tinstone
11. The western Pacific
12. 69
13. An aquamarine weighing 520,000 carats, which was found near Marambala, Brazil in 1910

DO YOU KNOW ART? . . . . page 36

1. The Louvre, Paris, France
2. Botticelli
3. Vlaminck
4. Degas
5. Impressionists
6. Fourteenth
7. Still Lifes
8. The Impressionists
9. Dante Gabriel Rossetti
10. Gilbert Stuart
11. American
12. Georgia O'Keeffe
13. Surrealist
14. Raphael
15. Fra Lippo Lippi
16. Action painting
17. Pieter Breughel
18. J.A.M. Whistler
19. Matisse
20. Vincent Van Gogh
21. The Spanish Civil War
22. William Blake
23. Delacroix
24. Wassily Kandinsky
25. Modigliani
26. Leningrad

COLOSSAL COUNTRIES . . . . page 38

1. U.S.S.R. (8,650,000 miles)
2. Canada (3,851,809 miles)
3. China (3,691,500 miles)
4. United States (3,615,122 miles)
5. Brazil (3,286,488 miles)
6. Australia (2,967,909 miles)
7. India (1,261,810 miles)
8. Argentina (1,072,763 miles)
9. Sudan (967,491 miles)
10. Algeria (896,588 miles)

SPELLING BEE . . . . page 39

1. Disastrous
2. Despair
3. Rung
4. Undoubtably or undoubtedly
5. Disbelief
6. Conference
7. Paraphernalia
8. Breakfast
9. Automatically
10. Retrieve
11. Immediately
12. Greased
13. Lightning

14. Vehicle
15. Vengeance
16. Suddenly
17. Appeared
18. Attendant
19. Impeccably
20. Relief

A PANOPLY OF PHOBIAS..... page 40

1. Heights
2. Beds
3. Thunder
4. Being buried alive
5. Cats
6. Depth
7. Enclosed places
8. Doctors
9. Open places
10. Water
11. Dead bodies
12. Bullets
13. Fears
14. Learning
15. Rain

THE GAME OF STATES .... page 41

1. Alabama—The Cotton State
2. Arizona—The Grand Canyon State
3. California—The Golden State
4. Connecticut—The Nutmeg State
5. Florida—The Sunshine State
6. Illinois—The Prairie State
7. Indiana—The Hoosier State
8. Iowa—The Hawkeye State
9. Kansas—The Sunflower State
10. Kentucky—The Bluegrass State
11. Maine—The Pine Tree State
12. Massachusetts—The Bay State
13. Michigan—The Wolverine State
14. Nebraska—The Cornhusker State
15. Nevada—The Silver State
16. New Hampshire—The Granite State
17. New Jersey—The Garden State
18. New York—The Empire State
19. Ohio—The Buckeye State
20. Oklahoma—The Sooner State
21. Oregon—The Beaver State
22. South Carolina—The Palmetto State
23. South Dakota—The Coyote State
24. Texas—The Lone Star State
25. Utah—The Beehive State
26. Vermont—The Green Mountain State

CAN YOU SPOT THE INTRUDER? .... page 42

1. PETER. Paul, not Peter, was one of the rock group, The Beatles.
2. BERTH. The rest are forms of wheeled vehicles.
3. CORONET. The rest are musical instruments.
4. CROCODILE. The rest are land animals.
5. LLAMA. The rest are horses.
6. EDSEL. All are names of cars, but Edsel is the only one not named after an animal.
7. ELBOW. The rest are parts of the face.
8. RULER. The rest are used for writing.
9. CONCERTO. The rest are forms of poetry.
10. SODA. The rest are alcoholic drinks.
11. PATHETIC. The rest are terms which imply laughter.
12. FLOUR. The rest are dairy products.
13. FEEL. The rest are past tense.
14. AUNT. The rest are male family members.
15. TEETH. The rest come in pairs.
16. SWAY. The rest are ways of walking.
17. COMMENCE. The rest mean to end.
18. SUN. The rest are planets which revolve around the sun.

PRESIDENTS AND VICE-PRESIDENTS .... page 43

1. Harry Truman—Alben Barkley
2. Herbert Hoover—Charles Curtis
3. Warren Harding—Calvin Coolidge
4. William Taft—James Sherman
5. Dwight Eisenhower—Richard Nixon
6. John Adams—Thomas Jefferson
7. Gerald Ford—Nelson Rockefeller
8. George Washington—John Adams
9. Franklin Roosevelt—Harry Truman
10. William McKinley—Theodore Roosevelt
11. Calvin Coolidge—Charles Dawes
12. John Kennedy—Lyndon Johnson
13. Theodore Roosevelt—Charles Fairbanks
14. Richard Nixon—Spiro Agnew
15. Woodrow Wilson—Thomas Marshall

GAME FOR THE GOURMET...... page 44

1. White wine and tomatoes
2. Hollandaise sauce
3. French pancakes with a flaming orange sauce
4. Steak Tartare
5. Spaghetti
6. Cake
7. Beef and onions
8. Spicy
9. Apricot jam
10. Scallops
11. Crushed grain
12. Saffron
13. A French roll made with lots of butter
14. Saffron
15. A fresh basil sauce
16. Barbecued in a tomato and molasses sauce
17. Egg yolks, sugar, and wine
18. Green peppers stuffed with meat or cheese
19. Mulligatawny soup
20. A dash

21. Celery, apples, and walnuts
22. Mozzarella cheese and tomato sauce
23. Ricotta cheese and sometimes ham
24. Cumin, coriander, turmeric, and other pungent spices
25. A choice steak dish, cooked in butter
26. Potatoes

ALL ABOUT EVE . . . . page 46

1. Poland
2. Hull House
3. Photography
4. Emmeline Pankhurst
5. 1558
6. Catherine Breshkovsky
7. A champion athlete
8. Harriet Ross Tubman
9. Elementary education
10. Ellen Swallow Richards
11. George Eliot
12. Film director
13. Elizabeth Fry
14. Birth control pioneer
15. The Crimean War
16. The first woman cabinet minister in Europe. She was Secretary of Labor under Irish President Eamon de Valera.
17. An anthropologist
18. Golda Meir
19. Sister Kenny
20. Mary Baker Eddy
21. Charlotte Perkins Gilman
22. Dancer and choreographer
23. Chingling Soong Sun
24. Anne Sullivan Macy
25. Rosa Ponselle
26. A freed slave who was the first black to win a court action against whites
27. 1926
28. Sigrid Undset
29. New Zealand
30. 29
31. Ruth Benedict
32. Virginia Apgar
33. Belle Starr
34. Marie Tussaud
35. Swiss

VOCABULARY QUIZ . . . . page 49

1. Blast of trumpets
2. Science of wines
3. Childish
4. Brilliant
5. Lustful
6. Painkiller
7. Secret
8. Brawl
9. Gauzy
10. Incisive
11. Praise
12. Charming
13. Essence
14. Habitual criminal
15. Unfeeling
16. Blunder
17. Outcast
18. Substitute
19. Revolutionary
20. Lowest point
21. Plunder
22. Sentimental
23. Have effect
24. Revoke
25. Journey
26. Continue to exist
27. Intruder
28. Omen
29. Shyness
30. Tranquil

BALLETOMANIA . . . . page 52

1. A rapid turn on the toe or ball of the foot
2. Tchaikovsky
3. George Balanchine
4. *Coppelia*
5. Sadler's Wells
6. Italy
7. 19th
8. Marius Petipa
9. *The Dying Swan*, created especially for Miss Pavlova by Michel Fokine
10. Aurora
11. Mikhail Baryshnikov
12. Peter Martins
13. *Swan Lake*
14. *The Firebird*
15. Alicia Alonso
16. *The Red Shoes*
17. Carlotta Grisi
18. *La Fille Mal Gardée* (1786)
19. *Petrouchka*
20. Margot Fonteyn
21. Two, a ballerina and a danseur
22. Jean Georges Noverre
23. Five
24. Romantic
25. *Nutcracker Suite*

THE DOODLE QUIZ . . . . page 54

1. Joan Miro
2. Frank Sinatra
3. Sir Alec Guinness
4. Igor Stravinsky
5. Norman Rockwell
6. Leonardo Da Vinci
7. Ginger Rogers
8. Richard Nixon
9. Jean Dubuffet
10. Bob Hope
11. Cornelia Otis Skinner
12. James Michener
13. Lily Pons
14. Pat Boone
15. Princess Grace of Monaco
16. Betty Grable
17. Pablo Picasso
18. Duke Ellington
19. Enrico Caruso
20. Paul Klee

STREETWISE. . . . . **page 59**

1. Paris
2. London
3. New York
4. Los Angeles
5. Rome
6. New York
7. Boston
8. Paris
9. Los Angeles
10. Atlanta
11. Copenhagen
12. Leningrad
13. Berlin
14. Nice
15. Tel Aviv
16. New York
17. London
18. East Berlin
19. Chicago
20. New Orleans
21. San Francisco
22. New Orleans
23. London
24. Washington, D.C.
25. London

FOR BOGART FANS . . . . **page 60**

1. *The Harder They Fall*
2. Magazine illustrator
3. A stage manager
4. *The Drifter*
5. Helen Mencken
6. $750
7. Victor McLaglen
8. *Three on a Match*
9. Betty
10. Sam Spade
11. *Casablanca*
12. *To Have and Have Not*
13. Katharine Hepburn
14. The Rat Pack
15. John Huston
16. *Swing Your Lady*
17. Two, a son, Stephen, and a daughter, Leslie, named after Leslie Howard, Bogart's co-star in *The Petrified Forest*. Both children were products of Bogart's fourth marriage, to Lauren Bacall.
18. Cancer
19. *The Caine Mutiny*
20. Claire Luce
21. *The Two Mrs. Carrolls*
22. *Dark Victory*
23. *The Santana*
24. Truman Capote
25. *Casablanca*, in 1943.
26. *The Big Sleep*
27. Peter Lorre

POT-AU-FEU . . . . **page 62**

1. Angola, Africa, with a rate of 30.2 deaths per thousand of population
2. Beginner
3. *A Bill of Divorcement*
4. 1947
5. A tortoise; the giant tortoise lives as long as 300 years
6. The cormorant
7. Feud
8. A list of books published previously
9. The Sahara

10. 1895
11. A cave dweller
12. Ostrich
13. The Battle of the Marne
14. Bright lights used in the theater
15. Taft
16. Children's apron
17. 1889, between Kilrain and Sullivan
18. $200 per pound
19. In the Great Lakes
20. Camel
21. *Midsummer Night's Dream*
22. Michelangelo
23. Manuscript in which later writing is superimposed on earlier writing
24. Feasting and rejoicing
25. Wandering knight
26. Coypu
27. Dover
28. Emily Brontë
29. Wasteful

WHERE, OH, WHERE? . . . . **page 64**

1. New York City, U.S.A.
2. Jerusalem, Israel
3. Paris, France
4. Cairo, Egypt
5. Rome, Italy
6. Leningrad, Russia
7. Giza, Egypt
8. Pisa, Italy
9. Rome, Italy
10. New York City, U.S.A.
11. Agra, India
12. Venice, Italy
13. London, England
14. Blarney, Ireland
15. Moscow, Russia
16. Milan, Italy
17. Granada, Spain
18. San Francisco, California, U.S.A.
19. Athens, Greece
20. London, England
21. Mecca, Saudi Arabia
22. Paris, France
23. Madrid, Spain
24. Boston, Massachusetts, U.S.A.

GRAND TOUR . . . . **page 65**

1. Paris, France
2. Nairobi, Africa
3. Jerusalem, Israel
4. Athens, Greece
5. Vienna, Austria
6. Marrakesh, Morocco, Africa
7. London, England
8. Rome, Italy
9. New York City, U.S.A.
10. Nice, France
11. Dublin, Ireland
12. Buenos Aires, Argentina
13. Hong Kong

462

14. Haifa, Israel
15. Madrid, Spain
16. Paris, France
17. Singapore
18. Miami Beach, Florida, U.S.A.
19. West Berlin, Germany
20. Seoul, South Korea
21. Zurich, Switzerland
22. Isfahan, Iran
23. San Francisco, California, U.S.A.
24. Melbourne, Australia
25. London, England

FOR CHAPLIN FANS . . . . page 66

1. The Little Tramp
2. 1889
3. Four
4. D.W. Griffith
5. Edna Purviance
6. *A Night Out*, made in 1915
7. Hitler
8. London
9. Mary Pickford
10. Eugene O'Neill
11. *The Kid*
12. *The Gold Rush*
13. The Lone Prospector
14. Two years
15. Paulette Goddard
16. *A Countess from Hong Kong*. Incidentally, this movie starred Sophia Loren
17. Five
18. Paulette Goddard
19. Switzerland
20. 1972
21. Joan Barry
22. Scraps
23. Geraldine
24. Orson Welles
25. 1977

GRAB BAG . . . . page 68

1. A person of low intelligence
2. Lhasa, Tibet, at an elevation of 12,002 feet
3. Alexander Pope
4. Deer
5. Guinea, Africa, with an average life expectancy of 27 years
6. Musical instrument which resembles a xylophone
7. Timbuktu, Mali, where the average temperature is 84.7°F
8. Reversion to characteristics in one's remote ancestors
9. Bette Davis
10. Gigantic, after Swift's land of giants in *Gulliver's Travels*
11. A quadrilateral rectangle having only two sides parallel
12. Walt Whitman

13. Goldsmith Maid
14. Eatables
15. 29.7 mph
16. The British Museum
17. Giuseppe Verdi
18. Golfer
19. Australia
20. Matthew Webb
21. Bees
22. New Jersey
23. Earth
24. Churchill Downs
25. Stretch of land off New Jersey

DRIVE, HE SAID . . . . page 70

1. One per two persons
2. Gottlieb Daimler
3. Panhard
4. 1893
5. 1895
6. 25 percent
7. Chevrolet
8. The Cadillac
9. 125 million
10. 1939
11. The United States
12. New York
13. 1914, on Euclid Ave. in Cleveland, Ohio
14. Austrians, with 386 auto deaths per million population annually
15. 55 mph
16. The Mercedes-Benz Co., whose Mercedes 600 Pullman retails for $90,000
17. Craig Breedlove
18. Augusta M. Rogers
19. Dusenberg
20. 40 mph
21. 1920s
22. Citroen
23. Le Mans
24. Evening, because the air is cooler
25. $850

HOOP-LA! . . . . page 72

1. Rhode Island State
2. Wilt Chamberlain, with a total of 31,419 points scored
3. James Naismith
4. Ferdinand Lewis Alcindor
5. Boston Celtics
6. 75,000
7. Mu Tieh-Chu, who is 7'9¾" tall
8. Nat Holman, also known as Mr. Basketball
9. 20,000
10. Canada, in 1893
11. Third
12. City College of New York in 1949-1950
13. The Stilt
14. 1890s

463

15. 22
16. Oscar Robertson, who sank a total of 7,694 free throws in his career with the Cincinatti Royals and the Milwaukee Bucks
17. Interference with the ball on its final arc toward the basket
18. Wesleyan and Yale
19. 12
20. 1936
21. Run holding the ball
22. 100, by Wilt Chamberlain
23. 24 seconds
24. .275
25. United States

ALTERNATE CHOICE . . . . page 74

1. Heifer (Judges, Ch. 14)
2. Painter
3. Liver
4. Foreman (of jury)
5. Apiary
6. Seesaw
7. Leo (lion)
8. Reynard (fox)
9. Bevy (of girls)
10. Moo (cow)
11. Numerology
12. Permit
13. Electrician
14. Kyphosis (bent forward)
15. Hornet
16. Peat
17. Honest
18. Oxygen (20% of air is oxygen, so breathe deeply!)
19. Insects (exudate)
20. Guildenstern (Hamlet)
21. 18th (Prohibition)
22. Cardinal (Your Eminence)
23. Unicorn (mythical)
24. Ichthyologist
25. Disparaging

PSEUDONYMITY . . . . page 76

1. Woody Allen—Allen Stewart Konigsberg
2. Fred Astaire— Frederick Austerlitz
3. Jack Benny—Benny Kubelsky
4. Sarah Bernhardt—Rosine Bernard
5. Voltaire—Francois Marie Arouet
6. Rocky Graziano—Tom Barbelo
7. Joseph Stalin—Iosif V. Dzhugashvili
8. John Wayne—Marion Morrison
9. Roy Rogers—Leonard Slye
10. Calamity Jane—Martha Jane Burke
11. Cary Grant—Archibald Leach
12. Adolf Hitler—Adolf Schicklgruber
13. Harry Houdini—Ehrich Weiss
14. Mark Twain—Samuel Clemens
15. Molière—Jean Baptiste Poquelin
16. Mary Pickford—Gladys Smith
17. Billy the Kid—Henry McCarty
18. Father Divine—George Baker
19. Gerald Ford—Leslie L. King, Jr.
20. Edward G. Robinson—Emmanuel Goldberg
21. Lewis Carroll—C.L. Dodgson
22. George Orwell—Eric Blair
23. Marlene Deitrich—Magdalene von Losch
24. Saki—Hector Hugh Monroe
25. Tintoretto—Jacopo Robusti
26. Leon Trotsky—Lev D. Bronstein
27. Sugar Ray Robinson—Walker Smith
28. O. Henry—William Sidney Porter
29. Nikolai Lenin—Vladimir Illich Ulyanov
30. Dean Martin—Dino Crocetti
31. Sophia Loren—Sofia Scicolone
32. Maxim Gorki—A. Max Peshkov
33. W.C. Fields—William Claude Dukinfield
34. Greta Garbo—Greta Gustaffson
35. Judy Garland—Frances Gumm
36. Marilyn Monroe—Norma Jean Baker
37. Paul Muni—Muni Weisenfreund
38. Joseph Conrad—Teodor J.K. Korzeniowski
39. "Legs" Diamond—John T. Noland
40. Boris Karloff—William Henry Pratt
41. Elizabeth Arden—Florence N. Graham
42. Hedy Lamarr—Hedwig Kiesler
43. George Eliot—Mary Ann Evans
44. Bette Davis—Ruth Elizabeth Davis
45. Bing Crosby—Harry Crosby
46. Marion Davies—Marion Douras
47. Rocky Marciano—Rocco Marchegiano
48. George Sand—Amandine Aurore Lucie Dupen
49. Ringo Starr—Richard Starkey
50. Vivien Leigh—Vivian Hartley Holman

DIAMOND 1 . . . . page 79

1. Alit
2. Altar
3. Apart
4. Arctic
5. Atrip
6. Capital
7. Carat
8. Cart
9. Lactic
10. Lariat
11. Pact
12. Part
13. Partial
14. Plait
15. Plat
16. PRACTICAL
17. Prat
18. Rapt
19. Ratal
20. Tail
21. Talc
22. Tapir
23. Tiara
24. Trail
25. Trap
26. Trial
27. Trip

DIAMOND 2 . . . . page 80

1. Ceil
2. Clevis
3. Clue
4. Else
5. Elusive
6. Evil
7. Excel
8. Excise
9. EXCLUSIVE
10. Excuse
11. Exile
12. Ilex
13. Isle
14. Levis

15. Lieu
16. Live
17. Luce
18. Sieve
19. Silex
20. Slice
21. Slue
22. Sluice
23. Veil
24. Vesicle
25. Vice
26. Vile

DIAMOND 3 . . . . page 81

1. Anvil
2. Avail
3. Avian
4. Aviso
5. Lava
6. Lavation
7. Naval
8. Nova
9. Oval
10. Saliva
11. SALVATION
12. Salvia
13. Salvo
14. Savant
15. Silvan
16. Vail
17. Vain
18. Valiant
19. Valonia
20. Vast
21. Vial
22. Viol
23. Viola
24. Visa
25. Vista
26. Vital
27. Volant
28. Volt

DIAMOND 4 . . . . page 82

1. Ailing
2. Align
3. Anil
4. Bailing
5. Baling
6. Balling
7. Bang
8. BILINGUAL
9. Billing
10. Blain
11. Bluing
12. Buna
13. Bung
14. Gain
15. Lain
16. Lung
17. Nail
18. Null
19. Unbag

DIAMOND 5 . . . . page 83

1. Fifer
2. Fire
3. FIREPROOF
4. Firer
5. Fore
6. Frier
7. Offer
8. Pier
9. Poor
10. Pore
11. Prior
12. Proffer
13. Proof
14. Reproof
15. Rife
16. Riff
17. Ripe
18. Roof
19. Roofer
20. Rope

DIAMOND 6 . . . . page 84

1. Egress
2. Engross
3. Gorse
4. GOVERNESS
5. Gross
6. Ness
7. Nose
8. Noser
9. Ogress
10. Rose
11. Roves
12. Seen
13. Seer
14. Sense
15. Sensor
16. Sere
17. Serge
18. Serve

19. Seven
20. Sever
21. Sneer
22. Snore
23. Soever
24. Song
25. Sore
26. Venose
27. Verse

DIAMOND 7 . . . . page 85

1. Elope
2. Leper
3. Lope
4. Peel
5. Peep
6. Peer
7. People
8. Plop
9. Pole
10. Poll
11. Pope
12. Pore
13. Prop
14. Propel
15. PROPELLER
16. Proper
17. Repel
18. Rope

DIAMOND 8 . . . . page 86

1. Amiss
2. Atom
3. Atomic
4. Cash
5. Cast
6. Chaos
7. Chasm
8. Chat
9. Chit
10. Coast
11. Coat
12. Coma
13. Hast
14. Iota
15. Mash
16. MASOCHIST
17. Mass
18. Mast
19. Match
20. Math
21. Mica
22. Mocha
23. Oasis
24. Oast
25. Oats
26. Scat
27. Sham
28. Shoat
29. Soma
30. Stoa
31. Stomach

DIAMOND 9 . . . . page 87

1. Abate
2. Abet
3. Arbiter
4. ARBITRATE
5. Attar
6. Attire
7. Bait
8. Barter
9. Bate
10. Batter
11. Beat
12. Biretta
13. Bite
14. Biter
15. Bitter
16. Brat
17. Irate
18. Rarebit
19. Rate
20. Ratite
21. Ratter
22. Rite
23. Tabaret
24. Tare
25. Tart
26. Tartar
27. Tear
28. Teat
29. Tiara
30. Tier
31. Tire
32. Titre
33. Trait
34. Treat
35. Tret
36. Tribe
37. Trier
38. Trite

DIAMOND 10 . . . . page 88

1. Gilt
2. Glim

465

3. Glint
4. Gloom
5. Holing
6. Hooting
7. Igloo
8. Ingot
9. Light
10. Ling
11. Lingo
12. Long
13. Looming
14. Looting
15. Might
16. Mongol
17. Mooing
18. MOONLIGHT
19. Moot
20. Nigh
21. Night
22. Thing
23. Thong
24. Tigon
25. Ting
26. Tooling

DIAMOND 11 .... page 89

1. Envious
2. ENVIOUSLY
3. Envoy
4. Envy
5. Evil
6. Evulsion
7. Levy
8. Live
9. Liven
10. Love
11. Novel
12. Olive
13. Oven
14. Ovine
15. Ovule
16. Sloven
17. Snivel
18. Solve
19. Unveil
20. Veil
21. Vein
22. Veiny
23. Venous
24. Vile
25. Vine
26. Vinous
27. Viny
28. Vinyl
29. Viol
30. Voile
31. Vole

DIAMOND 12 .... page 90

1. Aced
2. Acid
3. Ailed
4. Aimed
5. Alley
6. Ally
7. Amid
8. Call
9. Called
10. Calm
11. Calmed
12. Came
13. Camel
14. Clad
15. Claim
16. Clam
17. Clay
18. Daily
19. Dale
20. Dally
21. Dame
22. Deal
23. Decal
24. Decay
25. Declaim
26. Delay
27. Dial
28. Idea
29. Ideal
30. Lace
31. Laced
32. Lacy
33. Lade
34. Ladle
35. Lady
36. Laic
37. Laid
38. Lame
39. Lead
40. Lilac
41. Mace
42. Made
43. Madly
44. Maid
45. Mail
46. Mailed
47. Male
48. Malice
49. Mall
50. Mead
51. Meal
52. Mealy
53. Medal
54. Media
55. Medial
56. Medical
57. MEDICALLY

466

TYPESETTER'S HEADACHE ..... page 92

Reading through the clues you see that the letter combinations are: XY, TR, LK, and ES. Make a chart with these letters across the top, and Symbol and Number along the sides. Clues 1, 2, and 3 can be entered into the appropriate boxes on the chart.

	XY	TR	LK	ES
Number	57			
Symbol		$	%	

By deduction, you can use the remaining clues to complete the chart. Since TR and LK already have symbols, and XY already has a number, clue 5 must relate to ES. This leaves the symbol # for XY. If LK is not 39 (clue 7), TR must be 39 and LK must be 68.

TREE HOUSES .... page 92

	Owner	Color	Tree
Tree 1	Pete	red	elm
Tree 2	Tom	blue	maple
Tree 3	Jeff	yellow	oak
Tree 4	Luke	green	cherry

Clues 2, 5, and 7 can be entered into the grid immediately. Clues 4 and 8 together establish that the house that is blue is Tom's and is in the maple tree, so this can only identify tree 2. The red house which is Pete's (clue 1) can only be tree 1. Luke's house in the cherry tree (clue 3) must identify tree 4, so Jeff's tree 3 must be the oak with the yellow tree house.

FLY ME .... page 93

	Joe	Jim	Dan	John	Bob
Airline	Delta	TWA	PanAm	East.	United
Steward.	Lore	Lynn	Doris	Marge	Donna
Destin.	Dallas	L.A.	N.Y.	Miami	Chic.

Clues 1 and 11 immediately identify Jim's airline and destination. Clues 4 and 9 give Dan's destination and stewardess. Clues 7 and 10 give Bob's airline and destination. The only missing destinations are Joe's and John's. Clue 13 tells us that it must be Joe who is going to Dallas; so John must be going to Miami. John's airline is Eastern (clue 3). We now have all the destinations. The two airlines as yet unidentified are Joe's and Dan's. We known they are Delta and Pan Am, but which is whose? Clue 5 is a help. Since Dan's stewardess is Doris (clue 9), he cannot fly for Delta. So Joe flies Delta along with Lore, and Dan flies Pan Am. Now for the other three stewardesses: Clues 2 and 12 show that Marge can only work for John. Clue 8 tells us that Donna must work with Bob, and so Lynn must work with Jim.

TRIPLET TROUBLE . . . . page 94

Sue and Sarah both claim they walked Skipper on Monday. Since one of them is telling the truth, that means that Sandy did not walk the dog on Monday.

Sandy says she walked the dog Tuesday. Sue claims Sarah walked the dog Tuesday. Since one of them is telling the truth, that means Sue definitely did not walk the dog on Tuesday.

Only one of Sarah's statements is true. Since we know that Sue did not walk the dog on Tuesday, her other statement, that she herself walked Skipper Monday, must be the true statement.

So, Sarah walked Skipper on Monday. Sue did not walk him on Tuesday, so Sandy must have. It is therefore Sue's turn to walk Skipper on Wednesday.

TRUTH IN LABELING . . . . page 95

Make a grid with the five jar numbers across the top. Along the side, write What, Who, and When. Enter in the grid the information contained in clues 4, 6, 8, 11, 13, and 1.

Num-ber	1	2	3	4	5
What	sweet pickles	corn			
Who	Lois	Pat	Kris		Carol
When					

Now deduce from the remaining clues the information to complete the grid. Since Maggie is the only unidentified donor, she must have given jar #4, which was canned in 1973 (clue 7). Clue 14 indicates that jar #3 has green beans, and therefore jar #5 must have grape juice. Clue 9 dates jar #2. Clue 15 dates jar #5. Clue 3 dates jar #3, which leaves clue 10 to date jar #1. Thus, the information in the grid should read as follows: Jar #1 was given by Lois in 1969 and contains sweet pickles. Jar #2 contains corn and was given by Pat in 1972. Jar #3 contains green beans which Kris gave Ann in 1974. Jar #4 was given in 1973 by Maggie and contains tomato juice. Jar #5 contains grape juice and was given by Carol in 1971.

BUGS! BUGS! BUGS! . . . . page 96

Craig—Jackson High, ants, honorable mention

Joan—Lee High, flies, honorable mention

Margaret—Forrest High, butterflies, third place

Bert—Stephens High, beetles, second place

Peter—Davis High, bees, first place

Clues 1, 3, 5, 6, and 7 provide immediate entries. The Forrest student in third place (clue 4) can only be Margaret; the winner with his bee collection can only be Peter. Clue 8 makes the ant collector either Joan or Craig, but clue 9 eliminates Joan since we already know which her school is. Joan must be the fly collector, and Bert must go to Stephens High.

MATERNITY WARD . . . . page 98

	Baby	Ma	Pa
Apr. 29	Chuck	Wilma	Lee
Apr. 30	Bill	Barb.	Jim
May 1	Carol	Diane	Bob
May 2	Maur.	Donna	Tom
May 3	Geo.	Annie	Kevin

Clues 2, 9, 11, 12, and 15 provide entries right away. Clue 10 can now be used, followed by clue 5. Clue 8 establishes Carol's birth date as May 1, and clue 14 makes May 3 George's birth date. Clues 6 and 7 follow, and then clue 1. Jim must then be Bill's father. Clue 4 precludes Annie from being Bill's mother, so Annie must be George's mother, and Barbara is Bill's mother.

THE SOCCER TOURNAMENT . . . . page 99

Teams	Score
Central-Madison	3-4
Central-Lakeside	4-1
Central-Western	0-0
Madison-Lakeside	1-0
Madison-Western	0-0
Lakeside-Western	0-0

If Western scored no goals at all but still ended the tournament with three points, it must have held all three of its opponents to 0-0 ties.

Of Central's total of seven goals, four were scored against Lakeside and none against Western, so it must have scored three points against Madison.

Since Madison has a total of five points and one of them is the tie with Western, it has to win its games with Central and Lakeside. One must keep in mind, however, that all the goals scored in the Central-Madison, Central-Lakeside, and Madison-Lakeside games have to total 13. The Central-Lakeside game accounts for five, and Central's goals in the Central-Madison game bring the total already to eight. Madison's score in the Central-Madison game must then be four, and Madison can only have beaten Lakeside 1-0.

QUINTUPLET QUIZ . . . . page 100

	Fiancée	Sport
Pat	Alice	Football
Bob	Karen	Swimming
Tim	Pam	Wrestling
Steve	Sharon	Basketball
Bill	Susan	Baseball

Clues 1, 3, and 6 go right into the grid. Clue 5 identifies Alice's fiancé as the football player, who is Pat. Clue 8 makes Steve the basketball player, and therefore Sharon must be his girl (clue 7). Since Karen cannot be engaged to Bill (clue 4), she must be Bob's girl, and his sport must be swimming. This leaves wrestling for Tim, and Susan (Karen's sister—clue 2) for Bill.

CRIB CRISIS. . . . . page 101

	Baby	Mother
Crib #1	Paul	Alice Hamilton
Crib #2	Andy	Carla Moore
Crib #3	Todd	Sharon Adams
Crib #4	Sean	Susan O'Leary
Crib #5	Dennis	Melody Barnes

Clues 1, 6, and 7 provide entries right away. Sharon Adams' baby (clue 8) must be Todd, so crib #4 is for Sean. Clue 5 tells us Sean's mother is Susan O'Leary. Since Carla Moore's baby cannot be crib in #1 or #5 (clue 2), Andy in crib #2 must be Carla's. The only mother left for crib #5 is Melody Barnes. Since clue 4 says Melody's baby is not Paul, it must be Dennis, and Paul must be Alice's baby.

SUGAR AND SPICE . . . . page 102

	Bag	Boy-friend	TV Show
Lois	red	Scott	M*A*S*H*
Mary	blue	Ben	Happy Days
Margie	yel.	Andy	Hawaii 5-0
Shirley	grn.	Ed	Lav. & Shirley
Diane	blk.	Al	Maude
Sharon	pld.	Ken	American Bandstand

Clues 1, 3, 4, 5, 7, 11, and 12 provide immediate entries for the matrix. It is evident at once, from clues 2 and 11, that Sharon is Ken's girlfriend. Shirley's column is the only one with neither a sleeping bag nor a boyfriend, so she must be Ed's girlfriend and have a green bag (clue 6).

Lois and Margie do not yet have sleeping bags assigned; from clue 9, then, we know that Lois's is red, and from clue 11, that the yellow must be Margie's.

Mary has neither boyfriend nor TV show beneath her name, so clue 10 must pertain to her. *Maude* and *Hawaii 5-0* are the only programs left and must be assigned to Margie and Diane; clue 8 makes clear which show goes to which girl.

PAPA'S PLANTS . . . . page 103

Reading through the clues you see that the four plants are: African violet, spider, philodendron, and coleus. Make a chart with these names across the top. Along the side, write Room, Pot Color, and Direction. The information from the following clues can be entered in the appropriate boxes of the chart: Clues 1, 5, 10, 11, 9, 7.

	African Violet	Spider	Philo-dendron	Coleus
Room			Den	Kit.
Pot Color				Green
Direction	North	East		South

You will note that only one direction is missing; therefore, the philodendron must have a west window. Now go through the clues again, and by deduction, complete the boxes of the chart. Clue 8 implies that the African violet must be in the living room; and therefore, the spider plant must be in the playroom. Clue 3 thus tells that the spider plant is in a red pot. Clues 2 and 4 show that the African violet is in a yellow pot, and the philodendron is in a blue pot.

THE FIVE DWARFS . . . . page 104

	Tree	Cap Color
Tipsy	Spruce	Green
Greasy	Elm	Yellow
Cruddy	Oak	Red
Clumsy	Maple	Black
Shnook	Pine	Blue

Clues 1, 2, 6, and 7 provide ready answers, and clue 8 follows immediately from clue 6. Clue 4 can go only with Tipsy. Oak (clue 3) is the only tree left for Cruddy. Since Clumsy does not wear the yellow cap (clue 5), he must wear the black one, and Greasy must wear the yellow.

CRAZY QUILT . . . . page 105

	Ann	Barb	Chris	Dee	Edna	Fran
Proj.	Curt.	Jack.	Pants	Shirt	Dress	Toys
Color	Yellow	Red	Brown	Blue	White	Green
Cloth	Cotton	Denim	Cord.	Flan.	Satin	Felt

Clues 1, 5, 8, 9, 12, and 14 provide immediate entries for the grid. Clues 12 and 14 match clue 3 to prove that Barb is making a red denim jacket; clue 10 matches clue 5 to show that Chris is making pants. Clues 6 and 11 together prove that green felt toys are someone's project; Dee and Fran are the only women with blank columns, and clue 15 eliminates Dee, so Fran must be working on green felt toys. Dee is the only lady left without a fabric or a color, so the blue flannel of clue 7 must be hers. Edna is the only lady left without a project or a color, so the white dress of clue 2 must be hers. Dee's project can only be the shirt. The only gaps left now are Ann's cloth and Chris' cloth; clue 13 proves that Ann's yellow curtains are not corduroy, so they must be the cotton and the corduroy must belong to Chris.

RETIREMENT RIDDLE . . . . page 106

	Jones	Smith	Kelly	Robson
Hair	White	Gray	Brown	Bald
Game	Chess	Checkers	Horse-shoes	Croquet

Mr. Kelly's brown hair (clue 1) and Mr. Smith's checkers (clue 4) can go into the grid right away. Clue 2's bald croquet player must therefore be Robson or Jones, and clue 6 proves it is Robson. Clue 5's white-haired chess player must then be Jones. Clue 3's horseshoe player can now be only Kelly, and clue 7's gray-haired gent has to be Smith.

CHO . . . . page 107

1. Anchor
2. Anchovy
3. Chock
4. Chocolate
5. Choice
6. Choir
7. Choke
8. Choker
9. Cholera
10. Cholesterol
11. Chomp
12. Choose
13. Chopper
14. Chopstick
15. Chord
16. Chore
17. Choreography
18. Chortle
19. Chorus
20. Chow
21. Chowchow
22. Chowder
23. Dichotomy
24. Echo
25. Inchoate
26. Macho
27. Melancholy
28. Patchouli
29. Poncho
30. Rancho
31. Tachometer

ADE . . . . page 108

1. Abrade
2. Accolade
3. Adenoid
4. Adept
5. Adequate
6. Ambuscade
7. Bade
8. Balustrade
9. Blade
10. Breaded
11. Broaden
12. Brocade
13. Cadence
14. Cadet
15. Cavalcade
16. Charade
17. Deaden
18. Decade
19. Decadence
20. Degrade
21. Diadem
22. Escapade
23. Esplanade
24. Evade
25. Fade
26. Forbade
27. Glade
28. Grade
29. Headed
30. Invade
31. Jade
32. Laden
33. Leaden
34. Leader
35. Lemonade
36. Made
37. Mademoiselle
38. Motorcade
39. Orangeade
40. Parade
41. Pervade
42. Pleaded
43. Pomade
44. Promenade
45. Reader
46. Retrograde
47. Serenade
48. Shade
49. Spade
50. Threaded
51. Trade
52. Wade

NDM . . . . page 108

1. Endmost
2. Grandmother
3. Handmade
4. Handmaiden
5. Hindmost
6. Landmark
7. Landmass
8. Sandman
9. Windmill

COLLAR + BED − BEAR − L = COLD

H + RULER + BEAR − BARREL − R = HUE

G + WALLET − WELL + E = GATE

473

REBUS GAME NO. 25 . . . . page 133

VIOLIN + BERET – IRON – VEIL = BET

REBUS GAME NO. 26 . . . . page 133

H + BOOK – HOOK + HEART – H – T = BEAR

MARK TIME . . . . page 170

1. Toe the mark
2. Edwin Markham
3. Book mark
4. Mark Rothko
5. Mark my words
6. Mark Twain
7. Watermark
8. Magic marker
9. Mark Spitz
10. Hallmark
11. Alicia Markova
12. Buyer's market
13. Marksmanship
14. Markup
15. Countess Constance Markiewicz
16. On the market
17. Miss the mark; or below the mark
18. Enid Markey
19. Trademark
20. Markka
21. Market research
22. Mark of Cain
23. Mark down
24. Mark Hopkins, Top of the Mark
25. "On your mark…"
26. Remark
27. Mrs. Markleham
28. Mark Antony

ON ICE . . . . page 172

1. Lice or mice
2. Iceland
3. Triceratops
4. *Alice in Wonderland*
5. Nicety
6. Rice
7. Vice President
8. *Of Mice and Men*
9. Spice
10. Price
11. Iceberg
12. Trice
13. Break the ice
14. Bicentennial
15. License
16. *The Iceman Cometh*
17. Device
18. Triceps
19. Ice skating
20. Licorice
21. Slice
22. Choice
23. Precipice
24. Nice
25. Vice Squad
26. Advice
27. Entice
28. Reticent
29. Priceless
30. Leontyne Price
31. Licentious
32. *The Voice of the Turtle*

OF THEE I SING . . . . page 174

1. Thermometer
2. Theta
3. Zither
4. Pathetic
5. *Gone with the Wind*
6. Theft
7. Feathers
8. Lathe
9. Theatre
10. Othello
11. Bathe
12. Theme
13. Thespian
14. Thebes
15. Theology
16. Heathen
17. Leather
18. Mother Nature
19. Matthew
20. Mathematics
21. *Blithe Spirit*
22. Athens
23. Seethe
24. Loathe
25. Theory
26. Scythe
27. Thermos
28. *The Iceman Cometh*
29. Catherine
30. Writhe

MIGHTIER THAN THE SWORD . . page 176

1. Penny
2. Open, Sesame
3. Penniless
4. Pendant
5. Penthouse
6. Pensioner
7. Penguin
8. Pentagon
9. Aspen
10. Pennant
11. Expenditure
12. Penitentiary
13. Penny wise and pound foolish
14. Penobscot
15. Happenstance
16. Depend
17. Pence
18. Deepen
19. Pencil
20. Pentateuch
21. Appenines
22. Penicillin
23. *Pensées*
24. Repent
25. Henny Penny
26. Penates
27. Expensive
28. Sharpen
29. Penrod
30. Spent
31. Perpendicular
32. Compensate
33. Misspent
34. *Hey, Big Spender*
35. Cowpens

TRIPLE-HEADER . . . . page 177

1. Bookkeeper
2. Mississippi
3. Addressee
4. Tennessee
5. Whippoorwill
6. Successfully
7. Chattahoochee

RHYMING EXPRESSION . . . . . . page 178

1. Deadhead
2. Boob tube
3. Blackjack
4. Sweetmeats
5. Hurdy-gurdy
6. Claptrap
7. Willy-nilly
8. Hotshot
9. Hanky-panky
10. Helter-skelter
11. Tutti-frutti
12. Wingding
13. Hootchie-kootchie
14. Fat cat
15. Hocus-pocus
16. Mumbo-jumbo
17. Hoi polloi
18. Fuddy-duddy
19. Namby-pamby
20. Harum-scarum
21. Kowtow
22. Wear and tear
23. Pell-mell
24. Hobnob
25. Jeepers creepers
26. Honky-tonk
27. Hi-fi
28. Huff and puff
29. Voodoo
30. Hubbub
31. Hodgepodge
32. Bee's knees
33. Nearest and dearest
34. True blue
35. Fair and square
36. Pie in the sky
37. Fourscore
38. Heebie-jeebies
39. Plain Jane
40. Prime time

474

41. Fleet Street
42. Boo-hoo
43. Late date
44. Night flight
45. May Day

A PLACE IN THE SUN . . . . page 180

1. Sundae
2. Sunstroke
3. The sunny side of the street
4. To make hay while the sun shines
5. Billy Sunday
6. Sundries
7. *The Sun Also Rises*
8. "Here Comes the Sun"
9. Sun Valley
10. The Sunshine State
11. Sunnites
12. Sunspots
13. *Butch Cassidy and the Sundance Kid*
14. Sun Yat-Sen
15. Sundowner
16. *Little Mary Sunshine*
17. Sundial
18. Sunday school
19. The Sun King
20. *The Sunshine Boys*
21. Midnight sun
22. The Sunflower State
23. *Rebecca of Sunnybrook Farm*
24. Sun Devils
25. "Sunrise, Sunset"
26. "Sunflowers"
27. *77 Sunset Strip*
28. Land of the Rising Sun
29. *Never on Sunday*
30. Asunder
31. *Raisin in the Sun*
32. "Let the Sunshine In"
33. *Sunset Boulevard*
34. Misunderstanding
35. Whitsuntide
36. Datsun
37. Bosun
38. Unsung

THE GOLD GAME . . . . page 182

1. The Golden Rule
2. *Goldfinger* or
   The Man with the Golden Gun
3. Golden State
4. Cross of Gold
5. Gold Rush
6. Gold digger
7. Goldenrod
8. Gold mine
9. Golden touch
10. Goldilocks
11. Golden anniversary
12. Black gold
13. Pot of gold
14. Golden apples
15. Golden Horn
16. *The Gold Bug*
17. Golden Age
18. Goldbrick
19. Goldoni
20. Golden Fleece
21. Golden Gate
22. Metro-Goldwyn-Mayer
23. William Golding
24. *The Golden Ass*
25. Gold Coast
26. Rube Goldberg
27. Golden calf
28. Emma Goldman
29. Marigold
30. Harry Golden
31. *The Golden Bough*
32. Goldfinch
33. Oliver Goldsmith
34. Speech is silver; silence is golden
35. Barry M. Goldwater
36. Rheingold
37. Living in a goldfish bowl
38. Gold leaf
39. Silver threads among the gold
40. Gold dust twins

SIBILANTS . . . . page 184

1. Seamstress
2. Sassafras
3. Psoriasis
4. Subsistence
5. Success
6. Synthesis
7. Massachusetts
8. Psychosis
9. Suspicious
10. Classicist

I.R.S. CONFRONTATION . . . . . . page 185

1. First
2. Thirsty
3. Circus
4. Universe
5. Interest
6. Distress
7. Improvise
8. Iridescent
9. Increase
10. Fireside
11. Virus
12. Tiresias
13. Irascible
14. Waitress
15. Digress
16. Piraeus
17. Picturesque
18. Intersect
19. Cirrhosis
20. Verdigris
21. Hirsute
22. Circumspect

PARDON THE STUTTER . . . . page 186

1. Tintinabulation
2. Bonbon
3. Cincinnati
4. Murmur
5. Pom-pom
6. Barbaric
7. Vivisection
8. Couscous
9. Cancan
10. Bobolink
11. Beriberi
12. Tom-tom
13. Tutu
14. Vivify
15. Berbers
16. Mimic

EARNED INCREMENT . . . . page 187

1. Auburn

2. Robert Burns
3. Annapurna
4. Turnstile
5. Joseph Mallard William Turner
6. Diurnal
7. *The Turning Point*
8. Taciturn
9. Calpurnia
10. Tourniquet
11. *Journey's End*
12. Spurn
13. *Confessions of Nat Turner*
14. Saturnine
15. *The Turn of the Screw*
16. Sideburns
17. Carol Burnett
18. Turncoat
19. Sojourner Truth
20. *The Lady's Not for Burning*

ALL IN GOOD FUN . . . . page 188

1. A good-time Charley
2. Benny Goodman
3. One good turn
4. *Looking for Mr. Goodbar*
5. *Good-bye Mr. Chips*
6. A goody-goody or a Miss Goody Two-Shoes
7. Good Humor
8. The Good Book
9. Cape of Good Hope
10. *The Good Earth*
11. *The Good Sailor*
12. "O good grief!"
13. *The Good Woman of Szechuan*
14. Good-looking
15. To get the goods on
16. Good Neighbor Sam
17. Goodyear
18. A good name
19. Good Friday
20. *The Good-bye Girl*

BOTTOMS UP . . . . page 189

1. Upperclassman
2. Supper
3. "Up yours!"
4. Upheaval
5. Ups and downs
6. Give up
7. Seven-Up
8. "Why don't you come up and see me sometime?"
9. Upholster
10. John Updike
11. Upper
12. Cupola
13. Muppets
14. Upton Sinclair
15. Frameup
16. "Up, Up, and Away"
17. Live it up
18. Uppity
19. *Once Upon a Mattress*
20. Upset

100 PERCENT . . . . page 190

1. Supercilious
2. Imperious

3. Hyperbole
4. Prosperity
5. Persiflage
6. Perimeter
7. Chopper
8. Per se
9. Diaper
10. *Cries and Whispers*
11. Thumper
12. Temperature
13. Emperor
14. Perpendicular
15. Persecute
16. Cooperstown
17. Sgt. Pepper
18. Desperation
19. Experiment
20. Prospero
21. *The Perils of Pauline*
22. Tempera
23. Person-to-Person
24. Trylon and Perisphere
25. Permanent
26. Temperamental
27. Hesperides
28. Experience
29. Persimmon
30. Ampersand
31. *The Whisperers*
32. Permeate
33. *Topper*
34. Periwinkle
35. Propertius
36. Opera house
37. *The Adventures of Peregrine Pickle*
38. Aperitif or aperitive
39. Perennial
40. Caper
41. Coppertone
42. Imperative
43. Superman
44. Vituperative
45. Elmo Roper
46. Zipper

TONS AND TONS . . . . page 192

1. Tongue
2. Charleston
3. *The Tonight Show*
4. Plutonium
5. Platonic
6. Tonic
7. Estonia
8. Astonish
9. Carton (Sydney)
10. Croutons
11. Boston
12. Tonsure
13. Elton John
14. Marc Antony
15. Krypton
16. Richard Burton
17. Houston
18. *The Waltons*
19. Clara Barton
20. Cotton
21. Fredericton
22. Autonomy
23. Alexander Hamilton
24. Princeton
25. Detonate
26. *The Trial of the Catonsville Nine*
27. Kingston
28. Intone
29. Fronton
30. Baton Rouge
31. Dolly Parton
32. Piston
33. Canton
34. Wanton
35. *My Antonia*
36. Tontine
37. Tonga
38. Eton
39. San Antonio
40. Latona
41. Tonsils.
42. John Milton
43. Trenton

QUESTIONABLE THINGS . . . . . . page 194

1. Glocca Morro
2. Cock Robin
3. Day in June
4. Wrought
5. Keeper
6. On the bedpost overnight
7. Chattanooga Choo Choo
8. More like a man

LONG LIVE THE KING . . . . page 196

1. Old King Cole
2. Booth Tarkington
3. King's ransom
4. Peking
5. The King's English
6. Charles Kingsley
7. *The Man Who Would Be King*
8. Kingfish
9. The King of Swing
10. Kingston
11. Dr. Martin Luther King, Jr.
12. *Plain Speaking*
13. "In the Hall of the Mountain King"
14. King Kong
15. "My Kingdom for a horse"
16. Nat King Cole
17. King's College
18. Kingdom come
19. King Arthur
20. King-Size
21. Kingsley Amis
22. *Sky King*
23. King crab
24. Raking over the coals
25. *To Kill a Mockingbird*
26. *The King and I*
27. Vikings
28. *Looking for Mr. Goodbar*
29. "God Save the King"
30. Looking up
31. "The Conscience of the King"
32. King of beasts, or king of the jungle
33. King of the forest
34. Masking
35. *All the King's Men*
36. The March King
37. The Waltz King
38. Kingpin
39. Parking ticket
40. King Vidor
41. *The King of Marvin Gardens*
42. King James Version

THE LADY IN THE CASE . . . . page 198

1. Executrix
2. Mistress
3. Masseuse
4. Tigress
5. Marchioness
6. Hen
7. Queen
8. Chairwoman or Chairlady
9. Duck
10. Countess
11. Heifer
12. Couturière
13. Matriarch
14. Vixen
15. Chambermaid
16. Bride
17. Usherette
18. Doe
19. Lady
20. Abbess
21. Bitch
22. Doll (broad)
23. Peahen
24. Nun
25. Madame or Mademoiselle
26. Aviatrix
27. Dam
28. Ewe
29. Sultana
30. Duchess
31. Filly
32. Maharanee
33. Hostess
34. Sow
35. Lass
36. Niece
37. Mare
38. Tsarina
39. Fiancée
40. Maid of honor
41. Pen (swan)
42. Heroine
43. Hind
44. Señora or Señorita
45. Pierrette
46. Nanny goat
47. Dame
48. Goose
49. Squaw
50. Cow

PREVARICATION AS AN ART . . . page 201

Any fool can tell the truth, but it requires a man of some sense to know how to lie well.

Samuel Butler

BRAT AT A BALL . . . . page 202

Pretty pampered Polly peevishly pouted, prissily put on her purple pom-pom, and pettishly perambulated at a plodding pace.

ABSOLUTELY! . . . . page 203

The only thing that the artist cannot see is the obvious. The only thing that the public can see is the obvious.

Oscar Wilde

THE POWER OF MUSIC . . . . page 204

Into an inn entered an innocent nun. Ennui imminent, she intoned an air.

ERSE PHILOSOPHY . . . . page 205

I don't think there's any point in being

Irish if you don't know that the world is going to break your heart eventually.

Daniel Patrick Moynihan

THE CULT OF INCOHERENCE... page 206

Many a writer seems to think he is not profound unless he himself can't understand what he has put down on paper.

TALISMAN .... page 207

A fool there was and he made his prayer to a rag and a bone and a hank of hair.

Rudyard Kipling

RUBBING IT IN .... page 208

Of all the horrid, hideous notes of woe, sadder than owl-songs or the midnight blast, is that portentous phrase "I told you so."

Lord Byron

ONE-TRACK MIND........... page 209

The plump cook broke the back of the bookkeeper who nevertheless kept asking for coffee.

SOUND PERCEPTION .... page 210

Not many sounds in life, and I include all urban and all rural sounds, exceed in interest a knock at the door.

Charles Lamb

FOLLY! FOLLY! .... page 211

I can not give you the formula for success, but I can give you the formula for failure—which is "Try to please everybody."

Herbert Bayard Swope

ADVICE TO THE STRIFE-TORN.. page 212

Try praising your wife, even if it does frighten her at first.

Billy Sunday

AH CHOO! .... page 213

I sneezed a sneeze into the air,
And no one knew from whence or where;
But long and hard were the looks of those,
In whose vicinity I snooze!

YOUTH IS UNQUALIFIED....... page 214

The judge should not be young; he should have learned to know evil, not from his own soul, but from long observation. Knowledge should be his guide, not personal experience.

Plato

THE SUPREME JUDGMENT.... page 215

Not in the clamor of the crowded street,
Not in the shouts and plaudits of the
   throng,
But in ourselves are triumph and defeat.

NATURE, *Henry Wadsworth Longfellow*

ULTIMATE JUSTICE .... page 216

An appeal is when you ask one court to show its contempt for another court.

Finley Peter Dunne

INESCAPABLE DEDUCTION .... page 217

Mark how my fame rings out from zone to
   zone;
A thousand critics shouting: "He's
   unknown!"

Ambrose Bierce

LAMENT................... page 218

Sing me not in mournful dirges, "I am broke! Too many splurges!"

PLOY .... page 218

Then, drawing on my fine command of language, I said nothing.

Robert Benchley

DISDAIN.................. page 219

He looked at me as if I was a side dish he hadn't ordered.

Ring Lardner

PRAGMATISM . . . . page 219

If you cannot catch a bird of paradise, better take a wet hen.

Nikita Khrushchev

ARCHITECT . . . . page 237

1. Aitch
2. Arctic
3. Attic
4. Attire
5. Cache
6. Cachet
7. Caret
8. Catch
9. Catcher
10. Cater
11. Chair
12. Chart
13. Chatter
14. Cheat
15. Crate
16. Earth
17. Hatter
18. Heart
19. Hitter
20. Irate
21. Ratchet
22. Reach
23. React
24. Retch
25. Tacit
26. Tactic
27. Teach
28. Their
29. Thrice
30. Tithe
31. Trace
32. Tract
33. Trait
34. Treat
35. Trice
36. Trite

STEREOTYPE . . . . page 238

1. Ester
2. Otter
3. Pester
4. Pesty
5. Peter
6. Petty
7. Poetry
8. Poster
9. Pottery
10. Potty
11. Pretty
12. Prose
13. Protest
14. Repot
15. Reset
16. Retest
17. Retype
18. Spotty
19. Steep
20. Steer
21. Stere
22. Stereo
23. Store
24. Story
25. Street
26. Testy
27. Toper
28. Treetop
29. Tryst

CIGARETTE . . . . page 238

1. Agree
2. Attic
3. Attire
4. Cagier
5. Caret
6. Cater
7. Cattier
8. Cigar
9. Crate
10. Create
11. Eager
12. Eater
13. Egret
14. Erect
15. Grace
16. Grate

17. Great
18. Greet
19. Irate
20. React
21. Recite
22. Tacit
23. Target
24. Tiger
25. Trace
26. Tract
27. Trait
28. Treat
29. Trice
30. Trite

PLATITUDES . . . . page 239

1. Adept
2. Adieu
3. Ailed
4. Aisle
5. Altitude
6. Aside
7. Astute
8. Audit
9. Desalt
10. Detail
11. Dualist
12. Duelist
13. Duties
14. Elite
15. Ideal
16. Islet
17. Ladies
18. Lasted
19. Latest
20. Latitude
21. Least
22. Lusted
23. Paled
24. Patted
25. Pedal
26. Petal
27. Petit
28. Pitted
29. Plaid
30. Plait
31. Plate
32. Plead
33. Pleat
34. Plied
35. Sailed
36. Salted
37. Sepal
38. Sidle
39. Slate
40. Slept
41. Slide
42. Slitted
43. Spate
44. Spelt
45. Spied
46. Spite
47. Stale
48. Staple
49. State
50. Steal
51. Suited
52. Tidal
53. Title

MELANCHOLIC . . . . page 240

1. Aline
2. Alone
3. Amino
4. Anemic
5. Camel
6. Cancel
7. Chain
8. Chalice
9. Chance
10. Chill
11. Chime
12. Choice
13. Cinch
14. Cinema
15. Claim
16. Clime
17. Clinch
18. Clone
19. Comical
20. Colic
21. Conch
22. Conical
23. Echoic
24. Hello
25. Henchman
26. Laconic
27. Lance
28. Leach
29. Lemon
30. Lichen
31. Local
32. Machine
33. Malice
34. Manic
35. Melon
36. Niche
37. Ocean

DEPOSIT . . . . **page 240**

1. Deist
2. Depit
3. Depot
4. Despot
5. Estop
6. Poise
7. Poised
8. Posed
9. Posied
10. Posit
11. Posted
12. Spied
13. Spite
14. Tepid

MONASTERY . . . . **page 241**

1. Arose
2. Aster
3. Astern
4. Atone
5. Enamor
6. Entry
7. Manor
8. Manse
9. Marten
10. Mason
11. Master
12. Mastery
13. Mayor
14. Meant
15. Meaty
16. Mentor
17. Meson
18. Metro
19. Money
20. Monster
21. Moray
22. Nasty
23. Notary
24. Oaten
25. Onset
26. Orant
27. Orate
28. Rayon
29. Reason
30. Roast
31. Sentry
32. Smart
33. Snake
34. Snore
35. Snort
36. Sonar
37. Stamen
38. Stare
39. Steam
40. Steno
41. Stern
42. Stoma
43. Stone
44. Store
45. Storm
46. Story
47. Stream
48. Teary
49. Tenor
50. Tensor
51. Treason
52. Yearn
53. Yeast
54. Yeoman

PHANTASMAGORIA . . . . **page 242**

1. Again
2. Against
3. Agora
4. Amphora
5. Angora
6. Aorta
7. Apron
8. Argot
9. Arming
10. Astir
11. Ghost
12. Giant
13. Grain
14. Grant
15. Graph
16. Grasp
17. Gratis
18. Groans
19. Groin
20. Harming
21. Imago
22. Impart
23. Mania
24. Manor
25. Mantis
26. Margin
27. Martin
28. Matin
29. Minor
30. Orang
31. Orgasm
32. Phantom
33. Pinto
34. Print
35. Prism
36. Rasping
37. Ratio
38. Ration
39. Romping
40. Saint
41. Satin
42. Spigot

43. Sport
44. Sprain
45. Sprint
46. Stain
47. Stamp
48. Stomp
49. Strain
50. Strap
51. String
52. Strip
53. Strong
54. Train
55. Tramp

PENULTIMATE . . . . **page 243**

1. Alpine
2. Atilt
3. Elate
4. Elipe
5. Emulate
6. Entail
7. Entitle
8. Impel
9. Impute
10. Lament
11. Latent
12. Letup
13. Lineup
14. Lumen
15. Luminate
16. Mental
17. Metal
18. Paint
19. Panel
20. Penal
21. Plaint
22. Plait
23. Plane
24. Planet
25. Plate
26. Pleat
27. Plume
28. Taint
29. Tenet
30. Title
31. Ultimate
32. Unlit
33. Until

MOUNTAINOUS . . . . **page 243**

1. Amino
2. Amount
3. Animus
4. Anoint
5. Mason
6. Matin
7. Minus
8. Moist
9. Motion
10. Mount
11. Mountain
12. Nation
13. Notion
14. Ominous
15. Saint
16. Satin
17. Snoot
18. Snout
19. Stain
20. Suntan
21. Unanimous

MANIPULATION . . . . **page 244**

1. Amino
2. Amnion
3. Amount
4. Animal
5. Animation
6. Anion
7. Annual
8. Annul
9. Impanation
10. Implant
11. Input
12. Lamia
13. Lamina
14. Lamination
15. Lapin
16. Limit
17. Maintain
18. Mania
19. Manna
20. Manual
21. Matin
22. Minion
23. Mount
24. Mountain
25. Napalm
26. Natal
27. Nation
28. Nominal
29. Nuptial
30. Optima
31. Optimal
32. Paint
33. Patina
34. Patio
35. Pilot
36. Plain

480

37. Plaint
38. Plait
39. Plant
40. Plantain
41. Platinum
42. Pliant
43. Point
44. Tampon
45. Tonal
46. Tulip
47. Ultima
48. Ultimo
49. Union
50. Unman
51. Until

CHAPLAIN

1. Canal
2. Chain
3. Lapin
4. Panic
5. Pinch
6. Plain
7. Planch

DICTIONARY

1. Acorn
2. Acrid
3. Action
4. Actor
5. Adorn
6. Antic
7. Candor
8. Candy
9. Cantor
10. Carton
11. Cation
12. Corny
13. Crayon
14. Crony
15. Dainty
16. Dairy
17. Diary
18. Dicta
19. Diction
20. Dirty
21. Drain
22. Indict
23. Ionic
24. Ironic
25. Irony
26. Nadir
27. Notary
28. Ordain
29. Radii
30. Radio
31. Rainy
32. Rancid
33. Randy
34. Ratio
35. Ration
36. Rayon
37. Riant
38. Tardy
39. Toady
40. Today
41. Tonic
42. Train
43. Triad

CHARACTERIZE

1. Aerie
2. Archer
3. Cache
4. Cachet
5. Carat
6. Career
7. Caret
8. Chair
9. Character
10. Chart
11. Charter
12. Cheat
13. Cheater
14. Cheer
15. Crate
16. Crater
17. Craze
18. Crazier
19. Create
20. Earth
21. Eater
22. Either
23. Errata
24. Erratic
25. Etcher
26. Ether
27. Heart
28. Hearth
29. Heartier
30. Heater
31. Hirer
32. Racer
33. Reach
34. React
35. Rehire
36. Retire
37. Richer
38. Teach

39. Teacher
40. Terrace
41. Their
42. There
43. Three
44. Trace
45. Tracer
46. Trachea
47. Trice
48. Zither

TOGETHER

1. Egret
2. Ether
3. Getter
4. Ghetto
5. Greet
6. Hotter
7. Other
8. Otter
9. Teeth
10. Tether
11. There
12. Three
13. Toter
14. Troth

CONCENTRATE

1. Accent
2. Acorn
3. Anent
4. Atone
5. Caner
6. Canner
7. Canteen
8. Canter
9. Careen
10. Carton
11. Cater
12. Concern
13. Concert
14. Concrete
15. Connect
16. Content
17. Contract
18. Cornea
19. Cornet
20. Cotter
21. Crane
22. Crate
23. Create
24. Crone
25. Eater
26. Enact
27. Enter
28. Entrance
29. Entreat
30. Neater
31. Nonce
32. Oaten
33. Ocean
34. Octet
35. Orate
36. Ornate
37. Otter
38. React
39. Recant
40. Recent
41. Reenact
42. Rennet
43. Rotate
44. Rotten
45. Tanner
46. Tenace
47. Tenant
48. Tenet
49. Tenor
50. Trace
51. Tract
52. Trance
53. Treat

POMEGRANATE

1. Agape
2. Agate
3. Agent
4. Agora
5. Agree
6. Ameer
7. Among
8. Ampere
9. Anger
10. Apart
11. Apogee
12. Apron
13. Arena
14. Atone
15. Eager
16. Eaten
17. Eater
18. Egret
19. Emanate
20. Enamor
21. Enema
22. Enrage
23. Enter
24. Garment
25. Germane
26. Gnome
27. Goner
28. Grant
29. Grape
30. Grate

481

31. Great
32. Green
33. Greet
34. Groan
35. Groat
36. Grope
37. Magnate
38. Magnet
39. Manage
40. Manager
41. Manger
42. Manor
43. Marten
44. Mater
45. Meager
46. Meant
47. Menage
48. Mentor
49. Meteor
50. Meter
51. Neater
52. Oaten
53. Omega
54. Onager
55. Opener
56. Opera
57. Operant
58. Operate
59. Orang
60. Orange
61. Orate
62. Organ
63. Ornate
64. Parent
65. Paten
66. Pater
67. Peonage
68. Peter
69. Portage
70. Prate
71. Preen
72. Prone
73. Protean
74. Rampage
75. Rampant
76. Ranee
77. Range
78. Reagent
79. Regent
80. Remote
81. Repeat
82. Repent
83. Tamer
84. Tamper
85. Tampon
86. Taper
87. Tarpon
88. Temper
89. Tempo
90. Tenor
91. Toper
92. Tramp
93. Trope

DEMONSTRATE.............page 249

1. Amend
2. Armed
3. Arson
4. Aster
5. Atone
6. Attend
7. Demon
8. Demote
9. Dense
10. Deter
11. Detonate
12. Donate
13. Drone
14. Earnest
15. Eastern
16. Eater
17. Emend
18. Emote
19. Enter
20. Erase
21. Erode
22. Estate
23. Ester
24. Mason
25. Master
26. Meander
27. Meant
28. Mentor
29. Moderate
30. Modern
31. Modest
32. Monad
33. Monast
34. Monster
35. Motet
36. Nomad
37. Notate
38. Oaten
39. Orate
40. Random
41. Reason
42. Remand
43. Remote
44. Roast
45. Rotate
46. Senator
47. Sermon
48. Stare
49. Start
50. State
51. Stead
52. Steam
53. Steed
54. Steer
55. Stern
56. Stone
57. Store
58. Storm
59. Strand
60. Stream
61. Strode
62. Tenor
63. Tense
64. Trade
65. Treason
66. Trend

FRIENDSHIP .... page 250

1. Diner
2. Fiend
3. Finish
4. Fresh
5. Fried
6. Friend
7. Hinder
8. Infer
9. Inspire
10. Perish
11. Pride
12. Pried
13. Reship
14. Respin
15. Rinse
16. Ripen
17. Shine
18. Shiner
19. Shire
20. Shred
21. Shrine
22. Siren
23. Sniper
24. Spend
25. Spider
26. Spine
27. Spire

TRIUMVIRATE .... page 250

1. Arrive
2. Atrium
3. Attire
4. Avert
5. Erratum
6. Imitate
7. Irate
8. Irritate
9. Mater
10. Matte
11. Matter
12. Mature
13. Mauve
14. Merit
15. Miter
16. Mutate
17. Mutter
18. Remit
19. River
20. Rivet
21. Timer
22. Trait
23. Treat
24. Trite
25. Triumvir
26. Trivet
27. Trivia
28. Trivium
29. Truer
30. Utter
31. Virtue
32. Vitiate

MASTERFULLY .... page 251

1. After
2. Alley
3. Alter
4. Artful
5. Aster
6. Earfull
7. Early
8. False
9. Falter
10. Faster
11. Fault
12. Faulty
13. Fealty
14. Feast
15. Flatly
16. Fully
17. Lastly
18. Later
19. Least
20. Lemur
21. Mallet
22. Malty
23. Master
24. Mural
25. Muster
26. Musty
27. Rally
28. Ratel
29. Realty
30. Restfully
31. Rusty
32. Safer
33. Sally
34. Salty
35. Seamy
36. Small
37. Smell
38. Smelt
39. Stale
40. Stall
41. Stare
42. Steal
43. Steam
44. Sully
45. Surely
46. Surly
47. Tally
48. Tearful
49. Truly
50. Tulle

EXECUTIVE .... page 251

1. Civet
2. Cutie
3. Evict
4. Excite
5. Execute

VOCABULARY . . . . page 252

1. Bravo	7. Coral	13. Ovary
2. Burly	8. Curly	14. Ovular
3. Cabal	9. Curvy	15. Royal
4. Carboy	10. Labor	16. Valor
5. Carol	11. Larva	17. Vocal
6. Cobra	12. Lobar	18. Volar

BASEMENT . . . . page 252

1. Baste	7. Meant	9. Stamen
2. Beast	8. Semen	10. Steam
3. Beaten	5. Eaten	11. Tease
4. Beset	6. Manse	12. Tense

PICTURE-PUZZLE NO. 1 . . . . page 272

CORRECT SOLUTION: MECCA
Analysis: The word ME is spoken. What remains are two C's and an A. The word "Caesar" is phonetically equivalent to C's A.
Result: ME CC A = MECCA

PICTURE-PUZZLE NO. 2 . . . . page 273

CORRECT SOLUTION: DIOCLETIAN
Analysis: The girl who is "going to have this red dress made black" is going to DYE it. Her friend sits on an "acorn" which presumably fell from the tree above. This is ample evidence that the girls are under an OAK tree. The dog is held on a LEASH. The word AN is spoken.
Result: DYE OAK LEASH AN = DIOCLETIAN.
Notes: SITTING PRETTY and THE RED AND THE BLACK are general titles which cannot be doped out by constituent clues. LEAVES OF GRASS is extremely close. Both LEAVES and GRASS appear in the picture. But the syllable OF cannot be accounted for.

PICTURE-PUZZLE NO. 3 . . . . page 274

CORRECT SOLUTION: TACOMA
Analysis: The word TACK is found in the balloon. A state of insensibility or faint out of which one cannot be aroused is a COMA.
Result: TACK COMA = TACOMA

PICTURE-PUZZLE NO. 4 . . . . page 275

CORRECT SOLUTION: BULLDOG DRUMMOND ESCAPES
Analysis: A cow's husband is a BULL. A poodle is a DOG. There's a DRUM ON DESK. The men are wearing CAPES.

Result: BULL DOG DRUM ON DESK CAPES = BULLDOG DRUMMOND ESCAPES

PICTURE-PUZZLE NO. 5 . . . . . . page 276

CORRECT SOLUTION: BEFORE MORNING
Analysis: The syllable "by," hyphenated in the balloon, is pronounced BE. The word "figure" means FORM. There is an AWNING in the picture.
Result: BE FORM AWNING = BEFORE MORNING

PICTURE-PUZZLE NO. 6 . . . . . . page 277

CORRECT SOLUTION: CLARA BOW
Analysis: The word SEE, phonetically equivalent to the letter C, is spoken. The syllable EL, phonetically equivalent to the letter L, is spoken. This syllable is found detached and therefore may be used by itself. The sheik from Jaffa is an ARAB. The letter O is spoken.
Result: C L ARAB O = CLARA BOW
Notes: The WONDER EYE OF ABDUL just misses the boat. "Marvel" means WONDER, and all the other words are spoken, with the exception of the word OF. One-half of the missing link can be accounted for by the letter O. The F is the fly in the ointment.

PICTURE-PUZZLE NO. 7 . . . . . . page 278

CORRECT SOLUTION: THE SCARLET LETTER
Analysis: The word THE is found in the balloon. The mark on the complainant's cheek, which was caused by a cut, is a SCAR. The sign "To Let" on the building is equivalent to "Two Let" or LET LET. The syllable ER is found in the balloon.
Result: THE SCAR LET LET ER = THE SCARLET LETTER

PICTURE-PUZZLE NO. 8 . . . . . . page 279

CORRECT SOLUTION: ON A STEAMER COMING OVER
Analysis: The two merchants who are fair and upright are HONEST. The pair is a TEAM. Fog is MURK. The word A is spoken. MING is a period in Chinese history during which famous beautiful porcelain was manufactured. The word OVER is spoken.
Result: HONEST TEAM MURK A MING OVER = ON A STEAMER COMING OVER

483

Notes: BECAUSE I LOVE YOU can't place the L. CHINA SEAS, too, misses by a hair. Porcelain is CHINA. The word SEE is spoken. The S kills it.

PICTURE-PUZZLE NO. 9 . . . . . . page 280

CORRECT SOLUTION: HIGH FINANCE

Analysis: There is a HYPHEN in the picture. Jane's sister is Bob's mother; therefore, Jane is Bob's aunt. When Bob says, "This 50¢ piece is Jane's," in effect he says, "This 50¢ piece is my AUNT'S."

Result: HYPHEN AUNT'S = HIGH FINANCE

Notes: THIS IS MY MOTHER fails to fill the bill because the word "mother" cannot be removed as a clue out of the word "mother's." According to the note explaining picture-puzzle solutions, syllables separated by apostrophes may not be separately employed as clues. The word as a whole must be used.

ROBERT W. SILVER has one extra letter which invalidates it, since one-half of the letter W cannot be accounted for. In solving picture-puzzles, every last particle of a title presented as the correct title must be accounted for. It is true that the nickname Bob signifies ROBERT and that the half-dollar implies SILVER, but the W still remains unaccounted for. The word YOU is spoken, but there is no way to get DOUBLE.

PICTURE-PUZZLE NO. 10 . . . . . . page 281

CORRECT SOLUTION: ANYTHING GOES

Analysis: In the code, the N is under, or NEATH, the ING. There are two O's.

Result: N NEATH ING O'S = ANYTHING GOES

Notes: OWEN MOORE divides second money with OZONE PARK. There is an O in the code and an N. These letters, read together would form the name OWEN. The "rocks of silver" are silver ORE. There is an additional unused O in the code. Only the M cannot be placed. OZONE PARK is just as close. The two O's in the code are phonetically equivalent to the syllable OZ, while the N is phonetically equivalent to the letters NE. The name PARKE is spoken. Only one O is missing. It must be pointed out here that you cannot use the same letter or sound for two different purposes. The two O's in the code, having been used to form the syllable OZ, cannot be used again to supply the missing O.

PICTURE-PUZZLE NO. 11 . . . . . . page 282

CORRECT SOLUTION: STARS AND STRIPES FOREVER

Analysis: In the sky, there is a single STAR. On the beach there is SAND. The beach umbrella is decorated with STRIPES. Four times the young poet repeats the word "ever." This is equivalent, by count, to FOUR EVER.

Result: STAR SAND STRIPES FOUR EVER = STARS AND STRIPES FOREVER

PICTURE-PUZZLE NO. 12 . . . . . . page 283

CORRECT SOLUTION: ABOUT A QUARTER TO NINE

Analysis: The syllable A is found detached in the balloon. When the captain says, "Go forward," he indicates he wishes his men to go to the BOW. When the captain orders his men to change the course of the boat and turn her windward, he is telling his men to TACK. WATER is what the yacht is sailing on. One of the sailors in the picture is singing a TUNE. Two bells is NINE o'clock.

Result: A BOW TACK WATER TUNE NINE = ABOUT A QUARTER TO NINE

Notes: As for GIBRALTAR, although some nautical genius might somehow account for the syllable JIB, and although the word "change" means ALTER, how are you going to get around the R? The syllable "er" only suggests R, but is not equivalent phonetically or orthographically.

The difficulty with EIGHT TRAILS FORWARD is that two bells on the sea signify nine and not eight.

PICTURE-PUZZLE NO. 13 . . . . . . page 284

CORRECT SOLUTION: ICHABOD BARTLETT

Analysis: The word I is found in the balloon. The taxi is a CAB. The numbers on the license plate are all ODD numbers. The abbreviation for baronet is BART. The word "permit" means LET.

Result: I CAB ODD BART LET = ICHABOD BARTLETT

PE. . . . . page 286

1. Peril	8. Speck
2. Pekoe	9. Upend
3. Petal	10. Spear
4. Peary	11. Impel or expel
5. Perch	12. Viper
6. Speed	13. Ripen
7. Opera	14. Roper

15. Repel
16. Elope
17. Tripe
18. Shape
19. Scope
20. Gripe
21. Purse
22. Prove
23. Paste
24. Prime
25. Prune

1. Loose
2. Loupe
3. Loren (Sophia)
4. Logic
5. Local
6. Gloom
7. Clout
8. Sloan (John)
9. Block
10. Flout
11. Phlox
12. Alloy
13. Solon
14. Below
15. Helot
16. Hello
17. Marlo (Thomas)
18. Jello
19. Menlo
20. Cello
21. Lasso
22. Llano
23. Largo
24. Litho
25. Lotto

1. Serve
2. Sedan
3. Sever
4. Sense
5. Sepia
6. Setup
7. Easel
8. Miser
9. Upset
10. Inset
11. Nosey
12. Asset
13. Raise
14. Lapse
15. Blasé
16. Dense
17. Erase
18. Passé
19. Terse
20. Sabre
21. Scale
22. Skate
23. Shade
24. Spike
25. Sidle

1. Annul
2. Antic
3. Angle
4. Anger
5. Anode
6. Candy
7. Range
8. Manor
9. Panda
10. Dandy
11. Brand
12. Chant
13. Slant
14. Blank
15. Eland
16. Clean
17. Titan
18. Koran
19. Groan
20. Mayan
21. Again
22. Acorn
23. Amman
24. Apron
25. Alien

1. Cease
2. Cedar
3. Cello
4. Ceres
5. Cetic
6. Scene
7. Ocean
8. Scend
9. Acerb
10. Scent
11. Ulcer
12. Excel
13. Ricer
14. Lycée
15. Raced
16. Truce
17. Mince
18. Sauce
19. Bryce
20. Space
21. Canoe
22. Crete
23. Chore
24. Curse
25. Chive

1. Throw
2. Thorn
3. Thong
4. Think
5. Thief
6. Ether
7. Ethic (or ethos)
8. Ethyl
9. Athos
10. Other
11. Lithe
12. Bathe
13. Tithe
14. Pithy
15. Lathe
16. Mirth
17. Wrath
18. Barth (John)
19. Death
20. Booth (John Wilkes)
21. Touch
22. Trash
23. Tooth
24. Torah
25. Tough

1. Medal
2. Mercy
3. Melon
4. Metal
5. Meson
6. Smelt
7. Amend (emend)
8. Smear
9. Omega
10. Emery
11. Armed
12. Cameo
13. Women
14. Homer
15. Camel
16. Flame
17. Prime
18. Theme
19. Plume
20. Rhyme
21. Maple
22. Morse (Samuel)
23. Movie
24. Melee
25. Mauve

1. Robin
2. Rover
3. Roost
4. Rogue
5. Route
6. Proof
7. Broke
8. Grove
9. Irony
10. Aroma
11. Tarot
12. Carob
13. Arrow
14. Throb
15. Scrod
16. Metro
17. Ferro
18. Spiro
19. Macro
20. Morro
21. Romeo
22. Ratio
23. Rondo
24. Rodeo
25. Radio

A GIRL'S BEST FRIEND . . . . **page 330**

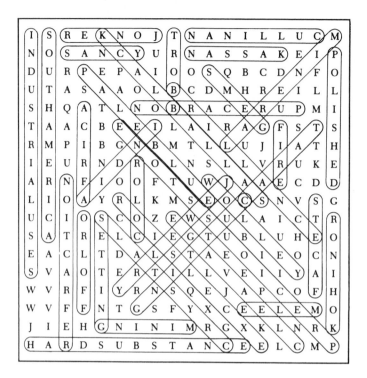

HOME GROWN . . . . **page 332**

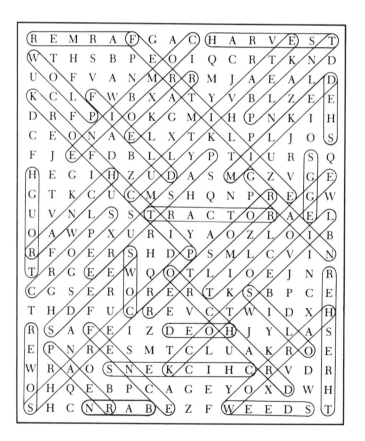

HOMETOWN . . . . page 334

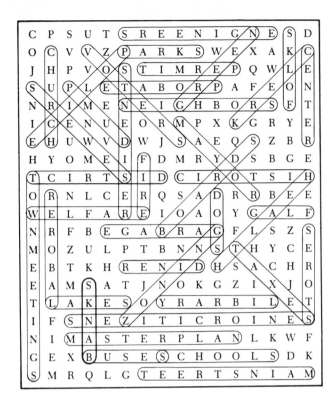

BREAKING POINT! . . . . page 336

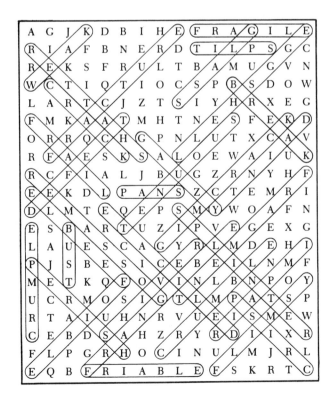

COLORFUL CAPER . . . . **page 338**

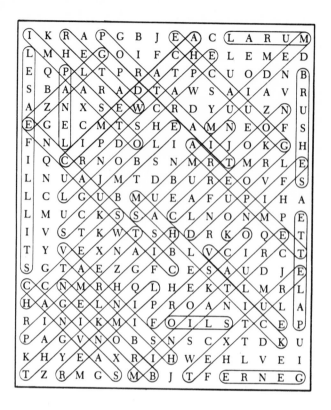

FISHY . . . . **page 340**

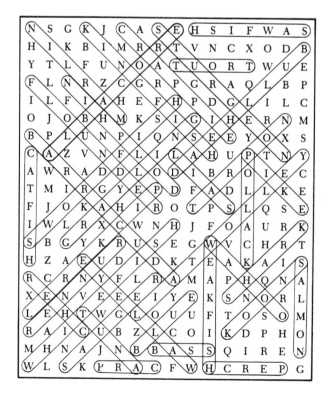

POPPIES . . . . page 342

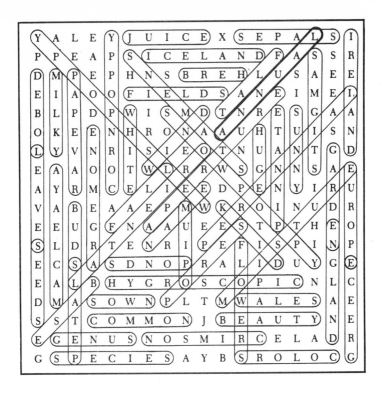

MYTHICAL MONSTERS . . . . page 344

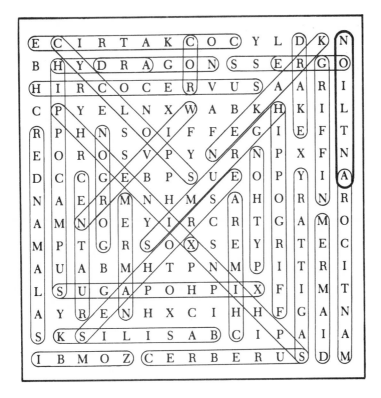

GET THE ANGLE . . . . page 346

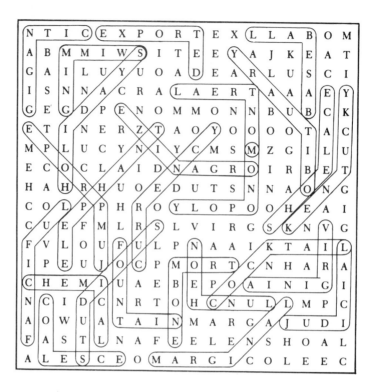

DRAGONS . . . . page 348

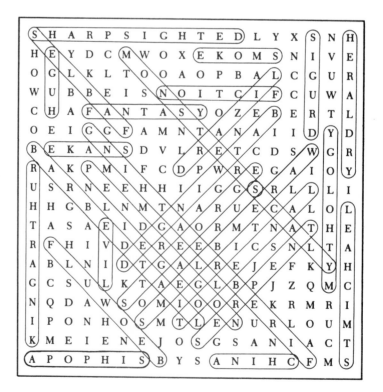

FEATHERED FRIENDS . . . . page 350

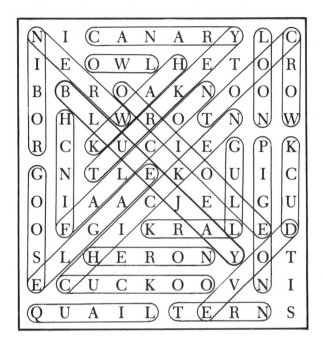

NO BED OF ROSES . . . . page 351

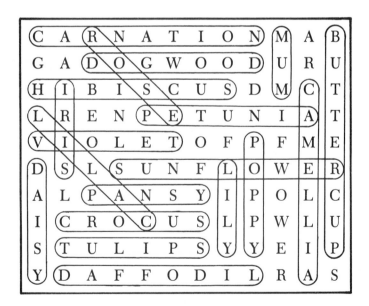

SECRET MESSAGE: A garden of flowers

VEGETABLE STEW . . . . page 352

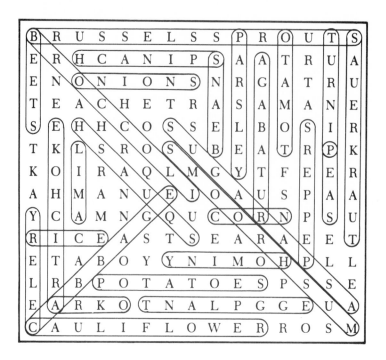

QUADRUPLE WHAMMY . . . . page 358

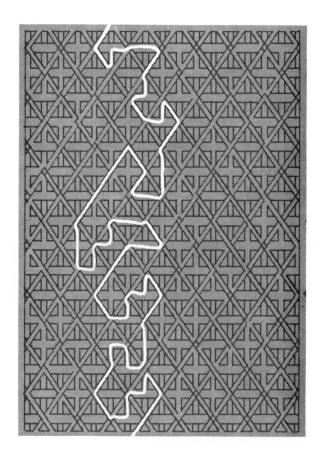

RATTAN RACEWAY . . . . page 359

DEAD ENDS . . . . page 360

SNUG AS A BUG IN A RUG ..... page 365

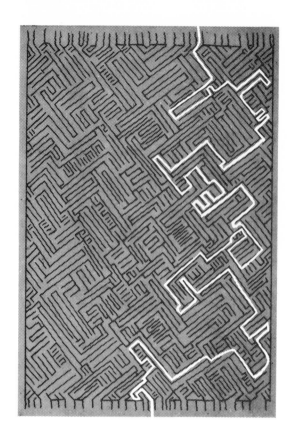

HOUSING DEVELOPMENT ..... page 366

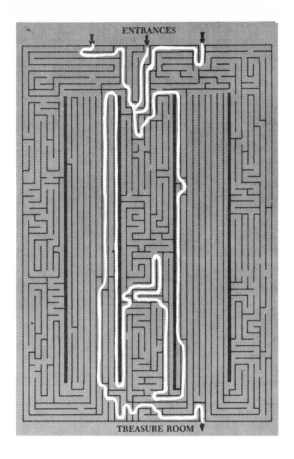

ENTRANCES

TREASURE ROOM

HOW SELF-ASSERTIVE ARE YOU? . . . . page 386

Count the number of A answers you have chosen, the number of B's and of C's. The A's represent introvert reactions, the B's, ambivert or "middling" reactions, while the C's are decidedly extrovert.

If you have six or more A's you probably avoid asserting yourself; six or more B's, you will assert yourself sometimes and at other times, avoid situations that make you come out front; six or more C's, you are a decided extrovert, and achieve your rights and goals.

Now add your A's and B's, and your B's and C's. If your total of A's plus B's is larger than the total of your B's plus C's, you have a rather "middling" temperament with a leaning toward introversion. A larger total of B's plus C's indicates a leaning toward extroversion.

WOULD YOU MAKE A GOOD COUNTERSPY? . . . . page 388

1. HASTE MAKES WASTE. Solution: Read the letters backwards. 10 points.
2. THEY SHALL NOT PREVAIL AGAINST THEE. Solution: Reverse the letters of the alphabet. A = Z, B = Y, C = X, etc. 10 points.
3. IN GOD WE TRUST. Solution: Substitute a sequential number for each letter of the alphabet. A = 1; B = 2, C = 3, etc. 10 points.
4. PUT ONLY AMERICANS ON GUARD TONIGHT. Solution: Find the junction of the two numbers on the vertical and horizontal scale to get each letter. 15 points.
5. AMERICA THE BEAUTIFUL. Solution: Each letter of the message is two *back* from the one given in the code. C = A; D = B; G = E, etc. 15 points.

497

6. MAKE HASTE SLOWLY. Solution: Each letter is represented by the configuration of the "pen" in which it appears. If there is no dot in the code configuration, it indicates the top letter in the designated "pen." The middle and bottom letters in each "pen" are indicated by one and two dots respectively in the code configuration. 30 points.

IF YOU SCORED BETWEEN:

80-90: A brilliant score, showing the mind of a super cryptographer. The maximum score is 90.

60-75: This is above average. You have a natural aptitude for this kind of thinking.

40-55: You are in the average bracket. Very likely, if you had worked longer on these problems you would have scored higher.

20-35: This is not a world-shaking score, but maybe you caught on now and will do better in the future.

0-15: Even if you are on the bottom of the heap on this test, don't worry. Your talents probably lie in other directions.

OBSERVATION TEST . . . . page 390

1. 10	9. a
2. c and e	10. c
3. a and e	11. 3
4. b and f	12. 2
5. a and e	13. 2
6. 8	14. 2
7. d	15. 1
8. a	

ARE YOU VAIN? . . . . page 393

1. a-10; b-0; c-0. In controlled research, it was found that those who themselves tended to be vain, saw vanity in the picture. Those who were more modest, saw the drawing either as a symbol of friendship or as having no special meaning.
  2. Yes-10; No-0.
  3. Yes-10; No-0.
  4. Yes-10; No-0.
  5. Yes-0; No-10.
  6. Yes-10; No-0.
  7. Yes-0; No-10.
  8. Yes-10; No-0.
  9. Yes-10; No-0.
10. Yes-10; No-0.

IF YOU SCORED BETWEEN:

80-100: This indicates you use vanity as a shield against your own insecurities. You may primp and preen, name-drop, and flaunt money in an effort to build up your own frail ego and be liked by others. "Vanity keeps persons in favor with themselves who are out of favor with others." (Shakespeare). If you would try concentrating on the other person instead of on yourself, you would begin to find people responding favorably to you.

40-70: This is quite a normal, human score. Most people keep up their self-respect with a certain degree of vanity. "Virtue would not go far if vanity did not keep it company." (Francois Rochefoucauld, French moralist).

0-30: This score sometimes indicates an "I don't care" attitude. However, it suggests you are usually liked because you are not vain. You probably view those who act like "big wheels" with a critical eye.

HOW SOCIABLE ARE YOU? . . . . page 394

Give yourself points for your answers as follows:
  1. If you placed your initials on: the large front block, 8 points; a block in the first bottom row, 4 points; a block in the middle row, 0 points; center block in the back row, 7 points; any other block in the back row, 6 points.
  2. a-6; b-8; c-1; d-5.
  3. a-6; b-3.
  4. a-2; b-5; c-4.
  5. Yes-2; No-1.
  6. Yes-4; No-2.
  7. Yes-0; No-1.
  8. Yes-3; No-2.
  9. Yes-2; No-1.
10. Yes-4; No-1.
11. Yes-0; No-2.
12. Yes-2; No-1.
13. Yes-2; No-3.
14. Yes-0; No-1.

IF YOU SCORED BETWEEN:

40-51: You are extremely sociable. Just be careful that in your casual, happy-go-lucky way, you don't spend too much time talking, and not enough time listening.

30-39: This score indicates a gregarious personality, but you can listen if you want to.

23-29: You often prefer to be alone than in the company of others. But you do speak when you have something to say. Words, to you, are a precious commodity.

16-22: You tend to be the silent type, prone to brood. Try to get out and mix more.

HOW DETERMINED ARE YOU?.. page 396

1. a-5; b-10; c-0. In studies that were done, testees who evidenced the greatest amount of determination chose the strong bricklike pattern b. A was the choice of those who were well-organized, and enjoyed their own personal growth, but were not as strong-willed as b. C was the choice of those who tended to bend with the "winds of fortune" rather than to buck up against life.
2. a-0; b-10; c-5.
3. a-10; b-5; c-0.
4. a-3; b-0; c-10.
5. a-0; b-5; c-10.
6. a-0; b-3; c-10.
7. a-5; b-0; c-10.
8. a-0; b-5; c-10.
9. a-5; b-0; c-10.
10. a-0; b-10; c-0.

IF YOU SCORED BETWEEN:

80-100: Testees in this bracket showed determined traits in their living patterns. They were not always easy to work or to live with, because, to their less determined associates, they sometimes seemed obstinate and bull-headed. "I like a person who knows his own mind and sticks to it; one who sees at once what, in given circumstances, is to be done and does it." (William Hazlitt, English critic).

40-78: This score shows a practical person who knows her abilities and limitations. "I hate to see things done by halves.—If it be right, do it boldly,—if it be wrong, leave it undone." (Bernard Gilpin, English clergyman)

0-38: This is the mark of those who usually have little ambition, are easily discouraged and have no strong motives for their daily actions. "Men must be decided on what they will not do, and then they are able to act with vigor in that which they ought to do." (Mencius, Chinese sage).

HOW WELL-LIKED ARE YOU?... page 398

Give yourself 3 points for each A answer; 1 point for each B answer; 2 points for each C answer. Highest possible score: 42.

IF YOU SCORED BETWEEN:

30-42: People like you very much. You obviously have the quality of winning friendship and respect. It could be that you sometimes weary of so much attention and applause, of being asked to do everything at all times. For your own sake, you must occasionally relax and let your host of friends take over.

20-29: You are probably thought of as reliable and likeable. This is a high score and one which is earned by good members of a community with a wholesome family life. You have very few friendship problems.

10-19: You have a few very good friends. "The friends thou hast, grapple to thy soul with hooks of steel." (Shakespeare). It might also be wise to try to expand your list of friends.

0-9: The score of a lonely person. The approval of others can only be gained by your trust in them. You must make the first step, give the handshake. You will be surprised at what will happen!

CAN YOU KEEP A SECRET?.... page 400

1. If either line was drawn to hole 3, give yourself 50 points, but no points for the second line. If both lines were drawn to hole 2, give yourself 25 points. All other lines 0 points.
2. A: a-0; b-10; c-4.
   B: a-0; b-10; c-4.
   C: a-10; b-0; c-7.
   D: a-0; b-4; c-10.
   E: a-0; b-10; c-3.
   F: a-5; b-10; c-0.
3. If you initialed block A, give yourself 20 points.

IF YOU SCORED BETWEEN:

100-130: This score indicates that you can be as silent as the Sphinx. You are trustworthy as far as secrets are concerned. People may complain that you are tight-mouthed, but they respect your ability to keep secrets.

60-99: This is an average score. Very probably when someone confides in you, you share a secret with someone else who is close to you, with the admonishment NOT TO TELL.

40-59: You are not a good risk with a secret. You must learn to think before you speak. Those around you know more about you and your friends than they probably want to know because you keep spilling the beans.

0-39: A very low score, which indicates that you are unable to keep a secret. You may even use your own imagination to embellish the facts. See if you can't make an effort to restrain yourself. You may find you enjoy knowing something almost no one else knows.

HOW WELL DO YOU CONCENTRATE?............**page 402**

1. 10. The number at the top is subtracted from the number at the left to arrive at the number at the right. 25 points.

2. The letters of the alphabet are sequentially numbered: A = 1; B = 2, C = 3, etc. a. Spain (19-16-1-9-14); b. Italy (9-20-1-12-25). 10 points each.

3. e (November). 5 points.

4. u (Sunday). 5 points.

5. n. 5 points.

6. Blind:did. In the other examples, the first letter of the first word is the same as the last letter of the last word, and the last letter of the first word is the same as the first letter of the second word. 25 points.

7. A N S W R T U K Z X M L F. 15 points.

8. Form a triangle as illustrated below. 25 points.

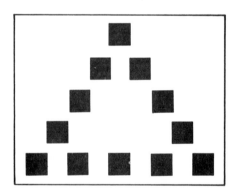

This test requires patient application. If you scored above 60, your powers of concentration are excellent and you are well disciplined. A perfect score is 125.

30-55: A score in this range indicates average ability to concentrate.

0-25: A score below 25 indicates a tendency to stare out the window and fidget at work. It also suggests poor concentration on the problem at hand.

DO YOU FEEL INFERIOR?......**page 404**

1. If you chose c or d, you generally wake up feeling it will be another hard day—give yourself 20 points; if you chose d, you're anticipating having to cope with problems— give yourself 7 points; if you chose b, you're not sure what awaits you—give yourself 2 points; if you chose a, you feel things will mesh for you—give yourself 0 points.

2. If you chose a, you clearly don't feel up to it—give yourself 20 points; if you chose b, you're not sure of your ability to do it—15 points; if you chose c or d, you feel grim, but determined—5 points; and if you chose e, you love the challenge, 0 points.

3. a-20; b-5; c-0
4. a-20; b-0; c-10
5. a-20; b-0; c-10
6. a-0; b-10; c-20
7. a-0; b-20; c-8
8. a-20; b-0; c-7
9. a-15; b-8; c-5
10. a-20; b-0; c-0

IF YOU SCORE BETWEEN:

100-195 points: You have the strength of a bowl of jelly. You punish yourself unmercifully with your feelings of inferiority. Make a list of the things you can do. You will be surprised how many items you can name.

60-99 points: You feel secure in some of your activities—but not as much as you might. Probably you sometimes have fearful dreams and an occasional sleepless night. Concentrate on your abilities instead of your shortcomings.

40-59 points: This is an average score. Being human and honest with yourself, you have moments when you feel inadequate. This is healthy, because complete self-satisfaction can stunt personal growth.

0-39 points: Little or no feeling of inferiority in this score, but watch out that you do not appear too cocky.

ARE YOU A PLEASURE TO BE WITH?..............**page 406**

Give yourself 2 points for each No answer. The questions fall under three separate headings:

1 through 6 are bad habits which you can break with thought and awareness of your actions.

7 through 12 may indicate thoughtlessness, nervousness, fatigue, or self-consciousness. By becoming aware of the cause, you may be able to develop the self-control to change these behaviors.

13 through 18 are concerned with characteristics which are more difficult to control because they stem from the inner you, your basic personality and needs.

IF YOU SCORED BETWEEN:

30-36: You have the appearance of being

calm and self-assured, even if you don't always feel that way inside. People like you, in all probability, and you have many close friends and many more acquaintances because you have hardly any annoying habits.

20-28: Since we are all human and imperfect, this is an average rating. However, personal growth keeps us alive, so keep working to eliminate the flaws which annoy others.

10-18: You are very likely a highly nervous person with many things on your mind which disturb you. Why not relax a bit and study the mannerisms of some very calm person whose traits you admire?

0-8: This score falls into the danger zone. Probably you annoy people and they annoy you, thus creating a vicious cycle. To break this cycle, you might seek the help of your mate, close friend, or a counselor.

MATHECROSTICS . . . . page 410

1.

4	×	4	÷	2	=8
×		×		+	
3	×	3	−	6	=3
÷				−	
6	+	4	−	1	=9
=2		=8		=7	

2.

5	+	9	−	8	=6
×		×		+	
3	×	2	−	4	=2
−		÷		÷	
9	+	3	÷	2	=6
=6		=6		=6	

3.

6	−	4	×	3	=6
×		×		+	
3	×	3	−	7	=2
÷		−		÷	
9	+	5	÷	2	=7
=2		=7		=5	

4.

3	×	6	−	9	=9
×		+		+	
3	+	7	÷	5	=2
−		−		÷	
2	+	9	−	7	=4
=7		=4		=2	

5.

9	+	7	÷	2	=8
+		−		×	
3	×	4	−	6	=6
−		×		÷	
7	−	3	−	3	=1
=5		=9		=4	

6.

6	÷	3	×	4	=8
×		+		×	
3	×	5	−	9	=6
÷		−		÷	
2	×	7	−	6	=8
=9		=1		=6	

7.

3	×	4	−	8	=4
+		×		+	
8	÷	2	+	3	=7
−		−		−	
5	×	3	÷	5	=3
=6		=5		=6	

8.

9	−	3	+	1	=7
÷		×		+	
3	+	6	−	5	=4
×		÷		+	
1	+	9	÷	2	=5
=3		=2		=8	

CROSSWORD PUZZLE NO. 1 . . . . page 416

CROSSWORD PUZZLE NO. 3 . . . . page 418

CROSSWORD PUZZLE NO. 2 . . . . page 417

CROSSWORD PUZZLE NO. 4 . . . . page 419

```
K I T   M A C A W   S C A M P
I D A   A D O R E   L A B O R
D E D U C E D   A F A R   L I
      P E N   C R E W   L A C
P E C O S   C A S E   F A R E
A L A N   L O G   T R A M
R I B   W A V E S   A M A S S
I T   C A P E   N A P E   L O
S E W E R   S C A N T   B A D
    I D E A   A F T   C O M O
P A L E   P E R U   C H A S M
A B E   T E N T   L O O
G I   A I D A   A I R W A Y S
A D A G E   T E N S E   R I A
N E W E R   E X I T S   A P T
```

```
C A R T     M U G     S T E P
R A T I O   T O R O   C O R E
A T O M   P I A N O   E A R N
Z E N   W A R N   D E N S
E R E M I T E   T W E E T E R
    A S H   P A I R S   L O
B R O T H   T A L L Y   P A D
R I P E   B E T E L   L A T E
A N T   D A N E S   V I R E O
I S   D I C E S   B I N
D E T R A C T   P A N T H E R
    H U L A   R I L O   A D O
A R I D   R O U T E   T R I M
R I N G   A N D Y   C R E T E
C A K E   T E E   A I M S
```

```
T E N D   S A N D   R O A R
H A I R   T I E R   E L V E R
I S L E   A R R O W   D A T A
S T E A D Y   O M A R   L I T
    M I S S   E Y E   O R E
C H A S M   H A D   D U N E S
O U R   E M A N A T E S
P E T S   A D O R E   E P I C
    P A R O D I E S   O R A
F L O A T   W E E   O T T E R
L O P   O R B   S I L O
I C E   M O O D   R E W A R D
T A N K   E X I L E   E L I A
S T E E P   E V E N   R O O M
    E D N A   S A G E   S E T S
```

```
C R A M   A L A S   D E M O S
A U T O   M A L I   E V A D E
S L O P E   W A N   V A L O R
T E M P L E   N E R O   E R G
    E D G Y   W I T S   S E
W A N D E R E D   G E T S
A L E   R E A R S   S A T A N
I T E M   T R O T S   B O R E
T O D A Y   S P A N S   N E W
    S P E D   S T I L L E S T
P A   S A Y S   E P E E
O L A   R E A D   S E V E R S
S A L O N   F I G   P E R I L
E M I L E   E V E R   R I T A
D O T E D   S A M E   S E E M
```

504

```
A R G O   B O A R   E A C H
C O O P   U R G E   A R R O W
M O R E   R E E D   S T A T E
E M E N D S     D R Y   V E E
    E A T   S E A   H E L D
W O R D Y   S I N G L E
E G O   C A R   L O N D O N
E R A   T A P   R A T   E V E
P E R S O N   B U N     L E E
    U N I S O N   B L E N D
F I L M   N E W   T O O
A C E   P E A     H A I L E D
T I A R A   R A T E   T I D E
E N V O Y   C H A R   E V E N
    G E T S   H A R E   R E N T
```

```
C A P E R   S L A T   S E R F
A L I N E   T A P E   O D O R
T I L E   W A T E R   F I L E
E V E   P A N E   R A T T L E
R E S P O N D     I R E S
    A P T   R O B I N   M E
S T A V E   W O R L D   P A W
H I V E   L E V E E   P I K E
O N E   H O N E S   L I N E R
W E   B A N D S   M A N
    P A R E     T A C T I C S
S T O N E S   B O R E   D O E
P A I N   O P E N S   C O R N
E L S E   M A N E   H O L E S
D E E R   E N D S   P O S S E
```

```
E V E N   O G R E S   C H O P
S I N E   S L A N T   H A L E
S N O O P   E R S E   A L E E
E E L   A L A E   P A S T O R
    S P I N   S T I E S
H A S T E N   S P U R S   G T
A S T E R   S T A R S   M E R
S P E W   S T A I N   W I N E
P E P   S T E R N   R E T I A
S N   S A R E E   D I E T E D
    S E V E R   W I S P
E L E V E N   D A N E   A B A
R A V E   G O O D   R A V E L
A V E R   T W E E D   L I D A
S A N E   H E S S E   E D E N
```

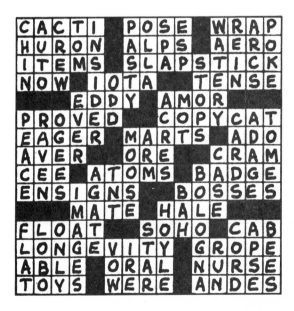

```
C A C T I   P O S E   W R A P
H U R O N   A L P S   A E R O
I T E M S   S L A P S T I C K
N O W   I O T A   T E N S E
    E D D Y   A M O R
P R O V E D   C O P Y C A T
E A G E R   M A R T S   A D O
A V E R   O R E   C R A M
C E E   A T O M S   B A D G E
E N S I G N S   B O S S E S
    M A T E   H A L E
F L O A T   S O H O   C A B
L O N G E V I T Y   G R O P E
A B L E   O R A L   N U R S E
T O Y S   W E R E   A N D E S
```

```
B A L S A   R A S E   S C O T
A G A I N   I B I S   C O N E
T E   P E R F E C T   I N C A
E N D   W I L T   E M O T E S
S T O P   P E T S   A N E
      U R G E   E L F   S M O G
A M B E R   A D I O S   P R O
P U L S A T E   D R I L L E D
E S E   M E R G E   D E A L S
D E B T   D I E   R E N T
      O A R   E N T O   T E N D
S T I L E S   E R O S   S I R
H O L E   A S S U M E S   M E
O M E N   L A I C   T A P E S
P E R T   E L S E   A M I S S
```

```
  R O M A     C A D   L O B S
H A V E N   S O M E   A S I A
O V E N   S L O O P   C I T Y
P E R   S P I N   L A K E
E N T I C E D   G E N E R A L
    N O D   P A T T Y   M A
B R U N T   S A L E S   A P T
L O S S   S I R E D   T I L E
A T E   T I L T S   T I M E R
S O   S A L L Y   D O N
T R A N C E S   P A S T E L S
  L O O N   R A M S   R O E
S O L O   C E A S E   G I V E
P R O P   E M I T   P A C E D
Y E W S   D U D     A L A S
```

```
R O C   S P A R E   S W A T S
U G H   K A T E J A C K S O N
T E A   E W E   E R A S   T O
S E R I E S   A C I D   G A B
    L O T   P I T A   P A L S
C H I N   B I D S   W E E
H U E   K A L E   B O S L E Y
I S   G A L E   F O O T   D O
C H E R Y L   L A D D   L E G
    R I O   R A C E   T U N A
B I N D   B E S T   H O G
A D E   G A P S   S I N G E D
N E   A U R A   B I G   A W E
J A C L Y N S M I T H   G E E
O L L A S   T I N E S   E R R
```

```
S T A G E   C A L M   D A W S
H O G A N   I D I O   E R I E
A D O P T   G A D   R A I S E
W A G   I M A M   G A R D E N
L Y   S T I R   B U N T
    H O L D   F R I G H T E N
S P I C E   T R A D E   A N I
H O N K   C R A V E   L I O N
O L T   C H I M E   R I L L E
D E S C R I B E   B O S S
    H O L E   B U S T   V V
D E M A N D   L O G E   T I E
A G I L E   C U M   T H O S E
L A N E   B U L B   T U T O R
E D I T   A B L E   E M E R Y
```

```
P R I M   D A M P   L I M I T
R I T A   O R A L   E R O D E
O P E N S   T I E   S A V O R
D E M O N S   N A B S   E L S
      R A M P   T I E R   S E
W H I S P E R S   G N A T
R I D   S A I L S   S C E N E
A R E S   R E A P S   K N O W
P E A L S   S T O W S   E T E
      S I T S   E R E M I T E S
P O   D A U B   T E A M
A C T   R E A D   T R A V E L
C A R A T   S I P   T R I B E
E L O P E   I R A N   E N O W
D A T E D   N E R O   T E N D
```

```
  P A C E     B E N     T H E M
E R R E D   H O R A   R O L E
G I B E   R A D A R   E R I N
A D O   H O S E   R O A D
D E R V I S H   L A N T E R N
    E R E   L U T E S   A I
T E P E E   C A R E S   E R N
O M A R   P L I E D   O G E E
P O W   B E A R D   M O O R S
I T   S E E M S   F E Z
C E N T E R S   S I L E N C E
    E A R L   M I N T   O A R
D E A R   E L A T E   T I L L
I N R E   S A N E   A I S L E
M E S S   S P Y     T E E S
```

```
S L A M   A M I D   C A R E S
T O T E   D A R E   A L I V E
I D O L S   R I P   B A S I N
R E M O T E   S O D A   E L S
      N A I L   T A R A   S E
C O N S I D E R   M E L T
A M O   R E G A L   T A I L S
S A V E   R I V A L   S N I P
T R E N D   T E N O R   E N E
      L I R A   R E V E R S E D
M A   D E L L   S E M I
O L E   S E A M   D I P P E R
R A T E S   B I T   T E A S E
A M O R E   O L E O   N I N E
L O N E R   R O A R   S L E D
```

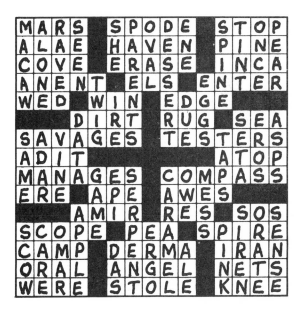

```
M A R S   S P O D E   S T O P
A L A E   H A V E N   P I N E
C O V E   E R A S E   I N C A
A N E N T   E L S   E N T E R
W E D   W I N   E D G E
      D I R T   R U G   S E A
S A V A G E S   T E S T E R S
A D I T           A T O P
M A N A G E S   C O M P A S S
E R E   A P E   A W E S
      A M I R   R E S   S O S
S C O P E   P E A   S P I R E
C A M P   D E R M A   I R A N
O R A L   A N G E L   N E T S
W E R E   S T O L E   K N E E
```

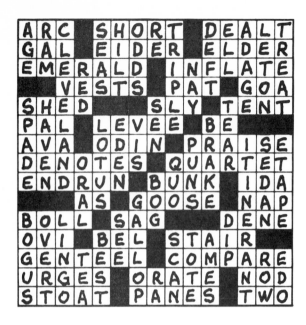

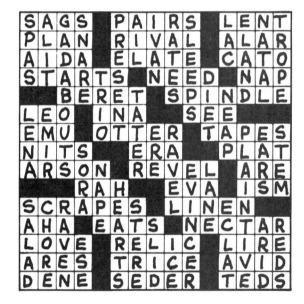

CROSSWORD PUZZLE·NO. 29 . . . . page 444

CROSSWORD PUZZLE NO. 31 . . . . page 446

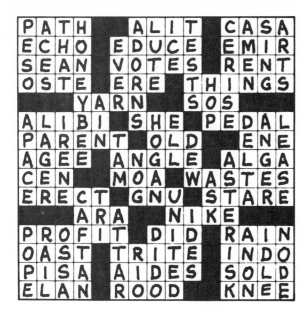

CROSSWORD PUZZLE NO. 30 . . . . page 445

CROSSWORD PUZZLE NO. 32 . . . . page 447

509

CROSSWORD PUZZLE NO. 33 . . . . page 448

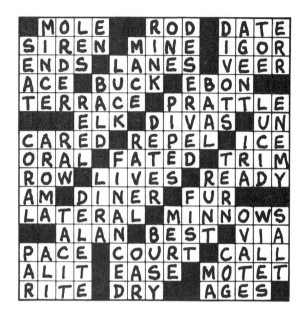

CROSSWORD PUZZLE NO. 35 . . . . page 450

CROSSWORD PUZZLE NO. 34 . . . . page 449

CROSSWORD PUZZLE NO. 36 . . . . page 451

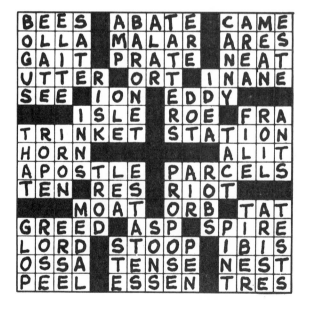

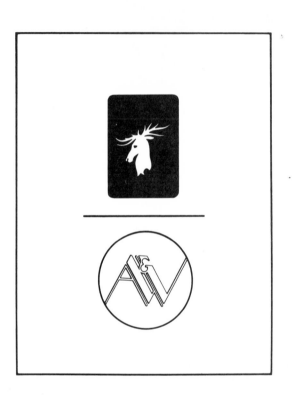